D0095460

The Wayfarers

THE WAY-FARERS

Dan Wickenden

WILLIAM MORROW
AND COMPANY
NEW YORK
1945

COPYRIGHT - 1945
BY DAN WICKENDEN

PRINTED IN THE UNITED STATES OF AMERICA

TO

Donald Stevens

AND

All the Gang

AT

The Press

Note

ALTHOUGH some aspects of this book's setting have been borrowed from a real city, there are many ways in which Broadfield differs from its original, and it should be thought of as an imaginary place. The people in the book have no living models, and any similarity of names to the names of real persons is unintentional. The author is indebted to Du Barry Campau for her assistance with the background material.

Appreciation is expressed for permission to quote in this book the following:

The passage on page 2, which is from "Walt Whitman and the Springs of Courage" by Haniel Long, published by Writers Editions, Inc., by permission of the author.

The passage on page 180, which is from "Mind, Medicine, and Man" by Gregory Zilboorg, by permission of Harcourt, Brace and Company, Inc.

The verses on pages 117 and 118, which are from "A Shropshire Lad" by A. E. Housman, by permission of Henry Holt and Company, Inc.

The lyrics on pages 102 and 305, which are from the songs: "It's the Talk of the Town," Santly-Joy, Inc., copyright 1933; "Good Night, Sweetheart" by Ray Noble, Jimmy Campbell and Reg. Connelly, used by permission of Robbins Music Corporation for United States and Canada; "I'm No Angel," copyright 1933 by Shapiro, Bernstein & Co., Inc.; "Ho Hum," copyright 1931 by Famous Music Corporation.

PART ONE

The Labyrinth

The problems of life loom largest to an egoist; they diminish if not fade as one feels the life of others.

*

A man's success or failure in business and profession is not interesting compared to his success or failure as a human being. We doubt the value of success achieved at the expense of love or friendship.

*

—Haniel Long, *Walt Whitman and the Springs of Courage*

1

He hadn't intended to visit the cemetery. It was a fine mild October Sunday and he'd had it in mind to ride out to Rush Lake and hire a rowboat; but in the dream which fell upon him whenever he was not at work he boarded the wrong trolley-car and was set down, presently, on the southeastern instead of the eastern edge of the city.

There were other passengers bound for the cemetery, some of them carrying bouquets of chrysanthemums and most of them wearing a mournful and sanctimonious look. He wasn't feeling mournful or sanctimonious himself, but he followed the others— a thickset large-boned man in a baggy tweed suit, with shoulders stooped from years at a copy desk, walking slowly, in a dream. He walked past a row of vacant stores, across the state highway and between the square brick pillars, beneath the wrought-iron archway upon which bronze letters spelled out *Cedar Knoll;* and then, as the others scattered to left and right, he was left alone, stranded on the curving central drive of crushed bluestone.

He took off his hat, which was at least five years old, with a stained ribbon and a brim gone limp, to fan his face; and presently a wind came across the fields and stirred his gray hair and flapped his necktie, and he walked on again. He walked unwillingly, though, as if some outside force were pushing him up the slope.

He noticed very little, all the time he was mounting to the highest ridge, and when he arrived at his wife's grave he felt confused and somewhat resentful, as a man will who has been forced into a meaningless gesture. He had not been here since the day of the funeral, more than ten years ago. Laura's grave, like Laura herself, was something he had refused to think about; but in a corner of his mind there must always have been a map of the cemetery, indelibly printed, so that his feet had carried him here without hesitation.

Now he didn't know what to do. He couldn't imagine why people visited cemeteries, unless it was to refresh their own sense of loss or meditate on dissolution—morbid, anyhow, he thought, clapping the hat on his head, and turned away.

But there was less vigor in him than he had supposed, and when he came to a stone bench among privet bushes he sat down to rest.

3

He sat at peace for ten or fifteen minutes, and then something strange happened. The golden afternoon was gone and he was back in a hospital room, sitting in a chair pulled close to the high white bed; behind him a yellow shade tapped in the breeze; mingled with the hospital smells was the scent of the roses he had brought, which she was too ill to notice. She was calling his name, over and over, and he kept assuring her that he was there. This she was eventually able to understand, and she spoke rapidly, as if she hadn't much time. Her eyes remained shut but her lips smiled— she'd always laughed at herself when she was most in earnest.

It would probably sound foolish to him, she said, but she had a horror of undertakers and of funerals and of graves, and he must not let them bury her. She wanted to be cremated, she said, and she wanted her ashes scattered from the far northern shore of the big lake, which had reminded her of the Maine coast. But you aren't going to die, Laura, he said loudly, knowing he spoke the truth, because it was obvious that if she died he could not go on living himself.

She had not died that day, nor the day after; but in the early morning of the third day the telephone woke him in darkness and by the time he reached the hospital she was gone.

Blackness moved in on him that day, and when it receded the world had moved in: his parents, his sister, his brother-in-law, none of whom had ever really liked Laura; behind them an army of friends, and behind the friends strangers—he was surrounded and unable to withstand them, and there had been a conventional funeral, costly, vulgar, and horrible, with Laura like a painted waxen image in the casket, and a procession to the cemetery in the clear summer morning, and burial in a plot which his brother-in-law had long owned and kindly sold to him, as it afterwards turned out, at a handsome profit. So he had failed Laura even in this; he had done her an irreparable wrong, he thought, the day he asked her to marry him.

But the funeral had been only the first of many betrayals. For he had tried to escape from his grief into alcohol: almost four years of heavy drinking, until his health collapsed and he understood that he was doing something worse to his children than he had ever done to Laura. There followed a struggle to end the habit, and although it was finally victorious, the effort had exhausted him; and in his weariness he had somehow forgotten why the effort had seemed important.

Since then he had been only half alive. His efficiency at work was something in which he could take pleasure, but each afternoon he walked away from his desk into a dream, and in the dream his children and his acquaintances and the world about him seemed as insubstantial as Laura, whom he was determined to forget. All

4

traces of her had been banished from his house; her name was never mentioned there; he had deliberately cut himself off from any intimate relationship, fearing that intimacy might resurrect his emotions about Laura.

He had thought himself safe, after ten years; he had held off his grief so long that grief could never touch him. And yet he must have been hovering on the brink of this moment always: again and again it had almost happened, when he woke in the night from a dream of desolation and found himself alone in the bed, when he moved down a street at dusk and caught a glimpse of some woman who walked like Laura, when he passed an open window and heard a voice that reminded him of hers; or when he was confronted with some problem he could not solve, which she would have solved without thinking. The truth was that his grief had always been with him; for years he had been locked up with his own pain, lost in self-pity.

All this he saw with great clarity as he sat on the cemetery bench, and it was in a way the most terrible moment of his life.

But he was aware of sunlight presently, falling warm on his face, on his hands which touched the cool stone of the bench. He saw that this was a flawless afternoon, perhaps the last perfect day of the year. From one horizon to another the sky was empty of clouds; the trees that stood above the tombstones and the cedars shed gold or russet leaves upon the stillness and the fields beyond were gold and russet also; the air was so clear he half expected it to ring when he moved his hand, and he could see for miles across the landscape, across the farm lands lifting and falling in wide smooth waves until they leveled out against the sky.

He had forgotten, along with everything else, how much he loved his own city and his own countryside, the places where he had spent most of his life; he thought what a fool he had been, what a shameful coward, and stood up abruptly, as if he could leave his old self there on the bench. He had thrown away ten years of his life, but there might still be time to make amends—to Laura and to his children.

The wind had died and the sound of crickets in the cold grass became part of the dreaming silence; it seemed that nothing could alter; time had stopped. But even as he stood here, high on the ridge, gazing out at the westward sweep of the continent, the shadows deepened and grew longer.

He walked forward. Shadows lay all about him as he descended the hill, but his face was fixed on the brightness which cast them, and for a little while he believed that it was brightness into which he was striding.

5

2

WHILE he waited on the corner for a trolley to carry him back into town, he could feel the strange moment in the cemetery receding. Already he was not quite sure what had happened; only that what had happened was important. You could not really leave your old self behind, in one instant become somebody quite different. The light of the setting sun made the line of stores, the still trees, the small white church in the distance, the people passing, seem somehow less ordinary than they had an hour ago; but he was only Norris Bryant, aged fifty-three, assistant city editor of the *Broadfield Chronicle*, waiting on a street corner on a Sunday afternoon in October for a trolley which took too long in coming.

Before the trolley arrived, in fact, young Vincent Rourke drew up in a maroon-colored convertible coupé and offered Norris a lift. Norris accepted, although with the other members of the staff he felt there were too many counts against Rourke and disliked taking favors from him.

Sitting at ease behind the wheel, driving with a dash and speed which took Norris's breath away, Rourke talked volubly for a while. He'd been out looking for scenery; he liked scenery, especially in October, but the colors around here seemed rather subdued.

"Compared with New England, I guess." Norris asked himself how in hell a kid making fifteen a week could afford such a car. "My wife was from the East. At least, not originally. She was born in South Dakota, of all the damn places, a few years before it stopped being part of Dakota Territory. But her mother took her East as a kid, and she grew up there." He talked about Laura deliberately; to mention her for the first time in so many years to a comparative stranger, whom he was not even sure he liked, was a kind of test. "New York City," he added, "and summers in Maine—Mount Desert Island, I guess it was."

"Pretty classy." Rourke looked a little surprised.

"Maybe it was somewhere else then, because my wife wasn't really what you could call classy. She used to be on the stage, as a matter of fact."

This time Rourke turned his head.

"Yes, from the age of about sixteen up to the time she married me, she was in show business. Good, too. She could have been a success." Norris looked at his hat, which he was holding on his knees. "She acted quite a lot with the Players here, later. In pretty nearly every show they gave. Good at comedy; liked to play character parts. Only mostly she had to be the ingénue. She always looked young, even when she—" He drew a breath, decided he was boring Rourke, and sat quiet. He hadn't been saying anything about Laura that mattered; even so, it was a relief, as if an inward heaviness had begun to lift away.

Presently Rourke said, "Better start giving me directions. I guess I don't know where you live."

Norris found that his hands were sweating slightly, and he had to look twice before he recognized the neighborhood.

"Turn left at the next corner," he said. "We're almost there."

By now the sun was level with the treetops and wide dark bars of shadow striped the asphalt and the neat lawns. They had come into a street of small houses, all very much alike, with narrow front porches and clapboard walls painted gray or brown, colors which were supposed not to show the winter soot.

"Third house on the right," Norris said, thinking how shabby, how unbelievably ugly it looked. The windows, catching none of the sun, appeared blank and dark, and a wave of loneliness swept over him; he was sorry the ride with Rourke had ended.

"Tell you what," he said, "if you don't have any plans for tonight, why don't you have supper with us?" He was aware of anxiety; hospitality was another of the things he had abandoned in the lost and foolish years. The boy's coming would be a sign that the moment in the cemetery had meant something, and that his life, which had drifted for so long, might now begin to march. "There's some beer on ice, and I'd like to have you meet my kids, the two of 'em who are home. Charlie, my older boy, he's in Detroit with his wife and baby, and Laurette's living there too, but Patricia and Joel—" He put on his hat. "You don't know many people here yet, I guess, and—"

"Thanks, I'd love to," Rourke said, after a moment's hesitation, and he smiled with great charm.

Norris's spirits soared. "No telling what you'll get to eat, of course. But after enough beer maybe that won't matter. You must get sick and tired, though, of eating out all the time."

The front door was unlocked, but Norris knew as soon as he stepped through into the living room that the house was empty; Patricia must still be out bicycling, and Joel was sailing, perhaps. He felt sad again in the dark kitchen; he'd had a vision of his two younger children running out to greet him, with cries of welcome. Only even if they'd been here, of course, they wouldn't have acted like that.

The air was so mild, although the sun was almost gone, that he and Rourke sat out on the old sagging porch swing to drink the beer; they propped their heels on the railing and watched the yellow leaves float down, the slow drift of leaf smoke from a bonfire along the street. Beer dissolved Norris's sadness and he thought

7

he liked Rourke, who was easier to talk to than either of his own sons. But how long had it been since he'd really tried to talk to his sons?

"We have a few things to thank Roosevelt for, anyway," Norris said, opening two more bottles. "I voted for Hoover myself, though right now I'm damned if I know why. Well, it's a relief, anyway, to have decent liquor around again." He drank deeply and looked out at the street. "Don't know if Roosevelt or anybody else, though, can get the country back on its feet. We were hit pretty bad here; still kind of down and out, the whole town—you must have noticed. And I guess Detroit's about the same. My kids there—" But Rourke was covering up a small yawn.

Norris was quenched for the moment, but he smiled at himself presently and said, "Well, Vinnie, you're the best new man we've had on the *Chronicle* in years. Not that you need to be told."

"It helps to be told."

"Oh, hell, if we ride you a little—" Norris's smile broadened. "Just keep going the way you have and you'll wind up our star reporter." Maybe he was overdoing it, but he kept liking Rourke better.

"Reporters are a dime a dozen these days," Rourke said. "I plan to stay put for a while."

"Well, it's a pretty good outfit. Most of us do stay put. I have myself. Started working there right after I was through college, and there I've been ever since." He could still feel frightened when he remembered how close he had come to throwing the job away with everything else; though even in his worst days he had contrived to turn up sober at his desk.

"Where'd you go to college?"

"Oh, just down to State. That was a long time ago. Turn of the century," Norris said. "I'm getting to be an old man."

He bent to pick up two more bottles of beer, and Patricia came along the street on her bicycle, followed by Johnny Wheelwright on his. The empty bottles stood along the porch floor in an incriminating row and Norris had to admit to himself that he was not, strictly speaking, cold sober. He refilled Rourke's glass and his own brazenly, though, and then rose, leaning across the rail.

"Well, you've had quite a day of it," he said. "Hi, Johnny."

They dropped their bicycles and came up slowly on to the porch. Patricia smiled only faintly at Rourke when she was introduced to him, and perched on the porch rail. Although there was a kind of glow about her from a day spent in the sun and wind, she seemed curiously remote, Norris thought—the glow was her private property, and she withheld it from the others.

"We did fifty miles," she said, and carefully avoided looking at the beer bottles.

8

"At least," said Johnny Wheelwright, who leaned on the rail at some distance from Patricia. He was trying to observe Rourke without appearing to do so, and he bristled slightly because he was in love with Patricia and inclined toward jealousy. "We went up to Long Lake, and, boy, was that water ever cold!"

"Swimming? In October?" Rourke asked.

"Why not?" said Johnny Wheelwright. "It was hot today." He kept measuring Rourke with his eyes, and in the new clarity Norris believed he knew what Johnny was thinking: that he was a good four inches taller than Rourke, and wider in the shoulders, and maybe fifteen, maybe twenty pounds heavier, and harder all over. Though he was only twenty-two to Rourke's twenty-four, he seemed older in some ways because his life had probably been a good deal more difficult; but he seemed really younger, too, because through his momentary sullenness there shone a candor and simplicity which Rourke, perhaps, had never had.

Gently Johnny thumped the rail with his fists and said, "I'll bet it was up to ninety, pretty near, around noon. Anyway, where we were."

"Maybe I passed you," Rourke said. "I was out near Long Lake myself this afternoon."

"Pretty nice up there," said Johnny. "Nice as anything you have back East, I'll bet."

"It's all right. But not what you'd call dramatic." Rourke was subtly different from the way he had been in the car, more like the slick, smooth, too-handsome bastard the *Chronicle* staff thought him.

"Anywhere looks dull," Patricia said, "if you whizz through at ninety miles an hour." She smiled sideways at Johnny, whose face promptly became radiant.

"I never do more than eighty," Rourke said. "And you see plenty with the top down. I was out West the summer before last—really West. I'd hate to do the Rocky Mountains on a bicycle."

"That's a pretty nice bus you have out there," Johnny said. "How many miles you got on her?"

"Around fifty thousand. Put a lot on that summer. It was quite a trip."

"I don't see why you ever came to Broadfield," said Patricia, "after seeing so many *dramatic* places. Why didn't you just settle down on a Rocky Mountain and stay there?"

"A bit chilly in winter. Besides, I have to earn a living."

"It's a shame, really. And to have to earn it in Broadfield, too," Patricia said.

The ruder Patricia was to Rourke, the more radiant Johnny became; Johnny had found a champion, and perhaps he needed one, but to avoid hearing any more of that kind of talk, Norris

9

went inside to get the supper. He was used to doing the cooking—he always reached home from work at least an hour before Patricia—and had acquired some skill at it; but tonight he wasn't in the mood for anything more complicated than scrambled eggs.

Johnny was in love with Patricia, but Patricia, Norris thought as he broke the eggs, didn't really seem to like boys at all. There had never been any other swains; Johnny came along too soon, and stuck, and it occurred to Norris for the first time that maybe he ought to do something about it. Johnny's mind was made up and you could see from his face and the set of his shoulders what a stubborn kid he was. A good kid too, a thoroughly nice one, but a husband for Patricia? Norris didn't know.

Johnny hadn't been able to go to college, or find a better job than as a filling-station attendant, and unless this so-called New Deal flipped out some shinier cards than it had so far, Johnny might very well go on being a filling-station attendant for the rest of his life.

Norris left the pan of eggs to keep warm in the oven and went into the dining room, where Patricia had begun to set the table.

"Joel say when he'd be back?" Norris asked.

"I haven't seen Joel today. He was still asleep when we left."

It wasn't really ungraciousness, Norris thought, looking at her flushed face, so much as a kind of stifling shyness; it wasn't that she scorned boys, but that she feared them. Laura would have known what to do about it, but Norris didn't. The effect of the beer had worn off, and he felt very tired again.

"Where's Johnny?" he asked.

"He had to put Tink to bed and see that he stayed there. You know what Tink is. Mr. and Mrs. Wheelwright were going to the movies."

"Poor Johnny. . . . All right, Vincent," Norris called through the archway. "I guess it's ready, such as it is." He fought against weariness, and searched for something lively to say; but that wasn't necessary, because Rourke began to give them a travelogue. He told them about the Carlsbad Caverns and the Grand Canyon and the White Sands of the Alamogordo and Mesa Verde and the geysers in Yellowstone National Park; and Norris, watching Patricia again, thought she was more interested than she let herself appear—not so much in what Rourke was saying as in Rourke himself. Rourke, after all, was a damn good-looking kid; much better-looking than Johnny, thought Norris, and became vaguely worried.

Vincent had worked his way around to a Pueblo Indian corn dance and Norris was pouring the coffee when Joel came in at last. He'd gotten becalmed, he said, right out in the middle of Rush Lake, and then couldn't find the oars and had to swim the boat in.

"Well, I hope you dried off all right afterwards," Norris said.

"You'll all be coming down with colds. Pull up a chair; I'll fix some more eggs for you."

"Naw, I had supper at Buzz Boonstra's. I'll just sit and watch you finish up." Joel placed himself solidly in a chair and proceeded to do just that, and Norris hoped Rourke wouldn't feel like an animal in a cage. "I would've telephoned," Joel said presently, "only I forgot."

"As long as you're finally here. Don't you think you better have some cocoa or something?" Norris asked.

"Naw, I'm fine. It was hard work, getting that boat in. Soon as I stepped ashore, I broke out into a sweat. I'm sweating right now," said Joel.

"Not noticeably." Norris wondered if things had always been like this in his house. "I guess there isn't anything for dessert."

"You could have crackers and cheese," Joel suggested. "I might be able to eat a little cheese myself." He rose and started toward the swing-door. "We didn't have much besides soup at Boonstras', and we had to say grace for that. Before *and* after. It sure is a relief not to belong to a religious family."

The swing-door flapped behind him and Norris could hear drawers being opened and slammed shut and a plate falling on the floor and breaking and a great jangle of cutlery, through all of which Joel cheerfully sang *Columbia, the Gem of the Ocean,* experimenting with new effects in his breaking voice. He was only thirteen, but like his brother Charlie was maturing early: it was as if he'd stopped being a small boy while his father's back was turned.

The commotion in the kitchen was still going on when Betty Lou Hanbury appeared. "I knocked," she said, "but I guess you-all were too busy talking to hear me, so I just swept right on in. And look what I brought!" She planked a large pie down on the table. "Some of those sour cherries off my tree that I *snatched* from the birds and bottled in the nick of time last summer," she said. "Something came over me the minute I jumped out of bed this morning. I began to get itchy in my fingers, and I said, 'Betty Lou, today's the day your piecrust'll turn out right.' And it has too. I made five pies, altogether, and I saved out the biggest for you. I've been distributing them up and down the street: largesse. I don't believe I've met you, have I?" she asked Rourke.

Joel returned with the cheese, which must have spent some moments on the floor along with the broken plate, and Betty Lou said, "Here's a pie I made out of some of those cherries you helped me pick, so you'll have to have the biggest piece. I wish you could have seen those birds, Mr. Rourke; the voracious way they went for my poor little tree. I declare, you'd have thought they were vultures. Joel had to fight them off. Now if somebody'd just get me some plates and a knife to cut this with—Oh, shoot!" she said, slapping her hand on the table. "Why didn't I think to bring along some ice cream too?"

She set to work on the pie. "You'll be thinking I'm just an old stuck-up thing," she said to Rourke, "and I have to admit I'm proud of my pies when they turn out right. . . . Where's Johnny tonight, Pat? When I first came in, why, I just took it for granted Mr. Rourke, here, was Johnny. Imagine! You must be of Irish extraction, Mr. Rourke."

"Vaguely." Rourke smiled at her. "And you're from the South?"

"I always say I'm from Dixie, and people can draw their own conclusions. . . . Black hair and blue eyes," said Betty Lou, studying him frankly. "It's a pretty devastating combination, let me tell you. There now! Have I cut the right number of pieces? If you *could* squeeze another cup of coffee out of that pot, Norris, I could use it. Sheer madness—I'll toss all night. But coffee is one thing I never could resist. Poor Sam Hanbury was the same way."

She chattered on, and they lingered at the table until Norris saw that she had turned the evening into a success. Rourke laughed at her, and baited her, and she bridled and fluttered and baited him back; Joel choked on his piece of pie; and even Patricia forgot to be self-conscious. When Rourke got up to go and said he'd had a good time, he sounded as if he meant it.

"You'll have to come again," Norris told him at the door.

"I'd like to."

"Just drop around any time."

Norris lingered at the top of the steps after Rourke had driven away, thinking he wouldn't come again because of the way Patricia had behaved. He must certainly have a talk with her, he thought; only perhaps it was too late, she had grown too old for that kind of thing. She was a young woman of nineteen, and since last June she had been working in a dentists' office, earning what Rourke earned on the paper—fifteen a week wasn't much, but somehow she managed to buy all her own clothes, besides helping with the household expenses. Norris had never asked her for help; it had been her own idea, and her insistence had hurt his pride a little. But under the prickliness she was a good kid, he thought; as good a kid as Johnny. . . .

The street was dark and quiet now; a few embers still glowed by the curb and their smell was pungent in the air. It was turning cold; there would be frost before morning.

Norris sighed and went back into the house. The dining room was empty, and Betty Lou, alone in the kitchen, was washing the dishes.

"This is the limit," Norris said, taking a dish-towel from the rail beside the sink. "You shouldn't be washing our dishes at all. Why don't you make those lazy kids help you?"

"Now, Norris, they aren't the least bit lazy, and you know it. They were worn out, so I packed them both off to bed. But *I'm* all hopped up with that coffee."

She seemed more subdued, though, than she had in the dining room; she had really, he supposed, been putting on an act for Rourke. Laura had done the same sort of thing in her own way; any kind of gathering that could be called a party went to her head like champagne.

It was the first time Norris had ever been alone with Betty Lou; possibly she felt shy, as he did the moment the notion occurred to him. He caught himself trying to straighten his stooped shoulders, and then felt too overcome with shyness to be able to speak at all for a minute.

Although she was at least forty, Betty Lou was Patricia's friend, not his. She'd lost no time, after having moved into the house next door three years ago, in making herself known to Patricia across the backyard fence. Now they held endless discussions about hats and dresses and different ways of doing hair; they went to the movies together once or twice a week; and Betty Lou showered Patricia with back numbers of the women's magazines and with recipes which Norris never tried out because mostly they were for ways of making food look like something else—halved pears were turned into girls' faces, bananas into candles, carrot shavings into pond lilies. It was surprising, really, that the pie had so tamely resembled a pie.

"How'd you like our cub reporter?" Norris managed to ask eventually.

"Is *that* who he is? I've been hearing things about him."

"What kind of things? And who from?"

"Oh, just that he was awful good-looking. From Milly Prentiss." Milly was one of Betty Lou's bosom friends; all Betty Lou's friends were of the bosom variety.

Norris chuckled. "Milly's old enough to know better."

"So am I, for goodness' sake! Just the same, my heart did give a little-bitty flutter when I took a good square look at him and realized he wasn't Johnny Wheelwright."

"We've been riding him, kind of, down at the office, and I thought maybe— Well, I thought being a little friendly wouldn't do any harm."

"Just so long as Pat doesn't lose her heart to him."

"I guess there isn't much danger." Norris sighed again. "Betty Lou, do you think—I'm wondering if there isn't some way I can help Pat. I've let her and Joel sort of go their own way, and Joel's

13

all right, I guess, but Pat—I couldn't help noticing the way she acted. She was rude to Vincent, Betty Lou."

"Oh, she's just— Shoot, Norris, she's only nineteen; give her time. And if she didn't like that Rourke boy, it's just as well. Though *I'm* not so sure she didn't." Betty Lou plucked the last dish from the water and set it in the draining-basket. "Blue eyes and black hair, and those *curls*. And did you see his eyelashes! He has a fatal charm, that boy, and don't you believe he doesn't know it!"

"M'm." Norris frowned, polishing the last dish over and over long after it was dry. "He's bright, anyway. Born newspaperman. We'll have to put him on a real beat, the way he's going." He laid the dish away and turned back. "I like him," he said.

Betty Lou took off her apron.

"Why don't you?" Norris asked.

"*I* didn't say I didn't like him!" Betty Lou opened her eyes very wide. They were blue, too—clear and guileless.

"You don't, though," Norris insisted; but he had found a more immediate interest than Rourke.

"Now, Norris, don't you go trying to pin me down. I won't *be* pinned down. And I'm not saying anything about Vincent Rourke, one way or the other. Vincent," said Betty Lou, hanging the apron on a peg. "I never did like that name for a man."

3

BEFORE Vincent left New York there had been a farewell evening with his uncle, Bertrand Vaughan, who had pulled the wires which had set in motion a train of events which resulted in the job; but Bertrand was apologetic about its having turned out to be in Broadfield. Going there, he said, was just like burying yourself alive.

"Not that I've ever been near the place," he added. "But I know exactly what it's like. Poor Vinnie! You don't *have* to go, you know."

"Oh, yes, I do," said Vincent.

"Well, yes, I suppose you must go somewhere. But I was wondering if I knew anybody human who lived there." Uncle Bertrand rubbed one hand gently over his thinning hair. He was a large, plump man, who had looked with some guilt on his nephew ever since 1929, when the crash had wiped out the larger part of Vincent's inheritance, all because Uncle Bertrand had been gambling with Vincent's money.

"It seems to me that years ago, in Paris, there was a rather

14

amusing woman," he said. "Carola Somebody. She was married to a princeling just then, one of those Central European things; she was divorcing him, so her name is probably different now. Anyway, she was from Broadfield, and I do believe she went back there eventually."

He lifted the telephone to call one of his innumerable women friends, and after fifteen minutes of persiflage obtained the information he wanted.

"She's Carola Wilmot now," he told Vincent. "That's what she started life as, but there was a British husband before the princeling, and I rather think there was an American one later. What a restless creature she must be! I don't think you'll need a letter of introduction; I'm sure she'll remember me, and once she's *seen* you it will all be plain sailing. She's a withered crone, of course, from your point of view, but if there *are* any amusing people in Broadfield, Carola will be sure to know them. But for God's sake, Vinnie, be careful this time."

So Carola's was the first number Vincent called, after he'd had a telephone installed in his broom-closet of an apartment. Her voice came over the wire low and throaty, and of *course* she remembered Bertie Vaughan, who was a rat for having lost touch with her but a lamb to tell Vincent about her, and Vincent must drop around for cocktails the very next afternoon; she was tired of being un-gay and some hardy souls were braving the threat of impending revolution to come, and it would probably be rather dreary but he might save the day.

Carola lived in a Victorian mansion on Warner Street hill. There was a sweep of lawn, rising steeply like a green wave, and breasting the wave was the tall pale-gray house; it looked a little shabby, but in the most genteel way, and the long windows gave it an air of raising its eyebrows at the town. The interior had not disappointed Vincent. The ceilings soared up into shadow and the brocade curtains hung in folds richly wine-red against gray-green walls; the furniture, which must have been new when the house was, had been thinned out judiciously so that now there was an effect of space instead of clutter; and the spaciousness was emphasized by large mirrors in gilt frames.

Vincent called there several times, once the ice was broken; Carola was typical of Uncle Bertrand's menagerie, and eventually Vincent took her out to dinner; and now, a few days after his Sunday supper with the Bryants, he had been invited to dinner in the mansion. Carola's mother was dead; her father had had a stroke five years earlier, after the crash, and lay paralyzed in an upstairs room; there was a manservant like a small sad monkey in a white jacket, and out in the back regions was his wife, reigning unseen over the kitchen; but the house always seemed quiet and empty and larger than it really was.

In a small room beyond the dining room, Vincent and Carola sat drinking bourbon and water; and presently Vincent told her about the Bryants and was inspired to impersonate Betty Lou Hanbury. He did it so well that Carola lay back on her chaise longue and laughed aloud.

"What a dreadful boy you are," she said. She was a tall woman, amply but firmly molded, with reddish hair and the creamy skin which goes with it; perhaps she was forty-five, but she was younger and certainly more vivid than Uncle Bertrand had suggested.

"Well, she's obviously set her cap at him," Vincent said of Betty Lou, after he'd finished his impersonation, "and the poor dope doesn't know it. She'll get him, too, sooner or later, with all her bewitching little ways."

"I wonder," said Carola. "I used to know Norris Bryant quite well. I knew Laura Bryant, that is, and Norris was often just there. Laura was really a rather remarkable person. She was Somebody, which poor Norris, of course, never was. I don't mean she amounted to anything socially, as society goes in Broadfield, but she was one of those people who knock down all the barriers because they won't admit there are such things. She was lovely, you know, really lovely, but she had enough of a common streak to be *most* appealing to anything male."

All traces of the Middle West were gone from Carola's accent, which had overtones of Boston, of New York, of Oxford, and even at times of something really foreign. Listening to her voice with the small throaty catch in it, that hurried over some words and drawled over others, always with an effect wholly calculated, Vincent thought that since her return to Broadfield she must have been almost as bored, as starved for the kind of society she loved, as she said she had been—each time he saw her she talked like this, avidly, as a drunkard would drink. All he need do was be amused by what she said, and prod her now and then with a bright enough remark to keep her talking.

"He said his wife was an actress, once. How'd she ever happen to land here?" Vincent asked idly.

"Ancient history, Vincent. She was the jeune fille in a stock company that struggled along here for a few months, back around 1906 or 1907. It was later that I knew Laura, after we started the Players. I had a little to do with the Players after my first marriage, and a good deal after my third. I suppose I was jealous of Laura, because she almost always played the leads. Well, you can see that to begin with she obviously wasn't respectable at all, not much better than a harlot from Broadfield's point of view then. And Norris was only a boy off a farm. But the years went by and

16

the background stopped mattering because it didn't matter to Laura. It was what she *was* that mattered; and somehow she made it so that it was what you were too that mattered to her. Not what you pretended to be, or how much money you had. Oh, the dowager duchesses—my late mamma, for example—never accepted her; but that was so much the worse for the dowager duchesses. They didn't know what they were missing. They still don't, poor dears."

"It sounds so small-town," Vincent said.

"Darling, that's what we are. We'd probably be that way if we grew as large as Detroit or Chicago; which I may say there's no sign of our doing. We've been shoved off, somehow, into a cozy little cul-de-sac, and if things go on at the present rate we'll wind up a ghost town. But what I started to say was that I doubt whether Norris will succumb to the wiles of your bouncing Betty Lou. What he had for Laura was a grand passion, I give you my word."

"Oh, now, listen," said Vincent, and laughed.

"It's true!" cried Carola, sitting up. "You're only an infant so you think it's absurd, but I give you my word he was mad about that woman. He very nearly drank himself to death after she died; how he ever managed to hold on to his job I don't know—though I believe he's good at it, and one rather had the impression, in those days, that most of the *Chronicle* staff was drunk the better part of the time. Well, the two elder children proceeded to go straight to hell, and the younger ones were farmed out—literally, I mean. His parents and his sister and brother-in-law are still out there on the family farm, and that's where the younger girl and boy spent their tenderer years."

"What a mine of information you are," said Vincent.

"It's what happens, you know, when you settle down in a place like this. One spends most of one's time raking over all the old scandals. I swore when I had to come back that I wouldn't let it happen to me. But behold, it's happened!"

She rose to mix more drinks. "Eventually," she said, "Norris climbed on the wagon, and after he'd been on it long enough, he got his children back."

"He fell off a little way the other night."

"Well, my dear, beer! His daughter does allow him a sip of beer now and then, I suppose. He can't have been a true alcoholic; they can't drink at all, I believe, or they're lost. But why do you suppose Bouncing Bet *wants* to marry him? Why did Laura marry him? I'd as soon marry a zombie, myself. I suppose there must be more to Norris than meets the eye. . . . You say Bouncing Bet is quite attractive."

"Quite."

"And the daughter?" Carola handed him his drink. "What did you think of her?"

"Very attractive indeed. In a way, beautiful."

"Ah, yes. The nice wholesome hausfrau type—I *knew* that's how your taste would run. I suppose your plans are all made."

"There seems to be somebody else with that kind of plan."

"Oh, Dick Wheelwright's boy. Dick, you know, is or was a really brilliant architect, but he— No," said Carola, "I refuse to get started on the Wheelwrights. But do ask me about them the next time you come. *There's* a story for you! I'm sure, though, that if you're really interested in the Bryant girl, you'll have no trouble with Johnny."

"Except maybe down an alley on a dark night."

"Yes, I see what you mean. He used to play football and I believe he was knocked out once in a Golden Gloves tournament. But you seem *fairly* substantial, Vincent. Couldn't you take care of yourself?"

"I'm a pacifist."

"Never mind, I dislike bullies. No, but if the Bryant girl should fall in love with you, that would hardly be your fault, would it? I'm sure Johnny Wheelwright could be made to see things reasonably."

"Doesn't the past give you enough to talk about?" Vincent asked.

"I suppose I have rather been leaping ahead. And on the whole I think you'd better not marry the Bryant girl. Think of having Norris as a father-in-law! You shed a bright light, Vincent, and I'd hate to see it quenched." Carola arched an eyebrow at her little flight and said, *"How* attractive is she? I'm sure you must be an expert already, even though you do appear so young and guileless. With the gifts God gave you it could hardly be otherwise."

"Well, if *she* sheds a light," Vincent said, "it's a very cold one. Like a reflection from an iceberg."

"No passion, then?"

Vincent laughed. "I'd have to see more of her."

"Perhaps it just needs to be kindled. And Johnny is not what I should call incendiary. *Do* you plan to see more of her?"

"Yes, I think I do," said Vincent, who had been thinking nothing of the sort. Partly because of the bourbon, he had felt a mild flutter of excitement as Carola talked; he had been thinking that if there were any games to be played it would be far more amusing to play them with Carola, and wondering if she hadn't something of the sort in mind. But if she had, she was too worldly to be obvious about it yet.

"She liked you?" Carola asked him now.

"I think not."

"There must be something seriously wrong with her. Or can you turn your light on and off? Well, you must keep me informed. I want to know how it all goes. Come along, now, and have dinner before I die of starvation as well as old age."

Vincent lay awake a long time that night on the bed which dropped from the wall and thereby occupied most of his living room. His apartment was on the top floor of another Victorian mansion, but one which had come a long way down in the world. Out from the veranda hung a neon sign reading *Furnished Apartments,* which flashed on and off until midnight, and even in its heyday the house couldn't have been the equal of Carola's. Through the thin walls and floor came a tinkle of jazz, murmured conversations, creaks from the stairs, an occasional girlish squeal or giggle, and mysterious bumps and thumps; it was like living in a house of ill fame, thought Vincent, who'd never been reduced to visiting one.

Tonight he felt oppressed and tried to divert himself by thinking about Patricia Bryant, who offered a challenge of sorts. Always, before, it had been so easy, too easy to be amusing beyond a certain point; but Patricia was the victim of fear, he thought, and to lull her fear out of existence would be a project to occupy him for a long time, to keep the boredom and the recurrent black moods at bay. It might be time to start making an effort again, instead of just letting things happen to him.

He smiled, but the oppression remained, and presently he could not think about Patricia or anything in the future; his mind traveled back into the past, as it did at such times—all the way back to the years with Aunt Lucy, who had become his guardian after his father ran off with a younger and prettier lady than his mother and his mother died: of a broken heart, according to his aunt, who had never married.

Aunt Lucy lived in a small New England college town, where one had the advantage of lectures and concerts and amateur theatricals and intellectual companionship, and she was a strange mixture of twentieth century and nineteenth. She had decided that she and the world were much better off without God; she had once fought for woman's suffrage, and she would discuss birth control at the dinner table; but she believed in rearing a small boy strictly and Vincent's childhood had mostly been unhappy.

Among her many crimes against him, Aunt Lucy forced Vincent to wear long black stockings to school, and other odd garments similar to those worn by nice little boys when she had been a nice little girl; and because everybody made fun of him Vincent didn't know for a long time how good-looking he was. Nor did he make any friends. As much as possible he lived inside a fantasy, a recurrent aspect of which was the sudden arrival of his father on a dark and stormy night, a violent battle with Aunt Lucy, and happiness ever after with his father and the lady who'd been prettier than his mother.

But the only person who ever arrived suddenly—and not once on a dark and stormy night—was Uncle Bertrand. He brought with him boxes of expensive chocolates which Aunt Lucy wouldn't let Vincent eat, and intimations of a wider and far giddier world than Vincent had ever known; and so, although Uncle Bertrand was much too fat and hardly a romantic figure, Vincent conceived an admiration for him.

The strife with Aunt Lucy, the corroding loneliness, the escape into fantasy, went on until Vincent was fifteen and a girl who was too young to be teaching English in a high school told him he had the face of a poet and asked if he never wrote poetry. The girl was not to blame, perhaps, and she never knew that she had turned Vincent's head, or that from then on the mirror on the wall was more than just a mirror to him. Nothing outward came of his friendship with her, except one or two afternoon tea parties in the fern-filled parlor of the boarding-house where she lived, at which they read aloud to each other from the works of Rupert Brooke and Edna St. Vincent Millay; only those spring afternoons among the ferns, and in June one A on his report card.

A short time after Vincent brought the report card home and flung it in Aunt Lucy's face, Aunt Lucy died; not of a broken heart, but of cancer. The knowledge that she was doomed had been with her for a long time, and perhaps she wasn't too much to be blamed, either, for what she had done to Vincent.

Now on the verge of sixteen, he stepped from Aunt Lucy's world into Uncle Bertrand's. There was a sun-struck summer at East-hampton, in the course of which Vincent discovered that he had a body as well as a face, became somewhat vain of it, and went in more for exercise than he had before. But in the fall he was shunted off into an expensive prep school, where he should have been going right along, said virtuous Uncle Bertrand, who had been tampering with legal arrangements and was now able to spend Vincent's money for him.

In this world Vincent was even unhappier than he had been in Aunt Lucy's. There were no pretty young English teachers to tell him he had the face of a poet; there was a snobbism different from anything he had so far encountered; and there were aberrations which appalled him, as they were more or less bound to after Aunt Lucy's dark references to immorality.

Uncle Bertrand was absorbed in himself, and to Vincent it seemed normal to feel miserable. It wasn't until the Christmas vacation of his second and last year at the school that his uncle emerged from himself long enough to notice Vincent's misery. The result was a week of theater-going and of visits to the more fashionable speakeasies, with large gay parties of ladies and gentlemen, all a great deal older than Vincent. Some of the ladies were not too old, however, to tell Vincent that he was simply adorable and flatter him with little pats on the hand and little entreaties not to be so bashful and little playful kisses now and then. Vincent could feel himself growing up very fast, that week, and when he put on the formal clothes Uncle Bertrand had given him for Christmas, he decided that he was already a man of the world. So far, though, he'd had nothing more dangerous to drink than ginger ale: Uncle Bertrand's conscience worked erratically.

The day after Christmas Uncle Bertrand was afflicted with a sudden distaste for New York, and off he and Vincent went to Canada to celebrate the arrival of the New Year in Quebec. There Uncle Bertrand became so thoroughly absorbed in his own affairs as to forget his nephew for a while, and some pretty ladies, younger than those he'd met in New York, gave Vincent champagne to drink, and Vincent learned how much more exciting it is to see yourself reflected in the way a woman looks at you than in the mirror on the wall.

The ghost of Aunt Lucy haunted him briefly, and then he thought he had laid it to rest; by the time he returned to the expensive prep school he was very sophisticated indeed. He had discovered what pretty ladies were for, and what his good looks were for, and made cautious explorations among the younger faculty wives; there were some rebuffs, of course, but there were also some rather astonishing successes.

He had made no friends at prep school, and he made none at Harvard, where he was not asked to join a club; but he didn't mind, because when his studies bored him there were always more pretty ladies. Twice before he was graduated there were pretty ladies who didn't abide by the rules. The first time Vincent was frightened because he felt suddenly out of his depth; the second time he discovered how to be ruthless, and it was in its way as important as the earlier discoveries had been.

But between the first time and the second, the black mood entered his life. It was different from the childish despondencies, for out of this he could not escape into fantasy. He sat for hours quite motionless in his room; he walked for hours back and forth along the river in the bitter wind; and lay awake all night wondering if he was going insane.

It lasted only that long, a day and a night; but later attacks, which came in his first year out of college, were more protracted. He was living then in his uncle's apartment; the crash had occurred early in his Harvard career, and Uncle Bertrand, who had been more cautious with his money than with Vincent's, had been dipping generously into his own pocket. Now he told Vincent not to bother about a job just yet; there had been an unexpected little windfall and Vincent must share it, and maybe there would be a turn for the better soon and more jobs available.

There were a great many parties that winter, but all the gaiety cost Vincent very little—it was fashionable to be poor. When the bad moods came he could climb into the car his uncle had given him as a graduation present, and drive far and fast enough to leave them behind.

It was because of the mood's most violent and prolonged attack that he had taken his grand tour, the summer before the one just over. During the winter he had acquired at last a friend of sorts, an insignificant little boy just out of Princeton who didn't really seem to belong in the Social Register; he worked in a bank and was quite content, when Vincent wasn't in the mood for girls, to sit and listen to him talk about himself. When Vincent suggested the trip, the little boy from Princeton gave up his job in the bank and changed all his savings into traveler's checks; and they set forth together. But the little boy from Princeton was a crashing bore; his tongue was somehow loosened by the unrolling miles, and he began to tell Vincent all about *him*self in a flood of confidences which could not be dammed. It also turned out that he had a delicate stomach and he was constantly being sickened by the food they ate at roadside stands and small-town cafés and tourist camps; and possibly his feelings about Vincent were more romantic than they should have been. So in Santa Fe one night they became very drunk and had a savage quarrel, and next morning the little boy from Princeton, jobless and penniless too after he'd paid for his railroad ticket, went back to New York while Vincent drove westward quite alone.

He thought of those weeks as the happiest time in his life; it was as if he had been suddenly set free—from the past, from his own personality, from even the most tenuous human relationships; he was only a moving awareness of mountain and sky, desert and weather. It had been an intense experience, and when he told Norris Bryant he liked scenery he spoke from the heart.

It was November before he returned to New York, and he found his uncle in a peevish mood. Now, it seemed, it was high time Vincent settled down and began to scratch for a living. Vincent reminded him that he, Bertrand Vaughan, was responsible for the fact that a living must be scratched for. Bertrand sulked, but eventually wangled a job for Vincent in a small advertising agency which was about to go on the rocks. When it did go on the rocks, Vincent loafed again, and by early spring was deep in the most disastrous of all his affairs. Ruthlessness worked, eventually, but it left a bad taste in Vincent's mouth; and before summer came his uncle was for the first time really upset about him, and decided Vincent would have to get out of town and stay there.

Vincent suggested that newspaper work might not be too bad. On the periphery of Uncle Bertrand's circle of friends was a scattering of journalists, and they all said a medium-sized provincial paper in a medium-sized provincial city would be ideal, the perfect bottom rung for a distinguished career. While the wires were being pulled, Vincent lay in the sun on Fire Island, which was just far enough out of town so that he wouldn't have any embarrassing encounters; chastened at last, he didn't even look at the girls walking by in their bathing suits.

And while he drove out into the Middle West, which had been only an area to get through quickly the last time he'd been this way, he devised the new rôle he was going to play. He was only a little frightened. Everybody knew that Middle Westerners were friendly, and it would just be a question of putting his charm to work in a new direction. (Charm, thought Vincent, consists largely in convincing other people that they are charming.) He would be humble and naive, and eager to learn; he would be such a brilliant success at the job that it wouldn't be too long, even in times like these, before he could mount from the first rung to the second, and from the second to the third; at thirty he would already be in Europe, a full-blown foreign correspondent. . . .

Norris Bryant, standing on the street corner that afternoon, had presented himself as a means to an end. He must be cultivated further, and if that involved cultivating his daughter too—cold and gauche she might be, but attractive she was certainly—so much the better, thought Vincent. Life in Broadfield might turn out to be far more amusing than he had expected.

4

VINCENT began to turn up on the front doorstep two or three nights a week, and Norris didn't know what to make of it at first. When Patricia was not present, he and Vincent talked shop; when she was, there occurred a curious kind of conversation, addressed to Norris but somehow aimed at Patricia, who sat off in a corner, her head bent above the cardigan she was knitting, saying nothing.

By degrees, a picture was being built up: of a sad young man, who did not, however, pity himself but had a deep understanding of other people; a gentle, wistful, dreamy young man, who appreciated these qualities in other people; a shy young man, who

23

probably created the wrong impression the first time he met other people. It was mostly a matter of overtones, but Norris became increasingly puzzled and a little worried when he noticed that Patricia's hands would sometimes pause in mid-air, the cardigan suspended, while she stole glances across the room at Vincent.

Over these evenings presided a photograph of Laura, which now stood on top of the piano. Norris had hidden it away ten years ago, but on the Sunday night of his visit to the cemetery, before he went to bed, he'd rubbed the dust from the glass and polished the silver frame and put it in place again. Possibly because of her stage career, Laura had known how to smile at a photographer; but through the evenings when Vincent talked so volubly about nothing, Norris began to wonder if there wasn't something mildly ironical in the curve of her lips. . . .

Then Patricia began reaching home from the dentists' office earlier than usual; and one night Norris, who was slicing string beans at the kitchen table when she came in, asked if she'd been taking the trolley. Patricia crossed the kitchen and started up the back stairs.

"Oh, no. Vincent's been driving me," she said, and went on to take her evening shower. Cleanliness was almost an obsession with her. She didn't use any of the oils and face-creams Laurette rubbed so lavishly into her skin. She applied lipstick with such discretion that no stains were ever left on napkins or cigarette ends or the rims of cups. She did not varnish her nails. And ever since she'd had her job she had gone upstairs for a shower the moment she reached home, as though a day spent in even so antiseptic an atmosphere had coated her with a subtle contamination.

When she came down again, shining and pure, her thick hair burnished from brushing, to set the table, Norris decided to make further investigations. But it was a delicate matter, and he trembled at the thought of blundering.

"You don't think he's so bad then," he said, going into the dining room to help her.

"Who? Oh, Vincent." Patricia's face remained calm and still. "He was just there waiting in his car one night when I came out. It would have been silly to say no. And he's been there every night since." She stood back from the table and looked directly into Norris's face. "Do you like him?"

"He's going to be a good newspaperman."

Patricia folded three paper napkins and laid them neatly in place. "I thought at first he was terribly conceited, but now—sometimes I almost feel sorry for him." Color flooded her face. "But that's silly, of course. I mean—"

A great happiness welled up in Norris; she was about to confide in him. But there was a hissing from the stove and then the smell of gas, and on her way to set things right Patricia said, "The beans. You always put too much water."

She looked so much like Laura, Norris thought a little later, while he and she and Joel ate their dinner, so very much like Laura when Laura had first come to Broadfield: the same thick honey-colored hair, the same wide-set gray eyes and generous mouth, the same smooth skin; but whatever emotions she had she kept tucked away out of sight, and Laura had never been like that. Laura at twenty had been a woman already, overflowing with love for life and the world, with humor, with generosity. She would give and give—you knew it to look at her—but all the giving somehow renewed the abundance. In imagination Norris set Patricia beside Laura and it seemed as though Patricia, touchy and proud and difficult, prey to secret woes, were not alive at all. He suddenly wanted to shake her, shout at her: Wake up, wake up before it's too late!

"Vincent asked me to go to the movies tonight," she said, as though her father's thoughts had reached across the silence. "But Betty Lou's coming in to help with a new dress."

"I hope she brings another pie," said Joel. "What's for dessert, Pop, anyway?"

"Canned peaches."

"I guess I won't bother then." Joel rose, grabbing two slices of bread from the dish, and started out of the room.

"Where are you going?" Norris called.

"Roller-skating," Joel said, cramming bread into his mouth, and was gone before Norris could tell him not to be later than nine or ask him how about the homework.

"Joel might just as well not live here at all," he said. "Do you ever get a chance to talk to him, Pat, about school or anything? I don't believe he's done a stroke of homework this fall."

"He leads such a completely physical life. Though he hopes to go to West Point," Patricia said, astounding Norris. "Do you want any more vegetables, or shall I get the peaches?"

"You can get the peaches," Norris said, and his thoughts strayed to Joel, who couldn't mean it seriously. Remembering Laura's ardent pacifism after the World War, her conviction that there would never be another, Norris decided he was going to have to do something about Joel too. But Joel could wait. When Patricia sat down again, Norris returned to the attack.

"I don't know how to say it, Pat. After the way I've acted—not taking any interest, really, in you or Joel, for such a long time. I suddenly woke up a couple of weeks ago—that's what it felt like, anyway—and saw, well, I hadn't exactly been doing my duty by you." It wasn't what he meant to say. "About Johnny Wheel-

25

wright," he began again. "You've been going with Johnny for a long time now, and if he doesn't stand a chance—"

"Johnny can't possibly get married anyway, Father, as long as he's helping to support his family."

"Times are bound to get better. His father'll be designing houses right and left again. But what I started to say, you can't keep him dangling forever, Pat. It isn't fair."

Patricia finished her peaches. Looking away from her father, she said, "I haven't seen Johnny since the trip to Long Lake," and went into the kitchen.

Norris thought how well she carried herself, how straight and strong she was, almost as lovely as her mother, and made for bearing children; you couldn't blame Johnny for feeling as he did about her. But against the barrier she set up, Norris was helpless; there was no way in which he could touch her.

Patricia, though, plugging the drain in the sink, turning the hot water on hard, set her teeth against the inward trembling her father had started. He wanted to be kind, he wanted to help; she knew that. But why couldn't he understand that his former neglect was infinitely kinder than this clumsy new effort to meddle in her affairs?

When he came out presently she could feel his irritation because of the haphazard way she always washed dishes. Her father, untidy about most other things, liked to make a science of this, stacking the dishes neatly according to size, washing them in an unvarying routine. She tried to ignore his irritation, but it was no use. Automatically, almost, quite against her will, she began to slam things into the draining-basket; she stared through the window and prayed that he would not try to talk to her any more.

"About Joel and West Point," he said eventually; his voice was like a peace offering, and unreasonably this irritated her further. "Does he really mean it?"

"I can't read Joel's mind. If he has one." Hateful, hateful she was, despicable, a bitch—she let the word explode in her mind, and part of her stood aside and mourned over the way she treated her father.

"How long?" Norris asked. "How long has it been going on?" His voice was humble now and Patricia could have wept into the soapsuds.

"I don't know, Father," she said wearily. "Ages, I guess. Buzz Boonstra's brother is there now, and Buzz wants to go too. Buzz and Joel are both dazzled by the uniform, I suppose. I told him he'd have to study harder if he ever expected to get in."

"Joel in the Army," Norris said.

"Well, he isn't even fourteen yet. Nothing will ever come of it. He'll change his mind."

"Yes, sure. Foolish to get upset."

"And the Army's safe at least," Patricia said. "Dull, but safe. You know where your next meal is coming from."

When the dishes were done she went up to her room and sat in a chair pulled over near the window, turning the pages of a magazine Betty Lou had given her. She wished Betty Lou herself were not coming over; she did not want to see anybody else today, or be talked at by anybody else, or invited to share any kind of intimacy.

But she went on feeling sorry for her father. It was as if he'd waked up suddenly, he had said at dinner; and she thought how her mother's photograph had reappeared on top of the piano. Something strange had happened to him, certainly—for several weeks now she hadn't been able to think of him merely as a kind of shabby ghost.

All these years he'd never mentioned his wife, and Patricia had supposed he was trying to convince himself that Laura had never lived. For a long time she had believed it must be true, as Aunt Maudie and Grandma Bryant said, that in some way Laura had been an evil woman, cruel to Norris, and that her death was a judgment, the wages of sin. And now, thought Patricia, after ten years, perhaps he had decided to forgive her.

It was difficult for Patricia, who had been only nine when her mother died, to remember what Laura Bryant had seemed like. Upon the earlier image of someone who shed kindness wherever she moved, a later and darker image had been superimposed, and it was this which seemed more vivid to Patricia. Her father had never said or done anything to make it otherwise.

And Grandma Bryant and Aunt Maudie were people who never left you alone. From morning to night they told you what to do, and even when you obeyed they didn't seem pleased. Always they looked at you hungrily, staring at the thoughts, it seemed, which moved behind your eyes. They talked with vehemence in their high flat voices, back and forth endlessly, from the moment they rose before daylight to the moment they carried the kerosene lamps upstairs at nine in the evening; you could not escape their voices, pounding into your head the vision of the world which they thought proper.

Joel had been too young to be affected, and Cousin Leon, a year older than Patricia, had developed a kind of immunity. Cousin Leon got far more gold-paper stars in Sunday school than Patricia did, but he knew all the words the hired men knew; he accepted cigarettes from the hired men and went down to the river-bank to smoke them; he swam stark naked in the muddy water and flaunted himself when Patricia once came on him like that by accident. And there was a rainy afternoon when he and Patricia

27

were doing stunts on the trapeze in the barn, and he began to feel her, and because she shrank away from him told her what all the animals did, and men and women too, and suggested they might experiment themselves. There was a queer look on Leon's face; his eyes seemed to be slimed over; and for a long time after that the same slime appeared in the eyes of everybody Patricia looked at.

If the animals were disgusting, the human beings were more so; all the loud virtuous words of Aunt Maudie and Grandma Bryant couldn't cover up that truth. Indeed what they really did was to proclaim it; they shouted the vileness of man. . . .

Several times, in those four years on the farm, Norris came out from town. Joel laughed at Pop's behavior so hard he fell down on the front lawn, but Patricia went up into her room and bolted the door and stuck her fingers in her ears, so as not to hear his voice rising, rising, screaming at Grandma Bryant and Aunt Maudie: "They're my kids; they're mine, God dammit, and it's time they came to live with me again." When the rage had spent itself, he wept. "I'm so lonely. Oh, Christ, if you knew how lonely I was you'd let them come. I'll be all right, I swear I will, if I have the kids back again. They're good kids; they aren't like Laurette and Charlie, and if I had them with me I couldn't drink, don't you see? Don't you believe me, for Christ's sake?"

Eventually they would pour hot coffee into him and bundle him back into his car; Uncle Homer would do the driving and stay with Norris all night, seeing to it that he reached the paper on time next morning. Complaining loudly, Aunt Maudie drove the farm truck in to fetch Uncle Homer back, and everybody was behind schedule all day, and nobody was restored to good temper for a week.

It was a mercy Norris hadn't killed himself driving in that condition, they kept repeating to one another, but the way they said it made it sound as if they wished he had. There was an accident finally; Norris wasn't badly hurt, but his license was revoked, the car went off to the junkpile, and after that he never came out at all except for Thanksgiving and Christmas.

Then there was the evening when Grandma Bryant fetched Patricia from her room several hours after she'd gone to sleep; there was something she had to decide.

At one end of the bare kitchen table sat Grandpa Bryant, at the other Aunt Maudie; Uncle Homer and Grandma Bryant peered at Patricia around the lamp with a white china shade. It was winter; when wind gnawed the corner of the house there was a little shifting of coals in the stove.

"Well, Patricia," said Grandpa Bryant, and his voice was very gentle; he'd always been kinder than the others. "Seems like your father has been all right for almost a year now. That's what we

28

told him, you know, if he could be all right for a year, then we'd give you your choice. You're almost fourteen, and I guess you can decide for Joel as well as yourself. Your father wants you to go back and live with him again, and in a way I guess it's right you should. But if you don't want to, why, your grandma and aunt and uncle and me, we'll be glad to have you stay right on with us."

He smiled at her faintly and polished his glasses, breathing on them heavily before he rubbed them with a blue bandanna handkerchief.

"You don't have to *worry* about your father," he went on, after the spectacles were back on his nose. "He had a very bad time, you see, and that can make people act queer. But he's a good man, Patricia, and he's all over his trouble now. But it's entirely up to you."

Patricia sat very still at the table, not quite fully awake. Years later she didn't know why they'd chosen such an hour to do this to her, unless it was to make sure Joel and Leon were safely out of the way. Their eyes bored into her, all except Grandpa Bryant's; he stared at the circle of lamplight on the ceiling.

Although her father was somebody she no longer knew, Patricia had finished weighing one thing against another before her grandfather was halfway through speaking; but it was hard to tell them her decision, choosing wickedness against righteousness—for that was how they would see it, despite what he'd said.

"I want to go back," she said finally, "and Joel does too."

Aunt Maudie opened her mouth, but Grandpa Bryant's glance flashed down the table at her. "No, Maudie," he said, and that was that.

For a long time Patricia felt nostalgic about the farm. What she had hated about it dwindled, and she remembered only the good things, the summers especially; the wind and the wildflowers and the great sense of space, birds rising up to sing in the sky, the coppery oceans of wheat, and the emerald oceans of oats that became a clear pale gold after the wheat had been harvested. She remembered the kindness of Grandpa Bryant, and how Uncle Homer taught her to swim and ride a horse; she remembered Aunt Maudie helping her with arithmetic and spelling, and Grandma Bryant's skill with knitting-needles, and the look on her tight wrinkled face when she kneaded bread-dough—the look of a priestess attending a miracle. . . .

She was homesick for the farm and then she became used to the new life. Charlie had gone away to Detroit and presently Laurette followed him, and life except for Patricia's mixed-up feelings about Johnny was peaceful. It never occurred to her that Norris too had a life of the emotions. And because she never entered the *Chronicle* building or saw any other members of the staff she

29

knew nothing of the affection and respect they had for him. His mind away from work seemed to move so slowly that she never guessed he was exceptional, a highly skilled craftsman—an artist, in fact.

He emerged briefly from the shadows the evening she came home and told him she'd found herself a job. She was so young, he said, and she didn't have to work; he was making enough for the three of them. She could not understand his distress; it was a time when having work to do and being paid for doing it still seemed more important than anything else in the world. Although it was a dull job and she knew she'd been given it mostly because of her appearance—as if she were to become the handsomest piece of furniture in the reception-room—it was better than frittering her time away at home; and fifteen dollars a week, in those years, in that town, could be stretched a long way if you were careful.

She sat all day long behind a little desk, overlooking the leather sofas and the tables bearing magazines, making appointments for the four dentists whose offices opened two on either side of her, being polite to their patients, mailing out the bills. What she liked best about the job was that it allowed her to remain impersonal; her desk was a fortress and she wore her impersonality like armor.

Three of the dentists were quite elderly, and she had been able to quell the fourth, who was young, red-faced, and dashing, and who had been inclined, at first, to make genial advances when his wife was out of town. He addressed her now as Miss Frigidaire, but because she really liked to think of herself that way, she had come to feel that this was almost a compliment.

It was different with Johnny, though. Two years ago Johnny had told her he was in love with her; a year ago he'd asked if they couldn't announce their engagement; recently, on the day they bicycled out to Long Lake, he said he couldn't stand it any more unless she loved him too.

She was fond of Johnny, up to a point, but she couldn't help thinking that he was a little dull; he would never understand half the ideas that went coasting through her head. Still, when she wasn't actually with him she could begin to work up an almost romantic emotion about him; it was his physical presence which disconcerted her. She didn't like the clothes he wore, and his trousers were never pressed; his hands were too large and thick and sinewy and he couldn't ever scour out all the grime that had worked its way into the skin; sometimes he smelled a little of sweat. He kept his hair cropped short, and his face had a bumpy look because his cheekbones and chin were prominent and he'd broken his nose playing football. More often than not he was just a nice boy, but there were also times when he seemed too male— his voice thickened and there was too much hunger, too much urgency in his eyes. She shrank from the fact of physical desire; when she became aware of it in him, she knew he was hateful. There had been clumsy scuffles, once or twice, and she had felt degraded afterwards; but now he knew better than to touch her.

The day they rode out to Long Lake had started well: the bright air made them a little drunk, and they sang as they pedaled, until they both were out of breath. Then they laughed at each other; they shared a love for the landscape they rode through, so deep there was no need to say anything about it.

When they reached the lake they found a cottage which had been closed for the season, and appropriated the dock, where they sat and ate their lunch. The sun was remarkably hot for October; the lake felt warm to their hands; presently Johnny retired to one side of the cottage, Patricia to the other, and they changed into their bathing-suits. The water was colder than they had expected and they lay breathless for a while when their swimming was done, sprawled in the sun. But all the time, and even though she was enjoying herself, Patricia avoided looking directly at Johnny, because he was more impressive with most of his clothes off and he started a conflict inside her, attraction and revulsion: which was stronger, and which ought to be stronger? She could never make up her mind.

Then, lying prone, his voice half muffled against his folded arm, Johnny began to talk to her. There was something he had to tell her. Maybe she'd be through with him after she knew what it was, and she would be right to feel like that, maybe, even though he didn't know how he could bear it. If she would just try to understand. It wasn't that he loved her less; it was in a way because he loved her so much that it had happened. It would be different for her, she was better in every way than he was, stronger, and maybe it was easier for a girl; he didn't know. But it went on and on, she wouldn't ever let him kiss her even, she gave him no hope. He'd had to do something; he'd felt as if he were going crazy; and there was a girl way out on Barrett Street, a girl Stan Wolenczik knew, and—

"Stop!" she said. "Oh, Johnny, don't say it!"

But of course he had said it already, and the brightness was gone, the day was slimed over; for a moment it was her Cousin Leon who lay there.

"If it had been just once," Johnny said, clenching his fist. "But it won't happen any more; not any more, Pat, I swear. Now I've told you, it's going to be easier." He lay quiet for a long time and she listened to the lap of water against the piles of the little dock; she watched an airplane cross the sky; she thought how there hadn't been any clouds all day, and there were none still. If she looked long enough at the sky the slime might go again.

31

"I guess it's all over then," he said finally.

"I don't know, Johnny. . . . We'd better get dressed. It's time to be starting back."

But he checked her a little later, as she was about to get on her bicycle; he looked neither humble nor ashamed, but angry, almost.

"You're wrong, Pat. You're all wrong," he said. "No, wait a minute." He caught her by the arm and held her; she had to look into his eyes and they weren't in the least like Cousin Leon's— quite honest, and blazing at her, she thought. "I've been trying to figure it out. You're—off on the wrong track, kind of. It doesn't have to be bad. Don't you know that? *Life* is good, isn't it? You believe *life* is good, Pat, don't you?" He was pleading with her, but pitying her too, she thought; and she pulled away from him.

"Let's go, Johnny," she said. "Please."

All the way back to Broadfield she could feel the place on her arm where his hand had gripped her; and she kept denying to herself what he had tried to say. Life was horrible, and since life included her, she was horrible too.

She was sure what had happened must lie naked in her face for anyone to read; and perching on the porch rail, glancing at Vincent Rourke and away from him again, she thought he read it there and scorned her. But she had been wrong about Vincent; he was more sympathetic than anyone she had known. Sympathique, simpatico; it was better in another language, describing more accurately what Vincent was. They could entertain each other, and even talk seriously together; but their secret selves remained inviolate—that was how she wanted it, and she believed he wanted it that way too.

She became so lost in thoughts of Vincent that she didn't know Betty Lou had arrived until her father called up the stairs to her. Presently she and Betty Lou went into the dining room to get to work on the dress, and although Norris had gone out for a stroll, they pulled the curtains across the archway.

Patricia stood very still while Betty Lou kneeled on the floor to pin up the hem of the dress; she continued to think about Vincent.

"All right, honey, turn around now—all the way around," Betty Lou said. "Oh, shoot! Still dips down behind. Enough to drive you crazy." She kneeled again, and with pins in her mouth said, "Your mother was lovely, you know it? Your father was showing me her picture. I guess he must have been pretty crazy about her."

"I don't know." Perhaps he had been, but Laura had deceived him cruelly, and it was to forget that, perhaps, that he had taken to drink when she died. Patricia wished she had paid more attention to the dark hints dropped by her grandmother and her aunt; the vague memory of what they had said created a discomfort in

32

her mind and an additional confusion, for she wished to believe that her mother had been a good woman.

"It's funny I never happened to notice that picture before," said Betty Lou. Patricia, looking at her attentively for the first time that evening, thought she seemed oddly distraught.

"It never happened to be there until a few weeks ago," she said.

"So that's it. But I wonder why—" Betty Lou rose and stood back. "There! Now it's right. But watch yourself taking it off; you could get a nasty scratch from one of those pins."

She sat pensively at the table, basting the hem and casting small glances from time to time at the sewing-machine, as if she expected it to answer a question for her.

"It's fun," she said, "just loads of fun, popping in here the way I do, or having you pop in on me. I never had a daughter, and I wanted children; oh, you don't know how badly. Sam did too. Only he never could seem to make up his mind to adopt any. 'Just like buying a pig in a poke, Betty Lou,' he said. . . .

"There! Guess I can start using the machine now. I'm talking too much. Chatter, chatter, chatter, and never say a thing. Sam Hanbury liked to hear me chatter; it's how I got into the habit, I suppose."

This was more or less how Betty Lou always went on when she and Patricia were alone together, but a sadness trembled over her words tonight; she seemed on the verge of tears. Patricia felt a more immediate unease, as she did whenever emotion came too near the surface, and took up her knitting. The sewing-machine made a small peaceful whir in the dining room, and the world was shut out until Betty Lou stopped working the treadle and looked up at Patricia.

"What I was fixing to say, honey—if I'm butting in here, if you don't want me, you and your father, why, I'll stop coming. I mean I'll come just when asked. Seems like I've been taking an awful lot for granted."

"Oh, Betty Lou. Don't be silly." Even with her Patricia did not find it easy to sound affectionate. "We couldn't get along without you."

"There was just something in the air when I came in tonight. Sometimes I think I'm psychic. Like with poor Sam. Half the time I knew what he was going to say before he said it. But I felt, oh, like I was intruding, Pat, tonight. I saw that picture and I asked your father about it before I had a chance to think. Well, I was embarrassed, that's what; just downright embarrassed." She sighed and glanced up at Patricia. "You're looking kind of pale yourself."

"I suppose I'm just tired." Patricia looked carefully at her knitting, at her hands moving as swiftly with the needles as Grandma Bryant's. Betty Lou was quite different from Grandma Bryant and

Aunt Maudie, but her wide blue eyes saw too much. Patricia began to feel naked and defenseless again.

"You haven't had a real fight with Johnny, have you?" Betty Lou asked presently. "What's become of him anyway?"

"He's still at the filling-station, I suppose."

"That isn't what I *meant*."

Patricia's hands flew faster; she jerked the wool almost viciously upward from the box beside her chair and set her lips.

But Betty Lou was undaunted. "He's a nice boy, Pat. A mighty nice boy. I wish I was your age, let me tell you, and had a boy like Johnny crazy about me. Goodness! I'm just so scared you'll let that Rourke boy dazzle you and forget all about Johnny."

"Oh, Betty Lou!" Patricia tried to laugh.

"Well, I've been around, honey. I've met all kinds of men, and I know his kind. There isn't a thing in the world he cares about except himself."

"You've only seen him once." Patricia tried to imagine herself sitting behind her desk; she tried to be Miss Frigidaire, quelling a too-garrulous patient.

"Once was plenty. . . . He's been driving you home at night, hasn't he?"

Patricia dropped her knitting and looked up. She felt almost panicky, and then her panic was translated into anger. "Have you been spying, Betty Lou?" she said.

"Oh, now, honey. That isn't kind. It just isn't kind at all. I'm interested. Naturally I'm interested. Just like you were my own daughter."

"Well, I'm not your daughter." Patricia rolled up her knitting and put it in the box; she stood, smiling frigidly at Betty Lou. "When I want advice, I'll ask for it," she said. Already she was appalled at herself—her terrible uncharity—but nothing could check the words now, not even Betty Lou's stricken face. "I was going out with Vincent tonight, as a matter of fact; it was all arranged, and then I thought you'd be disappointed if I wasn't here, so I put it off. And now you start criticizing him." Her voice was growing louder, and she wound up almost defiantly, "I'm going driving with him on Sunday."

"Don't tell me, don't tell me! I don't want to hear." Betty Lou's voice suddenly·shot up too, and she bounced to her feet. "I'll never say another word to you about the Rourke boy or Johnny either." She flung back the curtains from the archway in a real passion. "And I'm *not* coming around again either. You can finish that dress up all by yourself."

For a moment Patricia couldn't believe it; she had never seen Betty Lou in a rage. Miss Frigidaire died an abrupt death. "Betty Lou—please—don't be silly," Patricia said. "I only—"

"Silly!" Betty Lou snorted. "Well, they say there's no fool like an old fool, and I guess it's what I've been, all right. Isn't it? I certainly do thank you for telling me, and I wish you a very good night."

She tossed her head, turned, and stalked from the room; the front door slammed behind her. Patricia caught hold of the back of a chair and tried to laugh at Betty Lou, so small and plump, trying to sweep from the house in outraged dignity. She understood at last why Betty Lou had come in so often, and that too was surely something to laugh about. But she couldn't laugh. She felt more like crying, and didn't know if her tears would be for herself or Betty Lou or her father.

5

PATRICIA wanted to show him all her favorite views, and forgot that many of them had been Johnny's discovery. The advantage of an automobile was that you could see them all in one afternoon instead of having to choose and then approach laboriously on a bicycle. While they drove, Vincent explained what empathy meant, and told her that he empathized to mountains.

"You'll have to teach me how to empathize to the lack of mountains," he said. "There aren't even any rocks. It's all so rich and soft."

"And peaceful," said Patricia. "But wait until you see it in spring, when the orchards come out."

If Johnny had talked as Vincent did she would have felt embarrassed for him; but Vincent cut all the tight little knots of diffidence in her. It was like carrying on a conversation in one of those dreams in which you seem gifted with the tongues of angels, though the words you can remember, after you are awake, turn out to have been nonsense after all.

Melancholy came over her as they drove, though—it was a melancholy time of year, and Johnny was on her conscience and so was Betty Lou, who had come over the evening after the quarrel to patch things up, and from whom Patricia had childishly fled.

And the car really did diminish the landscape, so that she wondered if she'd been deluding herself all these years. When you rode a bicycle the country could take you by surprise; for half an hour you toiled along a straight dirt road in the sun, between flat fields, past the shacky farmhouses and the great proud barns; and then you discovered that all this time you had been climbing a hill, and suddenly the land fell away from you in smooth, tremendous waves, lifting and folding, one wide field after another, until it swept up again with a gesture of infinite grace to a ridge that ran almost level, from north to south, as far as you could see.

But the indolent curve of a river flashed upon them now and they had thundered across the bridge before they realized it was there; the hills which seemed so steep to a bicyclist were devoured by the car's wheels and left behind in an instant.

"Stop now," she said. "You really must stop here; this is the prize; after this it will all be anticlimax."

So they smoked cigarettes and gazed out at what had seemed, three months ago, a view too vast to be comprehended in one glance. Now there was a haze in the air and the world seemed smaller; the dim edges of the land had drawn closer, as if winter were moving in from the four quarters, quenching color as it came, casting a pall which would soon be universal. Before very long there would be snow, mysteriously flattening and altering the contours.

"Are you empathizing?" she asked, and smiled at him sideways; seen in profile, his face was amusing and much younger, with a small-boy quality. The eyelashes were very long, the nose was slightly snub, and the chin was strong enough to save him from prettiness.

"I'm trying hard," he said, "but it doesn't seem to work."

"I know it'll work next spring."

"If I'm here that long."

She hesitated before she asked, "Don't you expect to be?"

He turned and smiled at her. "Never can tell. If wanderlust grips me—"

"It must be nice to be—unattached like that. Just able to pick up and light out for somewhere else whenever you feel like it."

"It's not quite that easy. I need the money I'm making."

"You're lucky to have a car."

"I really shouldn't have one. But if I didn't know it was there waiting, with a tank full of gas, to carry me off wherever I felt like going *when* I felt like going—well, then I might start to suffer from claustrophobia or something." He smiled again. "I'll say this much for your views, Patricia; they don't give me claustrophobia. And the other thing—what is it? agoraphobia?—that's something I've never suffered from. Space," he said, "space and emptiness! God, how I love them!"

"How could you empathize to emptiness?" she asked, not much caring whether she was talking nonsense or not. "Wouldn't you have to be empty too?"

"That's just it!" he said with a queer eagerness. "It does empty you; it empties out everything. You even stop thinking." Now his face became somber, and he looked away from her. "I'd like to show you *my* favorite views," he said presently, "but they're scat-

36

tered from Arizona up to Wyoming. . . . Looked enough for now?"

Patricia nodded.

"Then let's try a little speed for a change." He started the engine. "Speed is pretty wonderful too. A plane would be the thing. Then you really would have emptiness. Only the sky."

"I've never been in a plane."

"We'll have to visit the airport someday and go up. They do that; I saw a sign."

"I'd disgrace you probably. Get sick or faint."

"I don't think you're the fainting kind. Or the screaming kind, or the giggling kind. God, how I hate women who scream and giggle," said Vincent; but they had reached the highway and now he turned all his attention to driving.

They came back into the draggled southern fringes of the city before she had expected; and Vincent said, "Here's the airport now. Want to go up?"

"I really ought to be getting back. I usually try to get the supper Sunday nights. Father—"

"Your father's a swell guy. God, the things he's taught me already about newspapering. And nobody else would take the trouble." Threading a way through the increased traffic on Broadfield Avenue, he continued to talk about Norris; but Patricia's mind moved off, back toward what he had been saying about emptiness. Some of the thoughts she had he must have too; some of the things she hated he must hate also.

But, "Talking of gasoline tanks," Vincent said prosaically, "mine turns out to be almost empty." He swung the car into a filling-station and drew it up beside the row of pumps; and it was only then that she saw where they were.

"No!" she said, and in her agitation she touched his hand. "Not here, Vincent. This is—"

But Johnny, who was on duty that afternoon, had immediately withdrawn into the pit beneath a car whose crank-case he was draining, and it was Stan Wolenczik who presently came toward them, wiping his hands on a lump of waste, and grinned and said, "Fill 'er up, Mister?"

After the coupé had driven off again he loafed over to Johnny and spat and said, "Hey, Johnny, that was your girl, wasn't it?"

Johnny emerged from the pit. "Not any more," he said.

"Since when?" Stan sat down on a pile of old tires.

"I dunno. Since about three weeks ago, I guess."

"Too bad," said Stan. "She's really built."

"Yeah, that's right." Johnny was surprised at being able to speak at all. "I'm getting a coke," he said, and walked off to the bright red cooler, because he knew that in another minute he would have socked Stan in the teeth, and he liked Stan; besides, he couldn't afford to lose the job. He jerked the cap viciously off the bottle and poured the fizzy stuff so fast down his throat that he began to choke. Stan came over and pounded him on the back, and after that Johnny felt a little better.

"What the hell!" said Stan. "There's plenty of other dames. But, Jesus, that guy in the coop. He looked like a bastard to me."

"Yeah, he's a bastard all right," Johnny said.

"He was here the other day too. I was wipin' off the windshield for him, see, and he says to me, 'Guy by the name of Johnny Wheelwright work here?' 'Yeah,' I says, 'but he ain't workin' today.' "

Johnny was relieved when another car pulled in for gas. He managed to keep busy after that until he was through for the day, and didn't have to talk to Stan any more or accept any more of Stan's oblique sympathy.

"You ought to kick his ass," Stan advised as Johnny swung on his bicycle, and Johnny said, "I'd like to, but it wouldn't get anybody anywhere," and pedaled off into the dusk.

He told himself that he was through now; he was going to forget Patricia Bryant. It had been hopeless from the beginning, only he'd thought then that it was because she was so young still, not much more than a child. Pity for her, that's all it was at first; life had been hard on her and she was so young, and so brave too, he'd thought. (Would he have felt the same way if she'd been homely? Be honest; it was mostly because she was the best-looking girl he knew that he'd felt sorry for her.)

Only pity, but pity had trapped him; very soon he couldn't get her out of his mind. It was because she looked so much like the idea he'd had of the girl he wanted to marry: somebody calm and quiet, with depth and seriousness to her; somebody who loved Broadfield as he loved it, and liked doing the things he liked to do, taking long bike rides, swimming, playing tennis, just being outdoors; somebody who would want to have kids eventually as much as he wanted to have them. Not somebody who was always fussing with her clothes or her hair, worrying about how she looked; who thought that having a lot of money to spend was important, or that the best way to have a good time was to sit up late drinking in bars and night clubs.

What the hell, said Johnny to himself, standing up on the pedals to mount the long hill. Plenty of other dames, said Johnny, and tried to see them in his mind's eye; but Patricia got in the way and dazzled him. Just wait till that bastard tries to make a pass at her, he said savagely, but that was a mistake—he felt almost murderous pumping his bicycle up the hill.

He reached the top sweating and breathless and turned into

Johnson Avenue—his own street, and hers too—and presently coasted until he had reached his father's house.

His father and his mother, his kid brother Tink, aged nine, were sitting about the living room listening to his kid sister Dorothy, aged fourteen, playing *To a Wild Rose*. Stepping from darkness into light, he stepped from despair into happiness. Happiness showed on their faces and it brightened now that he was there too and the circle was complete.

He stood in the hall doorway until Dorothy had finished her piece, and then he said, "Swell, Dot. You'll be soloist with the Symphony yet."

Dorothy said, "Well, I made four perfectly horrible mistakes, as a matter of fact. But now listen to me do my new Chopin étude. Miss Bummerslee was amazed by my progress."

"Before Johnny gets too amazed to eat," said Mr. Wheelwright, "he'd better have his supper. Come along, Johnny."

He sat across the kitchen table, with his delicately made and mildly humorous face propped on one fist, while Johnny ate cold roast beef and two baked potatoes and a large green salad and drank the better part of a quart of milk. Mr. Wheelwright's hair, which had gone quite white in the last few years, rose in a crest above his high forehead; there was a small nervous quirk at the corner of his mouth, and his free hand tapped on the table, keeping time with Dorothy's Chopin étude.

"You've had a bad day, Johnny," he said at last.

"Yeah. Kind of."

"It's no fun working on Sundays. It's no fun working," said Mr. Wheelwright, and grimaced faintly because by now it was such a stale joke. "Mr. Norman Frazier Trees came by in his Cadillac like Elijah in the fiery chariot this morning," he said, "and swept me off for a round of golf. I suppose he wanted somebody he could be sure of beating. Beating me put him into an excellent temper and he began to have some generous ideas. He says they're becoming aware of a slight upturn in the tool and die industry, and he thinks if they tried very hard they might just manage to squeeze an opening for a hard-working young man who's good with his hands. I haven't told your mother yet. I thought I'd sound you out and see how you felt about it."

"Gee," said Johnny, "I don't know."

"I thought you wouldn't, just at first. If you're interested, you're to call him up when you get through eating, and he'll arrange an appointment."

"What kind of opening? Did he say?"

"One at the very bottom, naturally. It'll only be part-time at first. But after a while you'll be getting fairly decent wages, and you'll have a trade, as he said, which will never let you down."

"He's right, I guess."

"We aren't proud, either of us, Johnny, about working with our hands. And an opening's an opening, and the filling-station is a cul-de-sac."

"Yeah, I know." Johnny prowled about the kitchen until he had found an unripe banana, which he peeled and began to eat. "I'll take the job, I guess, if he really does offer it to me. It's just that— well, working in a factory."

"I know, Johnny."

"I'm outdoors most of the time at the gas-station. . . . Wonder if I could get a job on a farm."

"Possibly. Possibly. Norman began to conjure up visions. He saw you becoming, as the years rolled by, a foreman; then a department manager; finally, perhaps, even a very minor executive with a nice white collar and a desk of your own. . . . It just depends on what you want out of life, Johnny."

"Yeah." Johnny swallowed the last of the banana and dropped the skin into the garbage-pail under the sink. "No point in a farm job, I guess. Thing to do, make a lot of money in the tool and die works, then buy a farm and farm it like a gentleman. A very old gentleman by then, prob'ly. . . . What the hell! I'll try for the job."

Mr. Wheelwright rose from the table. "And it's still a free country. You could always quit if the factory got you down. Well, Johnny, I wish you luck."

"Thanks, Pop."

"After you're through phoning, come on in and be amazed by Dorothy. I really think she's almost as talented as Miss Bummerslee says."

He strolled away to the living room and Johnny shut himself into the hall closet with the telephone. Presently it was as if Norman Trees were in there with him, exuding condescension and a Chamber-of-Commerce importance, a big-industrialist heartiness; and Johnny felt sweaty before he got through having the appointment made for him.

Three days later he sat in Norman Trees' office, which was all waxed blond woods and enormous crystal ashtrays, dramatic photographs of the plant, selected by Norman, and reproductions of the Post-Impressionists, selected by Norman's wife, who was on the executive committee of the Broadfield Art Gallery and knew about such things. He sat and stared past Norman at the industrial landscape beyond the window and listened to the faint vibration which penetrated even here, and was careful to address Norman as sir; and after he had listened to a discourse on the evils of the New Deal, he got the job.

Stan Wolenczik, though envious, was glad to let Johnny work at the filling-station the days he didn't have to go to the plant. So three mornings a week Johnny rode his bicycle a mile and a half to work, down the long hill and across the railroad tracks, across the river and more railroad tracks to the part of Broadfield which belched smoke into the sky. He felt a new kind of excitement; if he loved the growing world, he loved machines too, and now he was learning about machines more subtle than any he'd known before; he would become a creator; he would be where machines began. The eternal din of the plant got into his blood; the roughness of the men he worked with was something he could take in his stride; and his mind was kept so busy he didn't have a chance to think much about Patricia.

Also he would eventually be earning more money. It hadn't been an important consideration to his parents, but it was to Johnny.

When Wheelwright, Pattison & McLeod first went out of business, Johnny was anxious about his family; the foundations of the world, which had been shaky for years, had now given way completely, and it seemed as if the Wheelwrights must crack apart. But nothing of the sort happened. Mrs. Wheelwright was tired of being a housewife, she said, tired of the Women's City Club and the League of Women Voters; cheerfully she put her pride in her pocket and went to see the president of VanderLaan & Sons, Inc., who was her cousin twice removed, and began to sell clothing to ladies and junior misses; and it wasn't much more than a couple of years before she was running the department.

After such a long, losing battle to find the kind of clients who wanted to build the honest, solid houses his firm had designed, Johnny's father found housework soothing; and in time, he said, concessions might be made so *he* could join the Women's City Club and the League of Women Voters.

The Wheelwrights' good friends pitied them behind their backs, and their not-so-good friends sneered; but the Wheelwrights had never really cared about being conventional—it was just that life had worked out so they seemed that way, and now it had worked out otherwise; the new pattern went serenely on.

Johnny's love for his family was so great that sometimes he felt it would suffocate him unless he found a way to express it. Even when he was very young, long before the bankruptcy, he had felt protective toward his father; then there were Dorothy and Tink to be protective toward also. Johnny and his mother were joined in an alliance to see that nothing too hurtful ever happened to the other three.

From his love for them, Johnny drew his own strength and formulated his ideas about life and the world. He knew the world was in a very bad shape, and worried about it often; a dark cloud stood upon the horizon, and from Europe, from Asia, came premonitory rumblings which most of Broadfield didn't seem to hear.

Johnny believed that life was good and that all men wanted to be good in their hearts; well, most of them, anyway, and those who didn't had had their minds pressed out of shape by forces beyond their control. But those with their minds pressed out of shape somehow seemed to carry more weight than the rest, and so, to a greater and greater extent, life was becoming steadily less good for more people.

There ought to be something he could do about it, but he didn't know what. If he did something about it he would be helping Tink and Dorothy and Patricia and all the other people in the world who needed to be helped. At present he couldn't see anything else to do but to try, as far as he was able, to live a good life himself and fight his own particular devil whenever it reared its head. Later, maybe, there would be a chance to do something on a larger scale.

None of these things had become clear to Johnny all at once. He achieved his beliefs by painful stages, and words deserted him when he stood most in need of them, so that he was never able to clarify what he thought in conversations. He listened to what people said, and tried to hold on to anything which sounded important, and thought about it afterwards, smoothing and simplifying it until he could fit it in comfortably among his other ideas.

To lead a good life himself—that was the clear and straightforward kind of principle he liked; and having reached it he did his best to put it to work. It was why he had felt impelled to confess to Patricia that he'd found it impossible to remain wholly continent. Until he actually spoke to her, he had not felt any deep sense of guilt or disgust; it was better to do what he'd done than let his mind be pressed out of shape by the force in his body; and it had seemed there were only those alternatives. But he believed in honesty, and that a marriage not based on it couldn't succeed.

He had been so sure, even as he lay on the dock, with the sun hot on his back and the smell of the lake, the smell of his own good flesh, in his nostrils, that Patricia was going to marry him eventually. The truth might shock her at first, but in the end she would discover compassion.

The belief went on for a little while despite the way she'd behaved and what he had said to her about being on the wrong track. But as November drew to a close in a week of cold rain, as December came in with the first snowfall, his hopelessness returned, and now it was becoming a permanent condition. The time was past for him to make further overtures; and she would make none ever.

Well, then, to hell with her; but he still could not make himself mean that. What had begun in pity years ago was ending in pity—because she was blind, because she deliberately cut herself off from life—and he thought with a kind of desperation that this was only the beginning of a new involvement. She was woven into his life now, so intricately that he couldn't cut her out.

He wished it were possible to talk to his parents about it, to tell them the whole story, not omitting his excursions to Barrett Street. The trouble was that a special feeling had grown up among the Wheelwrights about Johnny and Patricia—a sympathy which defeated itself by having become too delicate. Against their silence he could do nothing; and that was really why he went to see Betty Lou one evening.

She was wearing an evening dress and her fingers flashed with rings. He'd never seen her so elegant, but didn't know if it would be tactful to say so; therefore he grinned and say "Wow!" and that was fine with Betty Lou.

"You don't know how glad I am to see you, Johnny. I'm sorry now that I'm going to Symphony. It's all right, sit down; I'm not leaving for another half hour. Been so long since I got all dolled up I didn't know how much time to allow, and I'm sick and tired strutting around like a lonely peacock. Peahen, I guess I should say, but they don't have any finery, do they?"

"Mom and Dot are going too," Johnny said, "but I didn't know you ever did."

"Well, I'm being taken. Dragged off, willy-nilly. Not that I don't like music," said Betty Lou, whisking restlessly about her little front parlor, which ran to countless knickknacks and photographs of all her relatives, "but I have to admit I prefer *Down by the Old Mill Stream* to Mozart and Brahms, which is what they're going to grapple with tonight. That's just between you and me. Keep it to yourself when my escort comes in."

"Who is he?" Johnny asked.

Betty Lou looked mysterious and said, "Wait and see. Though goodness knows I thought it must be all over town by now." She came to rest finally on a sofa with a curly back, and looked wistful for a moment, and then smiled, and then looked worried. "Pat's on your mind, isn't she?"

"Yeah. I hate to drag you into it, Betty Lou, but—"

"Well, she's on mine too. Has been for months. We had kind of a spat, oh, just ages ago. I don't often get mad, Johnny, but when I do I get just simply beside myself with childish rage. I walked out of the house swearing I'd never step foot into it again." Betty Lou twisted one of her rings and looked up with a twinkle. "My hot Southern blood, I guess. Someday I'll probably let slip where I really do come from, but that's neither here nor there. I was telling about my hot Southern blood, which cooled right down, and first thing I did the next day, I marched straight back there to patch things up. But, Johnny, she won't let things *be* patched up. She just got kind of sad and remote and said what she'd said to

43

me was unforgivable, and there was no sense going on that way any more, and ran upstairs. So from that day to this I've hardly seen her."

"She cuts herself off from people so," Johnny said.

"I know," sighed Betty Lou. "But people who don't want to be helped, you can't help them. She needs help, though, Johnny. She's gone and got herself caught in the toils of that snake from New York—no, what snakes have is coils—and I bet you any amount of money he's going to constrict her when the time comes. Oh, I try to make a joke of it," said Betty Lou, rising and beginning to fidget again, "but it isn't a joke at all, Johnny."

"You're damn right," said Johnny, and looked apologetic.

"Go right ahead and swear. *I* want to swear. I'm worried sick, but I can't say a word to Norris because he has enough to worry about already. *He* thinks the Rourke boy is fine, just because he writes such good pieces for the paper."

Johnny drew a careful breath. *"Has* she been—seeing a lot of him?"

"Too much, Johnny. Two, three nights a week, I see that car of his pulling up, and out he climbs, and ten minutes later, off they go together. Sometimes they don't get in till late either. I never can go to sleep until I know she's safely back again. . . . I've been mad at you too, Johnny; I might as well admit it. I don't see why you let this happen."

"What can I do?" Johnny clutched the arms of his chair. "Pat isn't my private property."

"No." Betty Lou paused before a mirror and fiddled with her hair. "I wish she was, that's what I wish. I wish you'd abducted her years ago."

"She's still pretty young, of course," Johnny said, and knew that he was wasting his time. Betty Lou had a kind heart, but she wasn't going to be any help.

"Her own mother married at twenty. Norris told me. And look at me! I married Sam when I was a tender bud of seventeen. And knew my own mind about it too. I'd had six proposals and Sam's was the seventh, and I never regretted my choice. And take my sisters. All four of them were married before they were twenty. That's the *time* to get married, while you're still young enough to enjoy it."

She crossed the room and tapped him on the shoulder.

"Don't give up, Johnny! You start going after her again."

"It doesn't work. It never worked. And I can't now. Look, Betty Lou, the last time I saw her I told her—" But he couldn't discuss Barrett Street with Betty Lou. "Well, I told her some things about myself she didn't like. I had to."

Betty Lou perched on the sofa and regarded him solemnly. "Oh, shoot!" she said finally. "Mountains out of molehills. Do you think I didn't know about the scarlet pages in Sam Hanbury's past? We're all human, I guess. . . . You just forget it ever happened. Don't *brood*, Johnny. It's bad enough to have Pat brooding, and Norris brooding, and—" She broke off and said, "Here he comes now. Brace yourself, Johnny."

Norris entered with snow on the collar of his Chesterfield, snow in the crease of his soft black hat.

"Coming down thick," he said. "I ordered a taxi. Well, Johnny; you're quite a stranger these days. Congratulations on the new job—saw your dad downtown the other day, and he told me."

"Thanks." Johnny rose and managed a smile. It was a very old Chesterfield that Norris was wearing, and his tuxedo was even older, but pearl studs gleamed bravely from the starched white shirt-front and the tie was crisply tied; in his own way Norris looked as festive as Betty Lou.

"Time I was running along," Johnny said. "I just dropped by to—"

"You can wait till the taxi gets here, anyway," said Betty Lou, going to the window. "Lordy, it really *is* coming down, isn't it? Slush from now to the middle of June, I suppose."

"Now, listen!" Norris protested. "The climate isn't that bad."

"It's a fiendish climate, and why they ever came and drove out the Indians I'll never know," said Betty Lou.

Johnny swallowed to ease the constriction in his throat and said, "How's Pat these days, Mr. Bryant?"

"Why so formal, Johnny?" But Norris didn't look at him. "She's fine. Just fine. Why don't you drop over and see her? She's all alone tonight."

Betty Lou turned from the window. "Here's the taxi," she said. "Yes, Johnny, you go ahead. Right now."

But after the taxi had vanished in a whirl of flakes, Johnny walked three times back and forth before Norris's house, and still couldn't bring himself to climb the steps and push the bell.

6

Two BLOCKS from the Civic Auditorium the taxi became hopelessly snarled in slush and traffic, and Norris and Betty Lou went the rest of the way on foot. He held an umbrella above her bent head and said anxiously, "You should have worn galoshes."

"Don't you worry about my feet. I've had them wet before and survived. And I *love* the snow, really, Norris. Makes it more exciting."

They climbed the broad stone steps, passed beneath the portico, and entered the lobby. Voices, laughter, the smell of perfume and gardenias broke upon them in a great wave, washing them under for a moment because darkness and snowflakes were still in their eyes; then they floated up and swam on the tide, which carried them forward into vastness. The auditorium had been built to house conventions, and space diminished the human beings, flattening out their voices, so that twiddles and squeaks sounded clearly; on the distant stage, the orchestra was tuning up.

Touching Betty Lou's elbow, Norris marched along the endless, level aisle, feeling that everybody was looking at him, even the people in the balcony. He hadn't been so acutely self-conscious since his young manhood and the first time he'd taken Laura into a public place.

When the usher paused, Norris's momentum carried him forward and there was almost a collision; he trod on a woman's foot, inching after Betty Lou to two empty seats in the center of the row; he helped Betty Lou out of her evening cloak and took refuge in the program notes. The thing to do was to memorize the high points of the opening selection—the "Academic Festival Overture" —as set forth by the annotator, who had found the information in a book; and then perhaps he would know what was happening once the orchestra started to play.

Betty Lou was like a child at a party. She turned this way and that, craning her neck, and merrily flapped her program at people she recognized, and made wide shapes with her lips: Why, hello there; the snow—terrible; oh, it's just an *old* dress, really, that I fixed over last week; I'll see you at intermission.

The conductor emerged from the wings, tall and lean in his tailcoat, and moved stalkily across the platform; applause began in the front rows and worked its way back gradually to the far reaches of the hall, where people were talking in a sudden frenzy, as if they had a great deal to get said before silence was enjoined upon them.

The house-lights dimmed; rap-rap went the baton; the conductor's thin black arms lifted in supplication and there was almost silence, though whispers still ran like a small wind about the balcony. The moment was not quite so magical as that before the curtain rises and the play begins; but it whirled Norris into the past, and he was a boy of twenty-five, and after the curtain had been up for ten seconds Laura would come running out on the stage laughing, carrying a basket of flowers, and he would lose his heart forever, then and there. . . .

Down swept the arms; the music broke forth; and soon Norris was lost, floundering in a welter of unintelligible sound. He stole a glance at Betty Lou; more like a child than ever, she leaned a

46

little forward, a little sideways, to watch the conductor between the heads in front of her. Her parted lips smiled faintly; she was amused by his emphatic, angular gestures.

Norris sighed and looked frontward again; he closed his eyes, and now, now, if he could just catch hold somewhere, he would start listening to Brahms. The woman in front of him leaned toward her companion. "Lovely," she whispered. "Just perfectly beautiful," her companion whispered back, and the beauty of the music appeared to generate heat in her, for she began to fan herself wildly with her program. "The piccolo player is new," said the first woman presently. "Beg pardon?" said the second. "The *pic-colo *player," the first repeated explosively. "Good, isn't he?" said the second. "I just said he was *new!*" said the first. "Who?" asked the second. "I don't know what his name is but I've never seen his face before," said the first. "The old one used to have the most enormous nose; he was just horrible." "Shhhh!" said Betty Lou sharply, and tittered at Norris. "Music-lovers," said the shapes she made with her mouth.

Brahms fought a losing struggle with Norris's attention; nothing passed between them. Now the orchestra was losing its grip on Brahms; ever more frantically jerked the thin black arms, trying to thrash the musicians back into line. Desperation was in the air; the audience, welded into one creature at last, held its breath. Ahhhhh! As one creature it sighed and broke apart into individuals again; discipline had returned, Brahms had returned, only slightly battered, and the last chords crashed out triumphantly. Bowing, sweating, the conductor left the platform and all about the hall programs quivered like butterflies and voices rippled gaily.

Now there was expectancy; now the craning of necks was general; the soloist of the evening, a violinist from New York, was about to appear. The conductor returned but the applause was perfunctory, saving itself up for the violinist. Here he was, younger than they had expected, far more handsome than he'd appeared in cuts in the *Morning Bugle,* the *Broadfield Chronicle;* young enough and handsome enough to be in the movies—the clapping went on as if all they asked of him was to stand and bow and smile and shed glamour on them.

But the delirium spent itself, and was succeeded by a violin concerto. In order not to disgrace itself with the violinist from New York, the orchestra had rehearsed Mendelssohn with a zeal it hadn't given to Brahms, and now it rose to the occasion and the black arms flailed the air less furiously.

"They're *good!*" whispered Betty Lou to Norris. Civic pride bloomed almost tangibly and Broadfield thought better of itself every moment; when the concerto was over the violinist was accorded what the *Bugle* critic and the *Chronicle* critic would quite accurately call an ovation; so he played *The Flight of the Bumble-Bee* for Broadfield, and Broadfield cheered.

"Shall we go out for a cigarette?" Norris asked Betty Lou when the house-lights came up and the players straggled off into the wings.

"I could stand a coke, anyway," said Betty Lou, rising. "Oh, Norris, I'm having the *best* time! I don't know a single thing about good music, but it's all so gay. I should have been coming to Symphony right along."

"You'll have to come again," said Norris.

"Yes," said Betty Lou, trotting beside him down the aisle, "only, Norris, there's something I have to tell you—"

She didn't get a chance, though, because out in the lobby they encountered Vincent Rourke and Carola Wilmot and a circle of Carola's friends.

"Norris!" cried Carola, bearing down upon him with her hand outstretched. "Norris Bryant! I haven't seen you for years! And aren't you looking distinguished! You must be Mrs. Hanbury," she said, clasping Betty Lou's hand. "How do you do? I've been dying to meet you. Isn't it all fun? The Brahms was too appalling, but the Mendelssohn amazed me. I think we may find ourselves with an orchestra yet."

The rest of the circle had drifted away, enclosing Vincent; Carola pinned Norris and Betty Lou against the wall and went on talking; they must come around for drinks afterwards—she was having just a few people in. She had tried to snare the violinist, but he was taking the midnight for Chicago.

"Did you drive, Norris?" Carola asked. "Oh, you haven't a car now, have you? Well, then, you must ride back with me. I'll meet you right here—don't fail me, now; I'm counting on you both. Isn't it a vile evening? You have no idea how I loathe the snow."

"I declare," said Betty Lou, after they were back in their seats, and became speechless.

"Would you like to go, Betty Lou?" Norris asked, and hoped she would say no. It wouldn't be their kind of party. It was only because Laura, so many years ago, had been exceptional in her way, and because Carola was exceptional in hers, that the invitation had been issued. The social barriers annoyed Norris, but only discomfort resulted when you tried to cross them. "We could always slip out a side exit," he said hopefully.

"Well, I'll make a fool of myself, I suppose, but I would kind of like to see the inside of that house, Norris." Betty Lou was gazing at him as if she had never really seen him before. "I didn't know you knew Mrs. Wilmot, Miss Wilmot, whatever she calls herself now."

"Well, I don't, really. Laura used to be mixed up with her the times Carola was living here. The Players," said Norris. "There used to be parties in Carola's house after opening nights. We got to go to them even if we weren't just the right people."

"Oh," said Betty Lou. "You'd think you were her long-lost dearest friend, the way she came up to you."

"Carola was always like that," said Norris, and the house-lights dimmed again.

The second half of the program wasn't Mozart after all; it turned out to be Haydn's "Surprise" Symphony, and Norris didn't try to pay any attention to it, although it was a kind of music which he might have enjoyed.

Laura was the real reason, he supposed, why he had decided to attend the concerts this season. At the last minute he had become a patron of the Broadfield Symphony Society by sending in a check for ten dollars; and now he was using a pair of the tickets distributed at the paper. The Society hadn't been organized until long after Laura's death, but there were smaller musical groups, run by women mostly, and Laura had been active in several of them. Occasionally, after the World War, some of the big orchestras passed through town, and he and Laura always went to the concerts.

To begin with Laura hadn't known much more about serious music than he did, although she played the piano and sang a little; but she learned more about it, as she kept learning more about so many things. While she was alive Norris had gotten over the feeling that the enjoyment of music and painting and books is effeminate. You and your masculinity, Laura said. You're always shutting doors, Norris, always shutting doors and windows, and making life smaller than it has to be. Music is just another window, and so are pictures. Why should women have all the fun of looking out?

Laura would have been happy about the Symphony Society; she would have gone about drumming up membership. He thought that because she had died was no reason for shutting the doors and windows again; and he hoped that Patricia, who liked music, might come with him; it would be a way of getting closer to her. She had come in November, but a week ago she'd told him she wasn't going to attend the December concert.

"I've had too many late nights," she said. "I'm going to start reforming."

"But we'd be out by ten-thirty," he protested.

"Why don't you ask Betty Lou to go?"

"Golly," said Norris, "I don't think Betty Lou—"

"She'd love to go," Patricia said. "Make a real evening of it, Father. Get your tuxedo out of moth balls and tell her to dress up too, and buy her a drink afterwards."

"You wouldn't be matchmaking by any chance, would you?"

She surprised him by going very white. "Of course not." She

paused and then said, "Betty Lou doesn't have very much fun, that's all, and she—"

"Why, she has a lot. All those bosom friends, and bridge parties, and book-club meetings, and—"

"She hasn't been out with a *man* since her husband died," said Patricia.

Norris couldn't help chuckling. "All right. I will ask Betty Lou. Only I hope she doesn't faint dead away."

Betty Lou didn't, when he went around to see her, but she became rather white too, and it occurred to Norris that she hadn't been doing much popping in lately. Things were becoming complicated, he thought, and fell into tactlessness.

"It was Pat's idea," he said. "She can't go, or I'd have sent you off together, but—"

"Shoot," said Betty Lou, tossing her head, "if that's the only reason you're asking me, Norris Bryant—"

"I'm sorry. I didn't really mean it that way. I'm just a crude old newspaper hack, Betty Lou, without any manners. I can't put things the way Vinnie Rourke can."

"Thank God for that!" cried Betty Lou, and began to laugh. "All right, Norris, I'll come. I'd love to. And wait till you see me all dressed up like a Christmas tree, three whole weeks before Christmas."

Before he left she said, "But it really was Patricia's idea, wasn't it?"

"Yeah, Betty Lou, afraid it was." Though his shoulders were so bent, Norris felt himself towering above her; what a little thing she was; what a pretty little thing. "But just because I didn't have sense enough to have the idea myself. People have to point things out to me, you know, and then I see the light. Saw right away it was one of the best ideas Pat ever had."

"Why, Norris Bryant, I declare! That's almost a pretty speech." Betty Lou wrinkled her nose at him, and he rather thought that as he went out she blew him a kiss. He crossed back to his own house feeling light of heart, but mildly apprehensive. No point in putting ideas in Betty Lou's head; he would never marry again, as he had more or less told her when she asked about Laura's photograph.

But hell, he thought, going in to tell Patricia that his mission had succeeded, if Betty Lou really wanted another husband, she could do a whole lot better than him. He might be able to start her into circulation again; once she'd been seen in public with a man at her side, even a shabby old bum, other men might begin to have the right ideas about her.

So really it was as a kind of benefactor that he took Betty Lou to the concert; and although he felt diffident at the thought of Carola's party, he was glad they'd been asked, for Betty Lou's sake.

You never could tell who might turn up in Carola's house; some eligible bachelor of an appropriate age, some wealthy widower young enough for a new romance. . . .

Applause spattered; Haydn had finished surprising the audience. Voices clamored too loudly now for the space to quell them; seats banged; feet shuffled down the aisles. A lovely concert, said the voices, just lovely; aren't you crazy about the way he conducts; why, hello there, I didn't know you were out of bed yet; I guess it's still snowing, isn't it? coming down thicker than ever; white Christmas, white Christmas; whole damn winter'll be white, we won't see the ground again before April. . . .

"Here you are!" said Carola, pouncing on them in the lobby, and after some moments of waiting in the portico, they swooped down the steps and into her limousine; wearing a chauffeur's uniform, her sad little manservant sat at the wheel.

No one spoke while they became disentangled from the jam and lurched away from the lights of Main Street, blurred with snow and soft as flowers; away from the lights and up a dark side street where the shape of trees stood out sharply because of snow along the branches; the tire-chains jingled like sleigh-bells all the way up Warner Street hill. Carola sat between Norris and Betty Lou; she held a hand of each, with an intimacy which seemed uncalled-for but endeared her to them momentarily. Norris thought his evening with Betty Lou was turning into a success.

Later, though, he wasn't so sure. In the tall, cool living room Betty Lou's finery looked suddenly garish, Betty Lou herself looked frightened and crushed; and when the others came in, five or six couples and Vincent Rourke with a girl Norris didn't know, he felt for the first time how shabby his tuxedo was, and a little foolish since most of the men were in business suits.

Carola herself served the brandy and soda, and for a while it was as if an invisible line cut the room in half; on one side lurked Norris and Betty Lou, like poor relations, on the other stood Broadfield's rich and mighty, with whom Vincent seemed quite at ease. Little bursts of talk died into silence; there was a clearing of throats; somebody pushed back a curtain and said the snow was slackening.

"Brandy, Norris?" Carola asked.

"No. No, I guess I won't take anything, thanks," said Norris, who had been staring at the girl with Vincent: a mane of gold hair, a daubed and voracious mouth, an evening dress of white satin, very décolleté. "But I *mean*," she was saying, "*after all* . . ." and Vincent was laughing down at her.

"There's beer, if you'd rather," Carola said.

"No. Thanks, I'm not thirsty, really," Norris said out of a parched throat, and watched her sweep away from him.

51

But now she began to fuse the disparate elements of her party; the line was crossed, it ceased to exist, and from the rich and mighty flowed a sudden graciousness and kindliness: noblesse oblige, maybe, thought Norris, and stood with his feet planted squarely on the carpet, determined that no one should patronize him.

Betty Lou had been captured by Norman Trees and now Mrs. Norman Trees, not to be outdone, proceeded to charm Norris. She did so enjoy reading the *Chronicle* editorials, she said; so sound, so sensible, so clearly expressed—he was still writing them, of course? Oh, no, not for years now, said Norris, whose six months in the library, sweating them out, had been as bad as penal servitude; but he'd tell Chuck Halsey; Chuck would be glad to know *some*body read them.

Mrs. Trees looked like an aging and somewhat neurotic mare; her lips curled anxiously away from long yellow teeth and you half expected her to toss up her head and whinny.

Well, she asked, what did he do on the paper then? Oh? And what were the duties of an assistant city editor? It sounded *most* impressive. Newspaper work must be *so* fascinating, so much more amusing, so much less nerve-racking in times like these, than the world of industry, for instance, said Mrs. Trees, and now she did toss her head toward her husband, and even whinnied faintly; it was the closest she could come to a titter. Well, yes, *he* found it exciting, said Norris, and realized that he did; after all these years it was still the breath of life, and he felt a sudden impatience to be out of here, home in bed and sound asleep, so that the dark morning when he would rise and go down to his desk through the snow would be so much the nearer. He stood a little straighter as he talked to Mrs. Trees, feeling the drama and the mild raffishness of his profession coursing through his blood; he did not envy any industrialist or lawyer or banker in the room.

In the way of such parties, though, he found himself suddenly not talking to Mrs. Trees, but explaining to empty air the difference between a three-head and a seven-head; and when Carola appeared once more at his elbow he said he thought he might have some brandy after all.

"Why do we see so little of each other, Norris?" she asked. "What on earth is the use of living in a place like Broadfield, if such very old friends lose track of each other? Do tell me about your children. How are they all?—All quite grown up by now, I suppose, and I hear that Patricia is her mother all over again. That naughty boy Vincent! Polly Peabody is up from Washington and seems to have bewitched him. An amazing child, isn't she?—but spoiled, my dear, utterly spoiled; her father worships the ground she walks on. Only seventeen, but she's turned several diplomatic heads already."

Carola glanced about the room at her party, inclined her head slightly as if to test the volume of noise it was producing, and turned back to Norris. "You must tell me seriously," she said, laying a hand on his arm. "*Is* my little gathering in the worst possible taste?"

"I guess I don't know what you mean."

"Oh, now, Norris, you do! We're all supposed to behave as if the wolf were at the door; otherwise the tumbrels may start rolling." She arched one eyebrow at him and said, "I have it on excellent authority that one of our very best families—now I'm not going to tell you which, but perhaps you can guess—has rigged up an elaborate system of barricades for the front door. *And* there's a small machine-gun in the hall closet. Literally, my dear!"

Norris laughed, and so did Carola.

"Well," she said, "that's the sort of thing I mean. Should I hang up a placard explaining the brandy was laid down in the cellar by my father, long before the World War? I call people up and say, 'Do come around for a drink,' and they say, 'Darling, but do you think it's wise?' And *if* they come, they come disguised as mendicants. Do look at Norman's suit! It's shiny, my dear, it positively is. And he must have fifty new ones at home.

"When the end of summer came," she went on, "I was *sick* of behaving as if life were one long perpetual funeral. I shall co-operate with the President, I told myself, I shall insist on happy days being here again. So far it has been an almost one-woman battle. You can have no idea, Norris, how charmed I was tonight when I saw you and Mrs. Hanbury in evening dress. There's somebody else who defies the rabble, I thought. Still, I felt a slight lifting of the gloom at the concert. Was I wrong, or wasn't it all rather festive?"

"Seemed festive to me," Norris said. "Lot of people dressed up, lot of women wearing flowers. I've been living in a kind of trance, I guess. Sort of noticed what you mean, but I thought it was just me. I—"

"In a trance? On a newspaper? I was sure your finger must be on the public pulse."

"All I do, really, is fix up the stories and write the heads. Most of the time it's just mechanical—hardly know what I'm reading."

"I suppose not. One must preserve one's sanity somehow." Out of words for the moment, Carola gave Norris another drink.

"But you must have seen who's coming here in spring to address the Ladies' Literary Club," she said.

"Anybody special?"

"My dear, Andrew White McBain!" said Carola.

"Andy McBain! Well, what do you know!" Norris gripped his glass tightly, glad now of the second drink.

"You've read his book, of course," Carola said.

"Why, no, no, I haven't. Been meaning to get around to it, but—"

"I was sure he'd have sent you an autographed copy, but perhaps fame has gone to his head. The book is fascinating, but it does rather make one's flesh creep. Europe is a powder-magazine, and Germany, he says, is *definitely* on the march again."

"Well, I don't know. This Hitler," said Norris, "he's just some kind of a crank, I guess." It was difficult to talk intelligibly about Andy McBain or his book; an old pain had stirred in Norris's heart. But it was foolish to suspect Carola of malice; she couldn't possibly know anything about the business.

"If I can persuade him to linger for a few days, we must have a real party," said Carola. "I invite you, Norris, this very minute. But I suppose he'll be on a rigid schedule, and will have to go tearing on as soon as he's made the literary ladies' blood run cold."

Norris was not sure, after that, whom he talked to or what he said. He felt the brandy just a little, and wished he felt it more because that might keep him from thinking about Andy McBain.

It was a relief when he and Betty Lou emerged from the party into a wide silence. The storm had ended and far down the hill the City Hall clock was chiming midnight; behind the curtained windows of Carola's house the voices and laughter went on; and somewhere upstairs her father must be lying, as motionless and almost as drained of life as the frozen trees supporting their burden of snow.

"How in the world am I going to get you home?" Norris asked.

"We'll walk," said Betty Lou cheerfully. "It's an ancient pair of shoes and I've wrecked them already. I could feel myself trailing little-bitty pools of water all over that carpet. My, Norris, that was quite a party!"

"Too much of a party, Carola thought. . . . It's a long way to walk, Betty Lou, and there must be almost six inches."

"We can walk in the road. It's only a few blocks, really. I don't mind, Norris—cross my heart—but if we stand still any longer I'll freeze to death."

So they walked in the road, and when they came to a drift there was still enough brandy in Norris to make him lift Betty Lou over. But he couldn't talk to her. He kept thinking about Andy McBain and wondering if there was, after all, some way in which Carola might have found out about Laura's last trip to New York.

"Come in for a minute, Norris?" Betty Lou asked when they reached her doorstep.

"Have to be at work in a few hours," Norris said, but he followed her into the living room. "You better get those shoes and stockings off right away and stick your feet in mustard and hot water," he said, and blushed like any adolescent.

54

"Oh, now, Norris, you quit fussing. You don't know how tough I am." Betty Lou picked up a pink sea shell and set it down again. "I started to tell you something, back at the concert, and then it went out of my head. You know, when you said maybe I'd come to some more."

"I hope you will. It's been a lot of fun, Betty Lou, for me."

"For me too. I don't know when I've had such a gay evening. But—I'm going away, Norris."

He looked up at her and said, "Not for good?"

"Oh, shoot, no! A month, maybe two months. I'm going down home. Mamma hasn't been so well lately, and it's just ages since I've seen her. I'm going down there for Christmas and I plan to stay on a while. We're all kind of afraid, my sisters and me, we're afraid maybe it'll be Mamma's last Christmas. She broke her hip a year ago, and she just hasn't been able to rally since. She's really awful old, Norris."

"My parents are getting old too," he said absently.

"I'm leaving tomorrow night, Norris, so I guess this is good-by. Au revoir, anyway. That's what I wanted to tell you."

"I'll miss you. We all will," he said.

"Well, I'll miss you too. What I was wondering, Norris, will you write to me now and then? There are so many things going on here I'd want to hear about. Patricia, especially, and that Rourke boy—did you *see* him tonight? with that thing in white satin?—and poor Johnny Wheelwright. I'll just sit down there and fret unless I know what's happening every minute."

Norris smiled. "I'll do my best. Don't know if I'll remember how to write a letter." Years ago, after they both were out of college, he and Andy McBain had carried on a correspondence, the best of Norris's life; but that had languished long since. And he must write to Charlie and Laurette, he thought; no word from either of them since September.

"Well, if you're going to write to me, you'll have to know where down home *is*," said Betty Lou, and drew a deep breath. "After all these years trying to pull the wool over people's eyes, I feel like I'm letting a really *horrible* skeleton out of the closet. I'm such a fool," said Betty Lou. "Norris, my home town is Muskogee, Oklahoma."

Norris laughed at her. "I don't see anything so horrible about that."

"Because you haven't seen Muskogee. Oh, it's all right, really. I had such a happy time, all the years I was growing up, I couldn't help but love the place. But it isn't exactly what you'd call Dixie. I'll write down the address."

After he had taken the slip of paper from her he solemnly shook her hand. "Thanks for coming along tonight," he said. "And I

55

will write. And I hope your mother gets to feeling better. And—come back as soon as you can."

He was feeling sentimental about her by the time he unlocked his own front door. She was such a little thing, so like a child, that he had a foolish notion of its being dangerous for her to travel all the way from Broadfield to Muskogee, Oklahoma, without somebody along to protect her and see she got on the right trains.

"Oh, shoot!" he said out loud. Then he said, "God damn," and laughed at himself.

7

HE WAS unaccustomed to staying up so late, and he did not get to sleep at all that night.

His mind at first moved tranquilly, away from all the things which might have worried him; the point was that it continued to move—faster as the hours melted and the notes of the City Hall chimes floated to him across the stillness. The alarm-clock on his bureau ticked impatiently, racing toward dawn; and his thoughts drew together, became concentrated into an eagerness, an arrow aimed at his desk in the *Chronicle* building three-quarters of a mile away.

Five minutes before the clock went off he climbed from his bed and set the catch and slid into the smooth routine of all his days: down the back stairs to the kitchen to start the coffee, up again to wash and shave and dress, down again to make toast in the oven while he fried bacon and scrambled eggs. At half-past six he snapped off the kitchen light and left his dark and sleeping house for the dark and sleeping outside world.

Minute flakes stung his cheeks; when he reached the street-light at the corner, he saw the snow sifting thinly out of blackness, and heard it whispering among the twigs of trees.

He should have been feeling tired and old, but instead felt extraordinarily alive. Today would be one of his good days, he knew, when everything would click neatly into place. The stories would come in with time to spare and would not have to be mangled; heads would crystallize of themselves and all the heads would be good ones, short clean words to make an exact geometrical pattern; Ack Guion would be in one of his sunny moods; the advertising department would not gum up the works by demanding puffs for its best customers; no unaccountable storms would break loose in the front office.

Norris whistled as he trudged through the snow and inhaled deeply when he pushed open the door and stepped forward on to the first floor of the *Chronicle* building. It looked rather like a bank. Marble barricades were topped with plate-glass and bronze grilles, and presently, to all the empty desks, the files and adding-machines, would come the members of the accounting and circulation departments. It looked rather like a bank, but it did not smell like a bank; the air was heavy with the strange sweetish reek of newsprint and of ink, and of oil from the great presses waiting in silence out beyond the splendor. It was the best smell Norris knew; the building was very different from the one in which the paper was published when he first worked for it, but the smell was eternal.

He climbed the stairs to the third floor, where the stink of old cigar butts fraying away to pulp in the spittoons enlarged and enriched the other odors. Lights burned above the state and telegraph desks, where men had been at work for an hour or more, and a single typewriter pecked at the silence; but the *Chronicle,* as a whole, still slept like the city.

Norris and the state editor, Don Hoeksema, exchanged comments on the weather; then Norris began to comb through the *Bugle* for local items, which he clipped, and which Ack would presently distribute for rewrites. Ack himself arrived, very soon, puffing and blowing from his climb upstairs, but Norris had been right; he was in a sunny mood.

"Who was that lady I seen you with last night?" he boomed, unwinding a muffler from his throat, hanging his coat on the rack against the wall.

"That was no lady—that was the Second Mrs. Tanqueray," said Don Hoeksema.

Norris laughed and went on clipping, too profoundly pleased to say anything; it was the first time in ten years that anyone on the *Chronicle* staff had tried to kid him.

"Jesus Christ," said Ack, settling himself in his chair, "of all the god-damned weather. No kidding, Bry, she was quite a doll. Where'd you find her?"

"Since when have you been a music lover?" Norris asked.

"Since last night. Mrs. G. has decided to take up culture, so now I have to take it up too so we'll have something to talk about at the dinner table. Holy God," said Ack, "I slept like a baby in that hard balcony seat and then I went home and went right on sleeping like a baby. Mrs. G. says to me this morning, 'See, that's what culture does for you.'" Ack leaned sideways and spat with gusto into the spittoon. He was an enormously stout man, some years older than Norris, with a round head which looked even rounder because he kept his hair cut down to thick gray bristles. When he walked he rolled like a sailor, but he was astonishingly light on his feet.

57

"Back to the grind," he said, lighting one of his stogies; with his arrival the day had really begun for Norris, and by degrees, as darkness thinned beyond the windows and the long room filled up, as telephones began to ring and two, four, six typewriters to chatter, the nonessential things dropped away and his mind became empty of everything but work. But it moved swiftly and unerringly, as he had known it would, until the mid-morning lull when most of the reporters were out on assignments and he leaned back in his chair to drink coffee from a cardboard carton.

Now was the time to gather his strength for the chaos soon to begin, the reporters returning, the phones incessantly ringing, the typewriters joining in a frantic chorus, the stories flooding the basket, flowing all over Ack's desk and his; the tumult which would mount to a climax at one o'clock, deadline for the home edition, and then be over for the day.

"Hey, you read Andy McBain's book?" Ack asked, dropping his own empty carton into the waste-basket.

"Nope," said Norris.

"Pretty good. Smart-aleck stuff, in a way, but it's good. The guy can write."

"It's what he's paid for. It's why he's famous."

"Funny how two guys can start out at the same point," Ack said, "with just about the same mental equipment, you'd say, and one of 'em winds up famous and the other winds up a god-damned city editor of a god-damned paper in a god-damned city like Broadfield."

"Or a god-damned assistant city editor," said Norris.

"Yah, that's right, I forgot you knew Andy even better than I did. You went to college with him, for Christ's sake. Why don't you read his book? Jealous?"

"Unh-uh." Norris looked down the room to the desk where Vincent Rourke sat talking at the moment with Will Eliot, who was about the same age. There were two more of them, starting at approximately the same point, and twenty, thirty years from now Will Eliot would still be working for the *Chronicle*, but where would Rourke be?

"Well, neither am I, by God." Ack spat again. "Going around the country talking to a lot of god-damned women's clubs. That's what fame gets you. Mrs. G. let out a yell they must've heard in Kalamazoo when I told her I used to know Andy. Didn't tell her he used to scoop me when he was covering police for the *Bugle*. He was a smart reporter; you have to hand it to him."

Ack's telephone let out its special ring, three nervous blurts of sound. "City desk," he bawled into the receiver. "Oh, Jesus Christ, another god-damned death. Hey, Rourke!" he yelled. "Quit chewing the fat and get this call, will you? What do you think you're paid for, for Christ's sake?" He left his own phone dangling while Rourke had the call switched, and muttered to Norris, "Fancypants! When I think two good guys had to go so there'd be a spot for him—"

"They were let off long before anybody'd heard of Vinnie. Be fair, Ack," Norris said, "be fair."

"Yah, and who's going to be fair to those two poor bastards?" But Ack's sunny mood, which always expressed itself in a wild excess of profanity—when he was in a rage his brain stayed cool, and he chose his vocabulary with great nicety and spoke softly— lasted for the rest of the morning. Some good stories came in; local news squeezed national news out of the place of honor on page one, always cause for quiet rejoicing to Ack and Norris, and out of the City Hall came some political stuff which really justified the inside streamer which had to run daily, whether there was actually any big news or not. Ack and Norris shared the particular triumph which came only rarely, when everything worked out exactly right.

"On the nose," said Ack at one o'clock, and went out to lunch, leaving Norris to hold the fort until one-thirty.

The snow had kept falling thinly all morning; a wind had come up and whirled the flakes in Norris's face when he slogged down Main Street to the Champ Diner, aware at last of his hunger. Usually he brought his own sandwiches and ate them at eleven-thirty in the back room; today he'd hardly thought of food.

Sitting at the counter, in a smell of grease and steam, eating a hamburger and drinking coffee from a thick heavy cup, he considered Andy McBain. It was the war, really, which had started Andy up the ladder. After less than two years on the *Bugle* he'd quit and gone to Chicago, and seemed stuck in Chicago until the war broke. Then he left his new wife and went up to Canada and enlisted, and presently his letters started trickling back to Norris; long before the United States went in, Andy had seen plenty of action. While he was overseas his wife found somebody she liked better than Andy, and presently there was a divorce; there was no reason for Andy to come back and he stayed in Europe a year or so after the war was over, living hand-to-mouth for a while but clicking at last, turning into a foreign correspondent —a comparatively rare breed, in those days—and after that he was set: a trip around the world, New York for a while, Europe again, and now his book, and fame, and the lecture circuit.

An exciting life, Norris thought; but it was true that he felt no envy. The pain in his heart was not envy; there was no reason for a pain to be there at all, and he tried to ignore it.

While Andy was fighting a war, Norris lived secure in a world which seemed to have no connection with the war, despite food shortages, rising prices, Liberty Loan drives, Navy recruiting campaigns, casualty lists. Laura worked for the Red Cross, Laura helped to run a canteen for service men passing through town, Laura appeared as the Statue of Liberty on a float in a Fourth of July parade. (July Fourth, 1918: what a remote era, what an innocent-seeming one, thought Norris. What had become of the zeal which burned in people's hearts in those days?) Laura had done as much about the war as anyone in Broadfield could, but Norris, preoccupied and worn out by his work on the paper, thought of the war chiefly in terms of the headlines he was writing. For by 1918 he'd been brought in off the streets to spend all his time at a desk: the telegraph desk, two years of it, and he might have become telegraph editor only Prent Hodges returned wounded from the war and was boosted into the job, which was only fair.

Then Norris was exiled to the library for six months as an editorial writer; he had to say things about Woodrow Wilson and the League of Nations which had thrown Laura into one fury after another.

"It's prostitution, Norris," she said, pacing in the living room, shaking the paper at him. "You can't go on like this! You'll have to quit. I don't care how hard things get, I'd rather starve, I'd rather we all starved, than have you write what you don't believe—molding public opinion with lies, lies, lies!" Then she laughed at her vehemence and said, "Not that anybody ever reads your wretched editorials. But oh, darling, what was the war *for*, if we're going to turn our backs on the world?"

"Well, I don't know. I'm not too crazy about the League myself. It *could* drag us into more wars, you know."

It was always a one-sided argument. Against her eloquence, against her passion (for she did feel it passionately; she really believed the war dead had been betrayed), Norris could say nothing. Just in time there was a death on the city side and a general shifting around. Ack Guion became city editor, Norris his assistant, and there they both had been ever since.

Sometimes Norris sighed for his reporting days, but his mind worked better at a desk. Swiftly, unerringly, his soft black pencil made clarity out of a garbled piece of reporting; he saw just where to twist a feature story, just where to cut it short, to make it punch home; he wrote better heads than Ack did, as Ack was the first to admit, and in a crisis he shared Ack's calm; his grasp on *Chronicle* style was the firmest of any staff member. If Ack died before Norris, Norris would certainly become city editor; but despite the frictions which arise between two men working in such close harness he didn't want Ack to die; he was content to be where he was. Dull, yes, it had certainly seemed dull much of the time, even to him. But there was always the satisfaction of doing his particular job as well as anybody could do it—it had pulled him through the bad days, through the worst of his hangovers; and now and then came a day like today, when he felt about his profession as he had last night, talking to Mrs. Norman Trees. . . .

The afternoon was quiet, as afternoons had a way of being, and the climax before the night edition went to press was only a faint echo of the noontime frenzy.

At loose ends for the moment, Norris pulled up his typewriter and batted out a letter to Laurette and Charlie and Charlie's wife, who were all living together now in a cramped Detroit apartment. He was expecting them for Christmas, of course; it would be nice if Charlie could get a couple of days off. Be sure to let him know, so he could tell them at the farm how many to expect. Folding the letter, shoving it into a *Chronicle* envelope, he wished it were not necessary to go to the farm for Christmas. Pat hated it, Joel was indifferent, Norris dreaded the occasion because it would make him feel what a bad son he had been to his parents, what a bad brother to Maudie.

Lifting his head, he caught sight of Vincent Rourke again. Vincent, with an air of long-suffering, was reading through Milly Prentiss's society copy for tomorrow's paper—one of the chores which had fallen his way, and as good a method as any, Norris had told him, for learning about desk-work.

On a sudden impulse, Norris hauled himself up from his chair, wandered down the room, and perched on the edge of Vincent's desk.

"How'd you like the concert last night, Vinnie?" he asked.

"It was all right. Very good, in fact," said Vincent, on guard immediately. "I mean, for a town like this to have a symphony orchestra at all—" The wrong note. Vincent felt nervous; he'd been feeling nervous ever since Carola had involved him with Polly Peabody and the concert and the gathering to which she had also dragged Norris and Betty Lou Hanbury.

"Still pretty much of an amateur organization," said Norris, who perhaps after all wasn't touchy about the orchestra. "Don't want to keep you from Milly's deathless prose, but I thought if you didn't have any other plans for Christmas, maybe you'd like to join us. We go out to the farm. Celebrate it there, after I get through on the paper."

"Gosh, that's swell of you, Bry. Sounds like a lot of fun. Only—" Vincent inserted a heavy black hyphen between "week" and "end"; the finer points of *Chronicle* usage were quite beyond Milly. "Well," said Vincent, with a feeling that he was being trapped, "I have another invitation already, as a matter of fact. I'm sorry."

"It's O.K.," Norris said, "it's perfectly O.K. Guess you're getting to know quite a lot of people around town by now. I should have asked you sooner." He smiled at Vincent before he slid off the desk and strolled away; but Vincent no longer felt sure that Norris was completely ingenuous; sometimes in those sad deep-set eyes there was almost a gleam of irony. So, just now, he might have seen that Vincent was lying.

But Carola would ask him for Christmas, surely; or if not Carola, then Polly Peabody. The Senator would be up from Washington; other personages would gather in the Peabody mansion and it might be possible to make some valuable contacts. Vincent spent a good deal of time, in the next few days, in trying to wangle an invitation to the Peabodys' Christmas dinner; but the first three times he telephoned, Polly was out, and when he caught her at last, she seemed almost to have forgotten who he was.

Vincent grinned at himself in the mirror that night and said, Rourke, you're slipping; but he didn't really amuse himself. It might be true; something might have happened to him because of the affair with Anne Bannister—the magic wasn't working any more.

He became a little frightened. The mood wasn't here yet, but it was waiting for him in the near future. Gray day followed gray day, and each one carried him closer to the terrible moment. He thought the weather might be largely to blame. Since the last week of November the sun had not shone on Broadfield; feeble spurts of snow came now and again from the low gray sky, and then the clouds thinned and bright spaces appeared; but they were deceptive and soon the gray closed in solidly and the snow started again.

Snow mixed with sand was churned to brown grit in the streets, and along the gutters the snow was forming sooty mountain ranges. Smoke from thousands of chimneys and the factories across the river seemed to accumulate in the raw stillness until it became palpable, too thick to be dispersed by the strongest wind. The whole city was becoming the color of ashes and soot; gray or brown or grubby yellow the houses and public buildings, black the lamp-posts and the rows of trees; you felt that whatever you touched would leave a smear on your fingers.

The Broadfield weather and homesickness for New York, which was not at all like this in winter, were all that ailed him. He could not be worrying about Christmas, which had never had a senti-mental meaning for him, and he would rather spend it alone than go out to the Bryant farm. But he wouldn't have to spend it alone because Carola, surely, would take pity on him.

He went to see her, when Christmas was only four days away, to remind her of his existence. The sad monkey left him standing in the front hall and climbed the stairs slowly and without making any noise. The house was so still that Vincent could hear the discreet tapping on a door, and Carola's voice, and the sad monkey's: "Mr. Rourke, Madam."

"Mrs. Wilmot will be down presently, sir," the sad monkey said, returning. "Will you wait in the living room?"

Vincent stood at the window, smoking one of Carola's cigarettes, which tasted faintly of perfume and made him feel sick. A truck was coming up Warner Street hill, by fits and starts, and men in shabby dark clothes were shoveling snow into it; even as they worked, new flakes dropped listlessly out of the weighted sky. Some boys lurched past, whooping in adolescent voices, pelting one another with snowballs; a dog explored the snow-range, sniffing from one yellowed patch to the next. It was as though a glass curtain slid down between Vincent and the world; everything went flat and brittle, and had lost all meaning.

In desperation he began to pace back and forth across the deep carpet, seeing his own reflection advance and retreat in the gilt-framed mirrors; the room was filled with Vincents, but they too lacked meaning. Carola found him pacing, and laughed, and said, "I hadn't thought of you as a panther before. You move very well, Vincent; you'd made a good ballet dancer."

He whirled on her, unable for a moment to conceal his fury, and then said, "This god-damned weather!"

"I know, my dear. But you'll be used to it before the winter's over. Either that, or stark, staring mad. Do sit down. I can't bear young men who pace. My first husband always paced before he got around to saying something unpleasant." Carola dropped into a chair and took up a cigarette.

While he was lighting it for her Vincent said, "I was wondering if you'd come out to dinner with me tonight." He smiled, though his face felt stiff and his voice sounded to him like a phonograph record which might stick any minute. "High time I made some return for all your kindness," he said. He continued to stand by her chair, looking down at her; this made him feel master of the situation, but she said, "Darling, *please* sit *down*. I can't see your pretty face properly. It's all foreshortened."

"First you call me a ballet dancer, then you call me pretty." Vincent laughed sharply, but he sat down.

"Dear me! We're touchy this afternoon," said Carola.

"Oh, it's just— I've been pining for New York."

"Not very original of you, Vincent. You'll have to do better than that if you want to fascinate me." She smiled again and said, "I'm terribly sorry, I really am, but I'm going to the country club tonight."

"Everybody's always going to the country club," Vincent complained.

"Oh, my dear, you're quite mistaken! The country club is a

barren waste, more often than not. Even though they have reduced all the fees and offer bargain rates for the Saturday night dinner dances. Haven't you seen for yourself? I was sure Polly Peabody would seize you by the hair of your head—how I envy you those curls!—and drag you out there forthwith."

"I haven't seen her again," said Vincent.

"Devoting all your energies to Miss Bryant?"

"I haven't seen her either."

"Then there must be some more bewitching damsel. Who is she?"

"I've just been stewing in my own juice," said Vincent.

Carola grimaced. "How repulsive you make it sound. . . . What has gone wrong? I thought Miss Bryant was fascinated. Likewise Miss Peabody. *Isn't* she a lovely child, Vincent?"

He sat quiet for a moment; his anger was over but his body was charged with nervousness. Carola saw through him, he thought, and he was overcome by an impulse to be frank; this was such a novel sensation that a little of the deathliness lifted away from the world. He smiled without any stiffness at all, winningly, and said, "I've been doing my best to get asked to the Peabodys' for Christmas. I thought the Senator was somebody I ought to know."

Carola laughed. "Vincent, there are moments when you melt my aged heart. I could almost fall in love with you myself."

"But Polly is being elusive," said Vincent. "She's being fêted so often at the country club that she has no time for a cub reporter."

"Perhaps it's just as well. Polly would never be able to darn your socks or cook you a good square meal. You'll be much better off with Patricia Bryant, even if she can't take you to the country club. That is, if you don't find somebody better than either. Really, you know," Carola said, "you disappoint me. You're so unenterprising. Stewing in your own juice, indeed! Surely you know better than that."

"I've been low in my mind," said Vincent.

"What happened between you and Patricia? I thought you were seeing her nightly."

"I was for a while. We went out and drank beer and talked, and she always paid for her own beer."

"Considerate. What did you talk about?"

"Ourselves."

"Fascinating. But the topic is now exhausted?"

"That topic never could be." Vincent smiled, more winningly than ever.

"Beer," said Carola, "beer and earnest conversation Dutch treat. It all sounds very wholesome. Why haven't you gone back to it? Has Johnny Wheelwright, after all, been lurking down dark alleys?"

"I squeezed Johnny right out of the picture," said Vincent, and

64

told Carola about the filling-station episode. He hadn't known until now why he'd gone to such trouble to contrive it; afterwards it had seemed like a false step; but now it became rather amusing.

"What a *wicked* boy you are!" said Carola. "But weren't you taking rather a risk? Suppose, instead of letting his heart break, Johnny had had it out with you then and there?"

"Johnny, it seems, is a clod," said Vincent.

"Or perhaps his passion has cooled. But I seem no nearer the root of things," said Carola. "Do you find, after all your trouble, that Patricia isn't worth it?"

"Patricia is all tied up in knots inside," said Vincent.

"And unraveling them is too much trouble? I should think it might be rather fascinating, Vincent. Niggling work, but fun."

"I thought so too for a while, but I— Well," said Vincent, "having started out by being a brother to her, I couldn't seem to get out of the rut. I—"

"Patience, patience. . . . It isn't surprising she's tied up in knots, I suppose." Carola took up another cigarette and lit it for herself. "Stay where you are, Vincent; I don't want to start you pacing again, or have you looming over me. . . . I wonder," she said, "I just wonder if Patricia has heard about Andy McBain. How I should love to know! It wouldn't surprise me in the least if she had. Her aunt and her grandmother are prime bitches; it's just the kind of thing they'd be likely to tell an innocent young girl. They never could abide Laura."

"What about Andy McBain?" asked Vincent.

Carola looked at her cigarette. "Is your interest in Patricia being rewakened? Well, Vincent, I don't think I shall tell you; I'm going to let you find out for yourself. Have one more evening of beer and conversation with Patricia, and bring up Andrew White McBain, and see what happens."

"How could I bring him up? I don't know the guy."

"Vincent, really, must I make up your speeches for you? 'Are you planning to go to McBain's lecture?' you could ask her. No, that might seem a little premature; he isn't coming until May. But you could certainly ask her if she's read his book. I'm sure you must switch off yourselves and on to books occasionally over the beer."

"It would be like—hide-in-the-dark," said Vincent. "Why not tell me all about McBain? How in the world could a man like that be hitched up with Patricia's neuroses?"

"Neuroses? Are they actually that? And she looks so placid, on the surface. Oh, you'd certainly be wasting your time with Polly Peabody. Patricia, I now begin to realize, has infinite possibilities. . . . No, I certainly don't intend to tell you; it would spoil all the fun. I shall drop a hint, however. Nearly all famous men have humble beginnings, and Andy McBain had his on the *Morning Bugle*."

"You mean he's from Broadfield?"

"The town isn't populated exclusively with cretins, darling. Though as a matter of fact Andy is not from Broadfield. I believe he was born on the banks of the Wabash far away. But he met Norris in college—they were rivals on the college paper and Norris won out; it was Norris who became editor; and then to make up for that, I suppose, he let Andy know, after *he'd* found a job on the *Chronicle*, that there was a job on the *Bugle* for Andy. So up from the banks of the Wabash came Andy, and laid the groundwork for his glittering career."

Silence invaded the room. Out in the street the shovels were still scraping and the truck still groaned occasionally as it inched up the hill; Vincent's interest was killed by these sounds and the whole weight of Broadfield in winter dropped on him again.

"You look as if you were going to burst into tears. Vincent, what on *earth* is the matter with you?" Carola asked.

"Nothing. Oh, nothing." Vincent went to the window and watched the men bending wearily to the snow, lifting it up in great frozen chunks on their shovels, dropping it into the truck. "I get this way sometimes, that's all," he said. "You'll know all about it when you know me a little better."

The stillness seemed to gather in the room behind him; he could hear Carola shifting in her chair.

"I'm not sure that I want to know you better," she said presently, "if you go in very often for this kind of performance."

He continued to watch the men shoveling snow; then he shut his eyes, clinging with one hand to the curtain. Another false step; but what he had said had forced itself out of him. It was better that way; it was more interesting, it aroused more sympathy, when it came spontaneously. When it happened with Anne Bannister she moved across the room to him, put both arms around him, pulled him close, and rocked him gently. Almost like a mother. . . .

"You have a few little pet neuroses of your own, it seems," Carola went on, after another silence. "Well, darling, I'm not interested. I'm just not interested. Keep them out of sight, or stop coming to see me—one thing or the other."

He heard her standing up; he heard her skirt swish as she came toward him. It was just that she was a good deal older, perhaps, and more experienced, and wanted to play with him a little longer, wounding him before she started to be kind. But long before she reached him she stopped moving.

"And now I think you'd better go," she said. "I'm due at the club in half an hour, and I must change."

He stood a moment longer at the window, and then turned.

"I'm sorry. It's just the weather; really, that's all it is." He saw himself again in one of her damned mirrors, and tore his eyes away. "I won't come again until the sun shines," he said, not quite achieving lightness.

"That would be in April," said Carola, "or possibly not until May. Unless we have a *very* exceptional winter. If my curiosity gets the best of me before then, I'll call you up. Good-by, and a very Merry Christmas to you."

"I've been asked out to the Bryant farm," Vincent said, "but—"

"How nice for you. It will do you good to see how the other half lives." Carola moved into the hall and pulled the door open; the sudden flood of gray light, washing over her face, gave it a ravaged look; she was older than he'd thought. "It's started to snow again. I hope you don't all get stuck in a drift on the way out."

Anger against her kept his depression from becoming absolute in the next few days, although he made up his mind that he would never see her again. But in the late afternoon of Christmas Eve he found a letter in his mailbox; Carola's name was on the flap of the envelope, and her tall angular writing marched right across the front: "Vincent V. Rourke, Esq." Up the three flights of stairs climbed Vincent V. Rourke, Esq., and sank into a plum-colored chair with a broken spring, and ripped open the envelope. . . .

My dear,

Forgive me if you can for the other afternoon. What I said was inexcusable, but bear with me while I make excuses. You know, I think, what my situation is—trapped in this mausoleum with a man who might just as well be a corpse. I too am susceptible to the weather and I've had to stand more of this *weather than you. I had been up all the night before, sitting with my father—there are times when he weeps like a child unless he knows I am there beside him—and I had spent the better part of the day with him too. When you arrived I had very nearly reached the end of my rope, as I sometimes do. I suppose I sensed that you were in a similar plight; for a time I did my best, but you would not have it that way—you had your outburst, I could not then help mine. I suppose you had been hoping to be asked here for Christmas, but really the Bryant farm will be far less dreary. I do not* celebrate *Christmas at all—nobody comes in, I go nowhere. Too much of the time I neglect my father but at Christmas a sentimental streak crops up. If you can forgive me, do come around in the evening, however, and we'll have something Dickensian to drink, and bind up each other's wounds. I have been feeling wretched about my behaviour and I cannot bear life when it becomes messy. Ever yours. . . .*

The writing dashed across the thick gray paper; the underscorings were double, and the pen, digging into the surface, had scattered small blots. Feeling suddenly almost hilarious, Vincent counted what money was left in his wallet and went out into the dusk to the nearest florist's, where he ordered three dollars' worth of flowers to be sent to Carola. On his card he scribbled, "For this relief, much thanks—but alas, we don't return from the farm until late." Then he kept on walking downtown, and presently he reached a bookstore. The windows were still lighted; there was a scattering of customers inside buying best-sellers at the last minute.

Vincent thrust his way in and prowled to the back beside a shelf of reprints. A brotherly gift for Patricia Bryant: somewhere on these shelves it must be waiting. He found it at last—a cheap edition which did not look too cheap (the format was outsize, the paper was thick, there were pen drawings) of *A Shropshire Lad*. Housman had been another of Miss What's-her-name's pets. A pessimist, of course, she said, but such lovely simplicity.

A harried woman with hair half coming down and beads of sweat on nose and forehead wrapped *A Shropshire Lad* in a gift wrapping, and Vincent carried it up the hill, buoyant still because of Carola's note.

But when he reached Norris's house he did not go in; he could not be so blatant. He walked on, resigned to a lonely Christmas; and next morning, when Ack Guion took the trouble to come all the way over to Vincent's desk instead of bellowing down the room at him, to ask if he'd mind staying until noon, when a member of the bulldog staff would arrive, Vincent couldn't find it in his heart to feel martyred.

The *Chronicle* published only one edition on holidays; it was off the presses and on the streets by ten-thirty, and by eleven the editorial room was empty, save for Vincent. By twelve, when he departed also, there was actually a pallid sun showing; the latest snowfall had covered the soot and glittered where the light touched it.

Vincent sat alone in his room, eating bread and butter. He was confined to his room until darkness fell; if he went out, Carola would be sure to see him, or somebody else would who would tell Carola; that was how things were in Broadfield.

He did not feel unhappy; he did not feel sorry for himself. He had spent strange Christmases, but this was the strangest; there would never, he was sure, be another one like it. When he had finished eating he put in a long-distance call to Uncle Bertrand, and because it was Christmas did nothing about reversing the charges.

"Bertrand Vaughan speaking." He might have been in the same room.

"Merry Christmas," said Vincent.

68

."Oh, Vinnie, you appalling fool. The same to you and how are you and why haven't you written?"

"Why haven't *you* sent me a check for Christmas? Or is it on the way already?"

"No, it isn't on the way, and it won't be. I am stony broke, Vincent; I'm gnawing an old bone at this very minute. I didn't get asked anywhere. Nobody is spending any money this Christmas. New York is a city of the dead."

"I don't believe a word of it. I hear voices and laughter in the background. I hear a great popping of corks."

"A sound-effects record I borrowed from a friend at NBC just to cheer myself up," said Uncle Bertrand glibly.

"Well, I didn't get asked anywhere either, and I haven't a phonograph even if I had a friend to borrow a sound-effects record from. *I* have just been eating plain bread and butter," said Vincent, "and that is the literal truth. So please take pity on me and send some money. You'd better wire it, as a matter of fact. My need is desperate."

"My dear Vinnie, *I* am one of the unemployed, *you* are a wage-earner. You must learn not to live beyond your income, and you'd better hang up right away. This silly conversation is costing you a fortune."

"I'll forward the bill to you. And I do need that money."

"Then you'll have to go out on the streets and sell yourself. Good-by," said Uncle Bertrand, "and I shall say Happy New Year to you now, so you won't be betrayed into any more extravagance. I'm glad to know you haven't died yet."

Vincent lay down and went to sleep. When he woke again it was dark, and Christmas was being celebrated all over the apartment house with the same kind of bumps and thumps, the same kind of screaming and laughter, that went on every other evening of the year. He took a shower, and had some tea to drink, and ate some stale crackers. He did not feel hungry at all, but he was beginning to mind his loneliness.

He walked out into the dark carrying *A Shropshire Lad* under his arm. He walked slowly, going several blocks out of his way, to give the Bryants a little more time to get back from the farm; he thought longingly of the Dickensian drink Carola had offered him, and even of the wound-binding. But it would be better not to see Carola again until he had something amusing to say to her; something so amusing that nothing ever need be said at all about that afternoon, or her letter, or the flowers he had sent. The best way to keep life from becoming messy was to forget all about such messes as sometimes occurred.

Long before he reached Norris's house he saw that his loneliness was about to end. There were lights blazing in all the windows.

8

WHEN Vincent rang the bell, Norris was in the living room having an argument with Charlie. It had been impending since last night, but until now there had been no chance for it.

Christmas began like any other morning, for Norris, and when he got back from the *Chronicle* there were the few presents they had bought for one another to be opened. Then Homer arrived in the truck and they rode out to the farm beneath the flapping canvas, across the white landscape which shone like a dream in the pale sun.

In the front parlor was a tree Homer had cut from his own reforestation project, strung with popcorn and tinsel; the dining room, which had been opened and warmed, was festooned with ropes of red and green paper like immensely elongated caterpillars, and a large red bell, sprinkled with artificial snow, hung from the central chandelier, which still looked new and brassy—Homer had only recently had the farm electrified. There was a bunch of mistletoe, strategically placed, and a good deal of coyness went on beneath it; sooner or later all the men had kissed all the women.

Despite these stabs at gaiety, though, it was not a gay occasion. Charlie had brought with him from Detroit a profound gloom which refused to lift; his wife had a cold; Laurette had too much paint on her face and wore a dress which clung too tightly to her opulent curves—Norris's mother, Norris's sister Maudie, kept looking at her askance; the baby cried; Joel vanished to the barn; Patricia withdrew into a corner and turned the pages of an old bound volume of *St. Nicholas*.

The others presented a hardly more cheerful aspect. Norris's parents had visibly grown older since the last time he'd seen them, and he kept thinking he should have come out to the farm more often; they might just as well have been in Muskogee, Oklahoma, for all he saw of them. His father was almost eighty now, and stone deaf; unable to hear what was going on or read lips, he had withdrawn into a private world; out of it he made sudden startling pronouncements which everybody ignored. Old Mrs. Bryant was going deaf too, and Maudie and Homer and Leon had grown so used to screaming at her that they screamed at one another unnecessarily also. It gave what they said an air of perpetual exasperation.

A drink would have helped; Charlie, pacing the floor, was obviously desperate for a drink; but there would be none for anybody. Homer Waldron's temperance had been one of the reasons why Maudie married him.

Dinner was served at two o'clock, and Norris's father asked a blessing on the turkey and the mashed turnip and the creamed onions and the potatoes and the bread and the pickles and the glasses of water. It was a long petition; Norris watched Charlie, who was staring belligerently at the bowed heads, and hoped he wouldn't resume the subject he'd started last night after his arrival from Detroit.

Like the other children, Charlie had a look of Laura, but mostly he conveyed an impression of sullen obstinacy. He was shorter than his father, with a square solid body, wide and thick in the shoulders, deep in the chest; his neck was too short, his head a little too large; at twenty-five he had furrows in his forehead, lines of discouragement about his mouth, which shouldn't have appeared for years yet. Once Charlie had been very much like Joel, but he'd never had the clear ingenuousness of Johnny Wheelwright; and now he was filled with bitterness.

He drew a breath, evading his father's eyes, and said, "It sure is good to be sitting down to a meal with white folks again."

"Why, Charlie, land's sakes, I didn't know you were living in a *nigger* district," Maudie brayed.

"I was speaking figuratively," Charlie said. "But you ought to see Detroit now."

"Charlie says you ought to see Detroit now," Maudie screamed at her mother.

"Why don't he come live on the farm?" old Mrs. Bryant asked. "Good healthy life. Plenty of work to do and we could let the hired men go."

"Now I guess Charlie's better off in Detroit, bad as times are," said Homer. "I say Charlie is better off in Detroit," he shouted. "What was it you were starting to say, Charlie, about conditions there?"

"Let's skip it," said Norris. "This is Christmas Day. Peace on earth to men of good will," he said, and the words suddenly moved him.

"It's good will to men, Norris," Maudie said kindly. "More turnip already, Joel? Still keep up your appetite, I see. Well, that's fine, it's just fine; a good hearty appetite for good wholesome food. Patricia, you're just pecking; don't you *like* the dark meat? Homer, give Patricia a piece of the breast—don't you remember, she always liked the white meat better, and why waste a drumstick on her, that's what I say. There's plenty of us think the drumstick's the tastiest part of the bird. They're good plump turkeys, but seems like maybe I didn't baste them enough. Now, Leon, you go right ahead and eat those creamed onions up. They're good for you; you're a grown man and you ought to learn to like onions. Would you pass me the cranberry sauce, Delores?"

But Charlie was not to be diverted. Eating hungrily, he talked about the Wops and the Hunkies, the niggers and the Kikes. The Wops and the Hunkies and the niggers were bad enough, but the Kikes were worst of all. The Kikes were running the country, they were damn near running the world, and everybody knew they were behind the New Deal; that was common knowledge, said Charlie, staring down the table at Uncle Homer.

"Yes, sir, Charlie, guess you're right." Homer poked at a scrap of meat that had caught between his teeth.

"The whole depression—they maneuvered that," said Charlie, "just so they could squeeze out the Americans and get their hands on things. It stands to reason. They've always had most of the money. Look at the millionaires; more than half of them are Jews."

"I never could stand a Jew," said Maudie. "Don't know why, but there's just something about a Jew makes me feel kind of sick inside. It all goes back to the way they crucified the Savior, I guess; it's a deep-seated instinct, you might say. I say it's only natural for Christians to hate the Jews," she shouted at her mother.

"They control the movies, they control the radio, they control the most influential newspapers in the country," Charlie said. "Molding public opinion. I'm not saying I'm crazy about Germany, but this Hitler has the right idea. You have to treat the Jews rough or they'll start kicking *you* around."

"Laurette, that dress is cut too low in front, and it fits too tight," said old Mr. Bryant.

"Trouble is," said Homer, still picking at his teeth, "how you going to get the upper hand, Charlie? They're smart, you know. Now, I like to think I'm a smart man myself, but by golly, I'm no match for a Jew, I'll tell you. Get the best of you every time."

"There are ways," Charlie said.

"Charlie belongs to a—" Delores started to say, but Charlie gave her a look.

"You just shut up about that," he said, and clenched his fist.

Delores went red and stared down at her plate; there were tears in her eyes. Delores was small and dark and almost pretty; she was brainless and cheap too, Norris feared; but he found himself feeling sorry for her.

"Come to that," Maudie said into the silence, "I'm not so wild about the Catholics, myself. You take the Pope, the control he exercises all over the world. You can't be a good Catholic and a good American citizen at the same time; that's my opinion. I say the Catholics in this country, their first allegiance is to the Pope of Rome," she shouted at her mother. "Being Americans is only secondary."

"Hell," said Charlie, "most of 'em aren't Americans anyway. Who belongs to the Catholic church? Wops and Polaks. Do the

72

Wops take out citizenship papers? Like hell they do. They come over here, they make their pile, then they go back to sunny Italy."

"Laurette, you look just like a harlot," said old Mr. Bryant.

"Now, Papa!" Maudie shouted futilely. "It's Christmas Day, after all. You just keep your remarks to yourself."

"Now you take Moosolinny," said Homer. "I don't like the Eyetalians any more'n you do, Charlie, but disregarding the fact Moosolinny *is* an Eyetalian, he's all right. Like to see a man like him in the White House. A strong man with good practical common horse sense, that's what this country needs."

"You're damn tootin'," said Charlie.

"You know," said Laurette, making her first contribution to the symposium, "I like Benito a whole lot better than Adolf. That silly little mustache—Adolf looks just exactly like Charlie Chaplin."

"Don't kid yourself; he knows what he's doing," Charlie said. "Europe was on the skids, what with the Kikes and the Commies and all, but before he's through, Hitler's going to do a hell of a lot of cleaning up. You just watch. Trouble is, *we're* all asleep, most of us here in the States. Just playing into their hands over there. Hell, we could run the world," Charlie said, "if we set our minds to it. But if we don't get wise in a hurry we'll be goosestepping for a bunch of damn Krautheads."

"Not the Jews?" Norris asked. "You can't have it both ways, Charlie."

"The Jews'll sap our strength, then Germany steps in and takes over," Charlie said.

Norris stopped listening. The more they talked, the more he thought about Laura, who would have left the table long ago. He thought about Laura in the war years, hating the war but doing what she could to help win it, knowing that most of what she did was absurd, but burning with hope, an enormous conviction. We've produced a great man, said Laura; it's one of the miraculous things about us, we do produce great men when we need them. He's the greatest President since Lincoln.

There would never be another war, Laura thought; the human race was learning at last. Oh, Norris, she said, it's a terrible time, but it's the time I'd have chosen. It's a tremendous time, darling, she said, turning to him in the dark; it was as though he could see her eyes shining. Darling, darling, I love you so much, she said. I'm wicked and selfish, but I couldn't bear it if you had to go away and fight too. . . .

He was almost glad she had died with her illusions, before she had seen the terrible sickness which was spreading over the world. The world had always been sick, of course; the sickness made the war and the war made the sickness worse. For a while one hadn't noticed but now it was touching everybody, even Laura's first-born. Norris could not have stood it if she'd heard Charlie talking like that. But perhaps Charlie would have been different if Laura had lived, or if Norris had tried to keep what Laura meant, what she believed, clearly before his children.

Betrayal, he thought again; so many ways in which he had failed her. When he had remembered her at all it was only the outward appearance that came into his mind, the loveliest woman he had ever seen, too lovely for him, a creature he was always afraid of losing, so that he had been shaken by jealousy every time she smiled at another man.

Well, he had lost the appearance and the real Laura too, and so made an emptiness in the lives of his children which need not have been there. But he could get her back, perhaps; the image was growing clearer.

"Norris Bryant, what in the world is the matter with *you* today?" Maudie brayed. "Expect us to wait all after*noon* while you poke along with your turkey?"

Norris looked up at her. "I'm sorry," he said meekly enough, but what they had been saying flowed back into his mind and he trembled with a sudden wild anger. "I was hungry when I sat down," he said, raising his voice, "but not any more." He tried to control his anger, but it was no use; he got up from his chair and he shouted at them. "It's a wonder the food doesn't choke you. God is hate, is that it? Well, I've had enough!"

He walked out of the room, through the back door and the barnyard and away across the frozen fields. He sank to his knees in the drifts, but plunged on until he reached the bank of the river; by then he could hardly breathe, and the whiteness was blinding him.

He found a fallen tree, pushed the snow away with his bare hand, and sat down, blinking in the dazzle. Their hatred, flung carelessly at whatever happened to be in the way—Jews, foreigners, those of another faith or color, what difference did it make?—had kindled only hatred in him. Hatred was foolish, but anger was better; anger could be turned not against them but against the bestial stupidities they had admitted into their minds.

He sat on the fallen tree, with the wide whiteness all around him, and felt a renewal of the resolve he had made in the cemetery, as if a new power flowed through him. But presently the intensity of the moment was gone, as it had gone when he left the cemetery.

I'm tired out, that's all it is, he said, and cupped his cold hand around a match-flame to light a cigarette.

He was not pure in heart himself. There was a darkness in him which had been pleased by Charlie's words. No one was pure in heart, perhaps; the darkness was in everybody and sought an outlet. So easy to choose the scapegoats conventional to your own place and time; so easy to see, not men, fellow creatures, but monsters born out of your own evil. He wished unsaid all the careless words of prejudice he'd ever spoken; he was no better than Charlie, who could be forgiven at least his sense of grievance.

He had no idea how long he'd been sitting there, but he was numb with cold when Patricia came toward him through the snow.

"Father? Are you all right?"

He stood up and tried to smile at her.

"Yup." He couldn't keep his teeth from chattering. "Cold, that's all."

"You didn't even put on your coat. Or your overshoes."

"I was mad clear through. That kept me warm."

"It was so strange, Father—long after they'd all stopped talking like that."

"I know. I got to thinking about your mother. It seemed as if they were— Oh, hell," said Norris, "I don't know what came over me. But that kind of talk. On Christmas Day."

"You'd better come back." Patricia touched his arm. "Father, you'll catch pneumonia."

He linked his arm in hers, enclosed her mittened hand in his bare one, and they walked back toward the farm. She did not try to pull away from him. "They think you've started to—drink again," she said presently, looking away from him. "Aunt Maudie even said she noticed liquor on your breath when you first came in."

Norris snorted and then he laughed. "Maudie's a damn liar," he said.

"I told them, Father, I *told* them, but they—it seemed as if they *wanted* to think you were drunk." Patricia turned her face back to him. "I never knew you felt that way about them too."

"They aren't bad people, Pat. Better than I am. It's just that—" Norris trudged on in silence before he said, "We've got to do something about Charlie. The state of mind he's in—"

"Charlie's lost his job," Patricia said. "Laurette told me last night after we went to bed. He's been looking for work ever since the end of September."

"Why didn't he tell me?" Norris closed his eyes for a moment. "What have they been living on?"

"Laurette. It's why she moved in with them. To cut down on expenses."

"But Laurette can't be making enough to—"

"Laurette isn't a stenographer any more. She's working in a beauty parlor. And she's singing too; she got to know some men in a band, and she's singing with the band, I guess, in a kind of night club. And Charlie does make a little now and then, selling things on commission. Just rackets, Laurette says, but he makes a few dollars almost every week. People are always slamming doors in his face, Laurette says; he's getting to feel like a bum."

"Maybe he ought to come back to Broadfield. If Johnny Wheelwright could get a job at Northern Tool & Die— I didn't know Laurette could sing."

"She used to sing enough when she was home."

"But professionally—"

"She croons," said Patricia, "into a microphone. You don't have to have very much of a voice. You just turn on the sex, she says, and let the rest take care of itself." Patricia flushed, but she still did not pull away from him.

"I don't like the sound of it," Norris said. "There's something *about* Laurette. She—it's true, what Papa said. I wish she didn't have to dress herself up like that and use so much lipstick."

"I never used to like Laurette." Patricia clung to his arm. "When I first came back from the farm she used to—scare me, almost. She was so noisy, she knew so many boys, and—well, *you* know. But Laurette is kind, Father. She didn't have to help Charlie and Delores out. And she's so cheerful."

Norris squeezed Patricia's hand. "How'd you find me, way out there by the river?" he asked.

"Followed your footsteps in the snow, silly." Patricia swung his hand. "A lot you learn, reading all those detective stories."

He was sorry they had reached the barnyard; the shadow of the house fell across them, ending the moment of intimacy. The clamor of voices and dishes and silverware in the kitchen subsided abruptly when they walked in through the back door; Norris kept going, without speaking a word, and found his father alone in the front parlor, which was very hot from a fire in the Franklin stove.

The old man looked up and smiled at Norris. Age had fined him down, purging away the flesh; the bone-structure of his face looked delicate and sharp, as though it might pierce the skin. "Sit down, Son," he said. "Talk to me." He dropped one arm and lifted from the floor beside his chair a kind of pad with a celluloid surface, and a bone stylus on a string. "Maudie's present to me," he said. "You can write on it, then you lift the cover—see, like that—and the words go away again."

"Magic," Norris said, and printed the word on the pad.

"Why did you leave the table?" his father asked.

The way they were talking, Norris scribbled. *You ought to speak to them, Papa.*

His father read the words with his lips moving; a little frown appeared on his fragile-looking forehead. "How do you mean, Son?"

76

They don't know what the Bible is trying to tell them. Norris scratched his head. *They were all saying how much they hated their fellow men.* He felt self-conscious and was afraid he was being literary.

"Just talk, Son. Have you rejoined the church?"

Norris shook his head.

"I wish you would, Son. It's a comfort. It's a great comfort. If you'd had the church, back when Laura died, you wouldn't have started to drink that way. No sense to mourn the dead. The dead are happy, Son. Laura is happy now, and you should rejoice for her."

"Laura wanted to live," said Norris. "And I wasn't mourning for her—only for myself." His father's eyes were fixed on Norris's face; his hand gestured toward the pad; but Norris couldn't write down what he'd been saying. *Yes, Papa,* he wrote, and this time the words looked piping. He was a small boy again, resented by his sister because he was the favored child; already he had a bookish tendency and they were saying he would have to go to college, he wouldn't grow up to be a farmer, but a doctor, maybe, or a lawyer, or even a minister of the Lord. Later his mother became disenchanted with him and switched her affections to Maudie; but there had been a special bond between Norris and his father; there was a gentleness and sweetness in his father, although it had to contend with violent prejudices. The old man had once called Laura a harlot, as today he had called her daughter one, and the word had festered in Norris's mind; from its utterance dated the estrangement between them, even though, later on, his father was the only one who became at all reconciled to Laura.

Laura was very fond of you, Papa, Norris scribbled on impulse.

Old Mr. Bryant nodded. "Laura was a good woman," he said. "Didn't use to think so, didn't see how she could be, the life she led before she married you, but you reformed her, Son."

NO! Norris printed in block letters. *It was the other way around.*

"I watched her change with my own eyes." Norris's father nodded. "But she was a good woman, Son, and don't you ever pay any mind to what your mamma and Maudie say about her."

What do they say?

"You know. I wouldn't repeat it. Your mamma and Maudie are good women too, but seems like it's in a different way. Laura was kinder than they are, even if she didn't have religion. Laura wouldn't ever say things about other people like they say about her."

Laura did have religion. Norris paused with the stylus in his hand. *Not church religion, maybe, but it was real; it went deep.*

"Maybe so," said his father, and shut his eyes. "Maybe so, Son."

There was a silence. Norris stooped down and put a lump of

77

coal on the fire and wiped his hand on the seat of his trousers. Then he took up the pad again and printed, *Charlie is out of work. Mamma said maybe he could live here. What do you think?* He laid the pad on his father's knees, but old Mr. Bryant had dropped off to sleep; he slept bolt upright in his chair, his mouth fallen open, the breath sawing at the back of his throat. Presently he came to with a little start, blinked, and read what was on the pad.

"I don't know, Son. Times are hard. I don't understand these new government regulations. I don't know much at all any more about the farm. Homer runs it all; Homer knows everything about it, and you'd have to speak to him. Kind of afraid Homer wouldn't like it, to have Charlie here, and Delores, and the baby. Charlie don't know a thing about farming, either. Never did come here much when he was a boy, and then only to swim in the river. Joel would be different."

Joel wants to go to West Point, Norris wrote.

"Joel would make a good soldier. A good farmer too. Don't tell Maudie, but I like Joel better than I do Leon. Joel is the best grandson I have."

Thanks, Papa. Norris scratched his head again; he wanted help from his father. *Can't seem to get close to him, though. Can't ever make him talk to me. I don't know what goes on in his head.*

Old Mr. Bryant smiled. "Just like you when you were a boy," he said. "But your mamma and Maudie, now, they used to have great talks together. Still do. Don't you worry about Joel. Joel is all right. Strong too. Big for his age."

I don't know if he has any brains, Norris wrote.

"Sure he does. He's a smart boy. Tell just by looking at him." Old Mr. Bryant went to sleep again and the pad slid to the floor; Norris's mother came into the room, wiping her hands on her apron.

"You better leave your papa alone, Norris," she said. "He needs his sleep. Don't sleep so much at night any more. He has to keep— Well, there are reasons. So you leave him alone. Going up now to take a nap myself, but don't know's I'll be able to, the way that baby keeps fretting. Delores, she's kind of useless, Norris; she don't know how to train a baby right. Why'd you ever let Charlie marry a girl like that? And Laurette! It's a disgrace the way she's painted up, and the clothes she wears, and the way she walks, even. Keep on like that, she'll come to a bad end. Well, blood will tell, I always say. Glad to say Patricia, she takes after your side more, even if she does look like Laura."

"Yes, Mamma." Norris walked over to his mother, so as not to wake his father by shouting; then he remembered that his father lived in a world devoid of sound. "They all look like Laura, really. I say they all look like Laura."

"Oh, they have a Bryant look about 'em too; yes, and a Norris one. Excepting Joel. Don't know who Joel looks like, but it certainly isn't you or any of us or anybody in any of our families." Norris's mother set her lips firmly together and moved out into the hall. "You'll be gone before I come down," she said, "so I'll wish you a Happy New Year right now."

"Thanks, Mamma. The same to you."

Very soon after that they left. If it hadn't been for Norris's outburst they might have stayed until evening; but the discomfort he had caused became worse instead of better, and before dusk fell they were piling into the truck to be driven back to town.

Delores and the baby were with Homer in the front seat; the rest squatted behind, beneath the canvas top, with blankets that smelled of horses tucked around them. It happened that Joel and Charlie were sitting side by side, opposite Norris, and he peered at them in the dimness—his mother's words had come back to him and for a moment they coiled like a snake in his mind. But allowing for the difference in ages, and for all the things life had done to Charlie's face, he looked as much like Joel as any brother could: Laura's looks coarsened and brutalized in Charlie, Laura's looks simply become masculine in Joel. The snake uncoiled and was gone; Mamma was getting old, and old people talked nonsense.

At home Norris studied Laurette and Patricia. If Patricia was Laura with the warmth and abundance left out, Laurette was Laura minus—what? the spiritual quality? Laurette's features too were thicker than her mother's; her nose was shaped more clumsily, her mouth was larger and had a loose look; her body was not so strong as Patricia's but no one could say it wasn't lush. You just turn on the sex, she says, and let the rest take care of itself. But Laurette wouldn't have to do any turning on, Norris thought painfully; Laurette looked cheap, there was no denying it—cheaper indeed than poor Delores, upstairs walking the floor with her baby.

They gathered at the supper-table presently to eat spoonbread and sausages; Laurette had done the cooking. She amazed herself by her own versatility, she said—she could do typing and shorthand, she was the world's best manicurist and now she was learning how to give a permanent wave; she could sing, she could cook, she could change a baby's diaper and mix a baby's formula.

"Gee," said Laurette, "there are so many careers open to me, I just don't know which one to pick."

"Cut out the singing," said Charlie. "That's the first thing to do."

"That's what I'd get paid the most for, finally. Why, I might even go on the stage, like Mom. *One* of us had to inherit her talent. Gee, Pop, remember what a good actress she was? That time she was an old Cockney woman? She came out on the stage and I didn't know who it was at all, even when she started to speak, and then you whispered, 'That's your mother,' and the

79

scream I let out! Boy, I bet it's echoing yet. You had to take me outside, remember? I just *couldn't* stop crying. But I liked it better when Mom was glamourous; and she really was too. Even in those god-awful clothes they used to wear after the war. Why, I remember when I used to be upset because I was starting to get what you might call a shape, and I just *couldn't* flatten myself out. Women were crazy in those days, you know it? Wanting to look like boys. Mom didn't, though. Mom kept right on being a woman. Gee, but I miss her. I guess we all do."

Patricia looked remote, Delores looked embarrassed, Charlie scowled; Laurette sat dreamily, both elbows resting on the table, indulging in a rich full moment of sentimentality—there were tears in her eyes; but Joel went on stolidly shoveling spoonbread and sausages into his mouth, as he'd shoveled turkey and turnip and onion throughout the talk at dinner. Joel in some ways was a great comfort—a rock, a monolith, whom nothing could shake.

"Golly," said Norris, "I just happened to think. I asked Vinnie Rourke to come out with us today. Good thing he didn't accept."

"You didn't, Father! You *couldn't* have!" Patricia stared across the table at him. "And have him meet those—"

"They're your own flesh and blood, Pat," Norris said mildly. "Anyway, he couldn't come, so no harm's been done."

"Is he young?" asked Laurette, letting sentiment go. "What does he look like? Has Pat been going around with him? Pat, why didn't you tell me? I could kill you!" said Laurette. "I might have known a new glamour boy had appeared on the scene. Gee, I'm all excited."

But now Buzz Boonstra came in. He was just such another blocky thirteen-year-old as Joel—towheaded, however, and with light-blue eyes. After he had wished them all a Merry Christmas he and Joel withdrew to the dumbbells and the punching bag in the cellar so as not to become fat from all the food they had eaten; Delores went up to her child again; Patricia and Laurette washed the dishes.

Norris sat in the living room with Charlie. "Pat told me about the job," he said. "Tough luck."

"Ahhh. Skip it, Pop." Charlie perched on the arm of the sofa and swung his foot nervously.

"Thought maybe they might find a place for you on the farm, like your grandmother said."

"Hell with that. Uncle Homer's a bastard and so is Leon. Anyway, I'm no farmer."

"While ago Johnny Wheelwright got a job at Northern Tool & Die. I think maybe things are starting to look up just a little. If you could find a job in Broadfield, Charlie—"

"Naw. If Johnny got a job at Northern, it's because his old man still has pull. Won't work himself, but he'll pull the wires for Johnny. What a bastard *he* must be."

"Dick Wheelwright's a good egg. I might be able to do a little wire-pulling myself, Charlie, if you want me to."

"Naw. I'll stick to Detroit."

"I don't like—I'm against big cities, I guess," Norris said. "Detroit's been doing things to you."

"Taught me how to get tough about it, that's all. And by Jesus, you have to be tough these days. Christ, Pop, you just don't know. You're all set on the *Chronicle*. It may look like a newspaper to you, but it looks like a goddam ivory tower to me."

"I earn my living there. And I don't have to get tough about it."

Charlie swung his foot and presently said, "I hope you aren't worrying about that break Delores made."

"Maybe I wouldn't have noticed, if you hadn't landed on her like a ton of bricks. What's it all about, Charlie?"

"Hell, it's just a club I belong to. We shoot pool, drink a little beer, go bowling sometimes. And the guys in the club that have jobs, well, they kind of keep their eyes peeled for the guys that don't. It's why I joined up."

"I thought the government was—"

"Hell with that too. I'm not taking any handouts."

"There's more to your club than you've said, Charlie."

"What do you mean? You can't get in if you aren't a hundred per cent American, if that's what you mean. What's wrong with that? Solidarity," Charlie said, gently thumping his fist on his knee. "The niggers have it, the Kikes have it, the—"

"Quit talking like that!" Norris said. "I won't have that talk in my house."

"Pop, for crying out loud!" Charlie stood up. "Come down out of the clouds. Ask the other guys on the paper what it's all about; ask your leg-men. They know. . . . Jesus, you used to talk that way yourself. What's happened to you?"

"I forgot about your mother," Norris said. "It's a strange thing. For ten years I wanted to forget her, but it was no good. It's why I went off the track. It's why you have. No, don't walk away," he said, because Charlie had started toward the staircase. "There's no sense feeling embarrassed. It's foolish not to speak out and say what you mean. Charlie, have you forgotten everything your mother stood for?"

"Mom was O.K.," Charlie said, drifting to the front window, "but she died ten years ago. Everything was rosy then."

"That's what some people thought. But things don't happen by accident, Charlie; what happens has roots. . . . I can see where this rotten club of yours is heading. It sounds like a cheap imitation of the Klan, and the Klan was going strong in those rosy post-war years, remember. Get out of it, Charlie. Get out before it's too late."

"Climb down off the soap-box, Pop. You're a good guy, but I don't like to be preached at."

"Don't shut your mind up. . . . It's one of the things your mother did," Norris said. "She opened up the doors and windows for me."

He sighed, gazing at Charlie's broad obstinate back, the sullen set of his head. How could you get through, past the bitterness and the wounded pride, to the part of Charlie that was still Laura's son? What happens has roots, and what had happened to Charlie was rooted in his earliest childhood. The guilt there was Norris's too; Laura had accused him of uncharity toward Charlie, and for the first time he acknowledged the truth of her accusation. In those years he had a little resented his first-begotten son, whose birth had brought an idyll to an end. . . .

He let the silence draw out. The baby's thin wailing was fainter; Joel and Buzz were shouting in the cellar; from the dining room came the flip of cards and Laurette's voice saying, "You make me sick! You're having *all* the luck tonight."

Norris decided to start off on a fresh tack. "Your mother was a great believer in Woodrow Wilson," he said. "Even after he failed. She never could see that he had any faults. She really believed the war *was* fought to make the world safe for democracy—"

"That crap," said Charlie, motionless at the window.

Norris was shaken again by rage, and got up from his chair; he could have struck his son across the mouth.

But just then the doorbell rang and Vincent Rourke came in with a present for Patricia.

9

For a second Vincent's smile vanished. Laurette and Patricia came in from their cards, Delores down the stairs, Buzz and Joel up from the cellar. Then Vincent sang out, "Merry Christmas, everybody," and the smile was back, fixed. "I wish I'd come in with a whole pack of presents, disguised as Kriss Kringle," he said, and laughed as he handed the square flat package to Patricia.

Norris had never seen such a look on her face; it was incredulous. She held the parcel as if she did not know it was in her hands, and gazed at Vincent as if he stood alone in the room. Pain touched Norris's heart; Patricia was coming of age.

"Open it, Pat, open it!" Joel shouted, breathing heavily over her shoulder.

Patricia sat down; her fingers fumbled at the gold ribbon.

"The wrapping's the best part of it," Vincent said, and there was dismay behind his smile; Norris thought she was attaching too much importance to this, and Vincent knew it.

"Oh, heck! A *book!*" said Joel. "Come on, Buzz."

"I knew it was a book all along," Buzz said, following him back toward the cellar stairs. "You can always tell from the shape."

"If you have it already," Vincent said, "I'll change it for something else."

"No," Patricia said, "no, I haven't, I— Thanks, Vincent, but you aren't making— You shouldn't have—"

Now Laurette was breathing over Patricia's shoulder. "Poetry," she said. "And look, Pat, there are pictures. My *God!* Are you sure they're *nice* poems, Vincent?" She tittered and turned away.

Charlie, who had been glowering at Vincent, propped a thick wrist on his hip and minced back to the window. Vincent hadn't seen, but Patricia had, and her face went scarlet.

"Just a cheap edition," Vincent said, "but they've gotten it up pretty well, I think. I just happened to see it, and I thought right away, 'That's for Patricia,' so I bought it. I used to know a lot of the poems by heart."

"Well, *say!*" Charlie lisped at the window.

Vincent straightened and swung around, looking murderous; but Laurette said loudly, "Charlie, come on out in the kitchen and help with the hot buttered rum." She hooked her arm through his, and tugged him toward the dining room. "That's what I brought that rum along *for,*" she said, "and Charlie's an expert. You wait and see."

Norris cleared his throat. "Come on in, Delores, and sit down," he said; for she had been hovering at the foot of the stairs. "Baby asleep now?"

Delores nodded; she dropped down on the extreme edge of the piano-bench. "I'm just so ashamed of the way he's been acting all day," she said, hardly above a whisper.

"Teeth," said Norris, "maybe he's cutting a tooth." He coughed; he offered Vincent a cigarette, and lit it for him with some ceremony. "Well, how was your first Midwestern Christmas?" he asked.

"Fun," said Vincent, who was still looking a little murderous. "Lots of fun."

"Yup, well, people around here are pretty hospitable, I guess, once they get to know you," said Norris. "Glad you decided to drop around. We're, uh, all a little tired out. Charlie, my older boy, it hasn't been such a merry Christmas for him—he's out of work right now."

"Tough," said Vincent, and blew a smoke ring, at which he smiled rather glitteringly.

"Yup, times are still bad," said Norris. He kept looking at Patricia and wondering why he'd wanted her to fall in love with Vincent. The boy was harmless enough, perhaps, but not the right boy for Patricia. "Been trying to get Charlie to leave Detroit, come up here to live."

"I wish you would," Delores said. Her voice was thin and high with a sudden urgency. "I mean—"

"Talk to him about it," Norris said. "We could squeeze you in here until he gets on his feet again."

"I can't—talk to Charlie." Delores pressed her thin hands together; with the long red nails they were like the claws of a bird. "I mean—"

"Well, stay on until New Year's, anyway," Norris said loudly.

"You ask him," Delores said. "Make him stay."

"I'll do my best. Of course, if there's some job he's on the track of down there, maybe he'll— But you could stay a while. You and the baby."

"Yes," said Delores. "I'd like that."

Norris switched on the radio. Vincent sat with his legs stretched out, languidly blowing smoke rings. Patricia was turning the pages of her book, and now and then she smiled at Vincent with the same dazzled look of unbelief. Delores still perched on the piano-bench, studying her clenched hands. Problems wherever Norris turned; he was sick with his need for Laura.

Presently Laurette came in with a trayful of steaming cups; Charlie loafed behind her, and returned to his post at the window.

"You're going to break down, Pop, just this once, aren't you?" Laurette asked, passing about with her tray. "One won't do you any harm."

The rum made things a little easier, or perhaps it was just Laurette. After Mr. Boonstra had arrived to collect Buzz, and departed again in horror, they all laughed.

"Must've smelled like a bar in here," said Laurette.

Norris shut off the radio and asked if she wouldn't sing for them.

"Nothing I'd like better." Laurette drained her cup and set it back on the tray. "Come on, Delores," she said, crossing to the piano, "you can kind of vamp out the accompaniment, can't you?" She smiled down the room at the others. "God, I'm lost without my mike. Got nothing to catch hold of in moments of need."

She and Delores whispered together; Delores struck a few chords; Laurette straightened, drew a breath, and began to sing. Her voice was low and a little husky; she swayed as she sang, and made the conventional gestures with her hands; Norris had no trouble seeing her in a dark smoke-filled place, with a spotlight on her, turning on the sex for the people at the small puddled tables. They were unhappy songs Laurette sang, self-pitying ones, songs to which the hard times had given birth; and even when the tempo quickened you were reminded of the depression.

Swaying, clutching an imaginary microphone, casting her eyes upward, she sang, among others:

> *Ev'rybody knows you left . . . me . . .*
> *It's the talk of the town . . .*

And:

> *Good Night Sweetheart . . .*
> *Till we meet tomorrow . . .*
> *Good Night Sweetheart . . .*
> *Sleep will banish sorrow . . .*

And finally: "Now my famous impersonation," said Laurette, "of the one and only, the buxom, bouncing, beautiful, and above all bazoomy Mae West." She put one hand upon her hip; she pushed up her back hair; she lowered her eyelids and slid her eyes back and forth in their sockets; and the quality of her voice changed as she sang now, becoming at once brassier and more insinuating:

> *Love me, Honey, love me . . .*
> *'Til I just don't care . . .*
> *I'm . . . no angel . . .*

Just above Laurette's head was her mother's photograph, and what would Laura have thought of this sort of thing, Norris wondered. He wished he'd never made his suggestion; but Laura had been flesh and blood, and known how to be ribald, and she might have laughed at Laurette as Vincent was laughing. And yet there was no health in this, Norris thought; it was a sickly carnality, with all the fire and passion left out.

"God, you're marvelous," Vincent was saying. "How long have you been doing it?"

"Only a couple of months for pay," said Laurette. "You really think it's all right? It's just a dive, the place where I work; I couldn't sing in a good joint yet. And of course everybody's impersonating La West these days. Aren't you crazy about her, though? She's the best thing that's hit the screen in years."

She left the piano and sat close to Vincent; they talked about the movies until Vincent, at midnight, departed, and in all that time nobody else had said anything.

Laurette and Patricia were left alone in the living room, eventually, and Laurette said that Vincent Rourke was just about the best-looking thing in pants she'd seen since *she* was out of diapers. "Gee, Pat, how do you do it? You just sit, and they come to you.

Look at Johnny Wheelwright. Maybe he's not so good-looking, but I always did think Johnny's sex appeal was terrific. And now Vinnie. Boy, oh, boy! Those bedroom eyes!" She sighed; she sat down at the piano and tinkled for a few minutes; then she turned and said, "You're kind of all gone on him, aren't you?"

Patricia looked at the dark window. She couldn't understand what was happening; she wanted to talk about what was most private to her.

"Maybe I shouldn't have monopolized him like that," Laurette continued presently. "But I could see how it was for you, you just kind of wanted to sit and look at him. And believe me, Pat, that's a bad policy, to let a boy know how crazy you are about him. So what I was doing, I was just kind of trying to distract his attention, that's all." She struck some more chords.

"Anyway," she said, "Vinnie's got class and that's what he likes in the girls he likes. I could tell. Mom had class, and she passed some on to you, but little Laurette got left out. A boy like Vinnie is not for me. Pat, you aren't jealous, are you?"

"No," said Patricia. The things about Laurette which distressed her began to matter less than the things she liked.

"That's O.K., then." Laurette stood up. "But don't fall for him *too* hard, baby."

"I have already, I guess. I didn't know it was happening. We just went out quite a lot, and talked. He's so much easier to talk to than Johnny. He's—interested in things. And he's traveled all over the United States. He told me about the Pueblo Indians. They— What are you laughing at?"

"Don't mind me," Laurette said. "Go on about the great *romance*."

"It was never like that," said Patricia. "That's why I never thought— Well, we'd been going out two or three nights a week. All through November. Then I don't know what happened. He put his car in storage for the winter, so we couldn't go driving any more—"

"Don't tell me he has a car too! On fifteen a week?"

"Well, he has some money of his own too, I think."

"Jesus," said Laurette. "Pardon my French, but honestly! Oh, Pat! A boy with looks like that, *and* money, *and* a car. What the heck is he doing in Broadfield?"

"He was unhappy in New York. He's an orphan, Laurette, and first he lived with an old aunt, and then she died, so he was taken over by an uncle and had to go to some awful school. And his uncle isn't very nice, I don't think. I think maybe he's even slightly, well, immoral. So Vincent just got fed up. He wanted to go somewhere where people—take life seriously."

"That's Broadfield," said Laurette, "in a nutshell. Well, so he was dating you two or three times a week, and then he put his car in storage, and then what?"

"He just stopped calling up." Patricia paused again, and thought about the weeks just past. "I didn't know what had happened. I kept thinking maybe—I'd hurt his feelings or something. Because he's terribly sensitive, Laurette. He gets moody. You never can tell what's going to upset him. One minute he'll be gay, and then something happens, just some little insignificant thing, and he—gets moody."

"It sounds like a wonderful technique to me."

"Oh, no, you're wrong! You don't—"

"You listen to Big Sister." Laurette leaned against the arm of a chair, cradling her elbows. "I guess by now I know just about every approach there is. I knew a boy like Vinnie once, only he wasn't so good-looking. If he had been, I hate to think where little Laurette would be now. But the moods, and the cozy chats about Indians—God, Indians, imagine!—and then turning on the silent treatment, and then suddenly bouncing in Christmas night with a book of poems. . . . Oh, Pat, you just don't know what you're letting yourself in for."

"He's sincere," Patricia said. "I know he is, Laurette."

"God, but you're young. You're an *infant!* That boy wouldn't recognize sincerity if it came up and socked him in the face. Honestly, Pat, I'm getting scared now." She paused, gazing at Patricia. "Has he ever tried to make a pass at you?"

"No," said Patricia, looking away.

"Not even a chaste little kiss on the brow at parting?"

"I don't think he's—interested in me—that way—at all. . . . He makes me feel so—" Patricia stood up. "I'm stronger than he is," she said. "I know that. I keep feeling sorry for him."

"Well, don't get to feeling so sorry for him you decide to part with your dearest possession just to make him feel better."

"Oh, Laurette, you're so—"

"I know my way around," said Laurette, "that's all. You never knew any guys in a band, did you? Boy, I've learned a lot about life from that bunch. Fun, sure, never a dull moment. But do I ever have to watch my step! Zowie!" said Laurette, and laughed.

"No, but look," she went on seriously, "if Vinnie's playing for keeps, and that's what you want, O.K. But me, I don't think he is. That kind of boy never does. Johnny's different. Johnny would—"

"Why does everybody keep trying to marry me off to Johnny?"

"*Does* everybody?" Laurette fluffed her hair up. "Maybe it's because we know you better, in some ways, than you know yourself, Pat. Now with me, it's different. I take my fun where I find it, and no regrets. If some smooth millionaire came along and offered me his hand and his yacht, I'm not saying I wouldn't accept. But it doesn't look like that's going to happen, *so,*" said Laurette, "I lead my life accordingly. No little traps like poor Delores has walked into for yours truly. No, thanks!"

"It would be the same kind of trap if I married Johnny."

"Not necessarily. Gee, my nails are a sight. Johnny's a sweet kid, but Charlie— Poor Charlie," said Laurette. "Poor Pop too. I guess we're a terrible disappointment to him. You hear the way he was talking to Charlie while we were playing cards?"

"I tried not to listen," Patricia said.

"Pop isn't going to get anywhere, so he might just as well leave Charlie alone. Charlie's got his head full of screwy ideas, and there isn't anybody can shake 'em out. Not even Pop."

"Mother might have."

"Spilt milk, baby, spilt milk." Laurette sighed profoundly. "You know, it's funny, isn't it, this idea Pop's got into his head all of a sudden, about how Mom had these ideals and all. I don't remember that about her. Do you?"

"I hardly remember her at all."

"God, you knew her nine whole years. But I guess when they got hold of you at the farm— It was tough luck, all right, you and Joel having to go out there to live. No, but what I started to say, the way I remember Mom, she was wonderful-looking, and she was full of fun. That was the chief thing about her, she always had a good time and she made everybody else have a good time too. Just any little thing that happened, she could make it seem like something extra-special. Always laughing.

"Except when she got mad. Boy, she had a temper too! Remember the fights they used to have, her and Pop? I can't remember what about. Once I was really scared. I wasn't more than nine or ten years old, but they had this terrific fight, and then Mom packed up her things and took a trip to New York to cool off. Don't you remember? Maybe not. You were only around four. Well, she took this trip to New York, and she was gone the better part of a month, and I thought she was never coming back. Somebody said that to me, I guess, some little girl I knew. You know the way kids are, but I believed it, and I got to bed that night, and started to cry, and I couldn't stop. Then you woke up and you started to cry too, and poor Pop came running, and— *Don't* you remember?"

"Yes," said Patricia. "Don't talk about it any more, Laurette."

"God, that's a long time ago. . . . They had their fights, but Pop sure must have been crazy about her. The way Johnny would be about you, baby, if you'd give him a chance."

"But I don't love Johnny. I don't even— Oh, let's stop talking this way! I'm not going to marry Johnny or anybody else."

"O.K., if that's the way you want it. But don't say I didn't warn you about Vinnie Rourke. . . . Gee, but I'm sleepy. And *I* have to mush back to Detroit tomorrow. Come on, baby, let's catch some sleep."

But tonight was like the night before, once the lights were out, and Laurette went on talking from the other bed in Patricia's room. In Detroit, perhaps, the past had ceased to exist, but now it lay thick and deep about her.

"You know, I like Charlie," she said. "We used to fight like cats and dogs when we were kids, but underneath—well, it was like being twins, almost. Me only a year younger, after all. Solidarity, like Charlie was saying to Pop. Especially after Mom died and Pop began to hit the bottle.

"Jesus, you just don't know what it was like! Maybe it was terrible out at the farm, but here—boy, oh, boy! Charlie was only fifteen, I was only fourteen: it was a tough situation for a couple of kids that age. Everybody knew about it. And Charlie was always getting into fights. All a kid had to do, just say something to Charlie about his old man being a drunk, and Charlie'd try to knock his block off. Started getting tough way back then. Always a chip on his shoulder.

"Then he went girl-crazy, and they wouldn't even give him a tumble, most of 'em, because he was a kind of ape, when you get right down to it, and anyway, all their mammas knew about Pop and thought Charlie wasn't fit to associate with 'em. There was one girl he was nuts about, I don't remember her name, and he used to pester the living daylights out of her. Finally he said he'd kill himself if she wouldn't go to Junior Prom with him. Well, he got her scared or something, and she said she'd go, and Charlie went out and hired a tux, and he bought her a corsage, and he went around in a taxi to pick her up, and her father had locked her in her room, wouldn't let Charlie in the house. God, I remember just as plain!

"He came back here in the hired tux and went upstairs, and Pop heard kind of a queer noise in the bathroom. He broke the door in—I guess he must've been slightly looping himself, at that point, or he wouldn't't've had the strength—he broke down the door and there Charlie was with his face stuck down in the wash-basin, trying to drown himself. Sounds funny now, but it sure wasn't funny when it happened. Pop reeling around and yelling at Charlie, Charlie bawling like a baby and saying he wanted to die, life wasn't worth living. . . . Boy, we lived through some lively times all right."

Laurette sighed into the darkness and said, "Bedtime stories for the kiddies, hey?"

"Go to sleep, Laurette. Please."

"What I think, it was that night, really, made Pop start to get ahold of himself. He was scared. He thought Charlie really meant it. Heck," said Laurette, "I guess Charlie really did, only thank God he chose a damn fool way of committing suicide."

She sighed again, and Patricia thought she was going to sleep at last; but presently Laurette went on talking. "It's a funny thing; I hated the way Pop drank, I was ashamed and all that, but somehow I never seemed to mind so much as Charlie did. And you'd think a girl would mind more, in a way. Charlie was crazier about Mom than I was, I guess. I used to think she was pretty wonderful, but Charlie, he was really nuts about her. He had some idea it was really Pop's fault she died, on account of the *way* she died—and then to see Pop carrying on like that. But I kind of sympathized with Pop. I guess I knew even then why he just had to drink or land in the loony-bin. Things might have been worse. And at least he stayed sober on the job. He sure loves his old *Chronicle*, doesn't he? . . .

"Well, you can't really blame Charlie for being the way he is, but I *still* think he shouldn't take it out on Delores." Laurette sat up and thumped her pillow. "That's one reason why I moved in with 'em. Afraid he might just go berserk some night and kill her."

"Laurette, don't say things like that!"

"I'm not kidding. Charlie's a violent guy when he gets worked up. It was all my fault, really, in a way—what happened."

Patricia could see her silhouetted dimly against the windows; she was running her hand through her hair. "Kept feeling sorry for Delores," she said. "She never did have much fun—the baby started so soon, and then all those nine months just dragging around, and Charlie out most nights, helling around with a bunch of guys. Well, after she began to feel better, I told her she ought to start stepping out. 'Charlie owes it to you,' I told her.

"But poor Charlie, of course, he didn't have any dough, even before he got fired, so— Jesus, it was crazy of me, really; I don't know why I was such a fool. But I knew all these guys in the band, and the leader, he's kind of crazy about me right now, and he had a friend—a nice little guy, very short, with kind of an olive skin and little black eyes and patent-leather cheveux, but in the money. Just got a divorce from some babe worked in a burlesque house and feeling kind of lonesome, so my pal in the band says don't I know some girl would go out with this little guy and take his mind off his troubles.

"So," said Laurette, "I fixed up some dates between this little guy and Delores. I didn't see any harm in it. Delores looks kind of meek, but she knows her way around, and anyway, all the little guy wanted was somebody he could hold her hand and tell her how sad he was feeling. Delores parked the baby with a woman across the hall—she's all right, real nice, about sixty years old and likes babies.

"So about five different nights when Charlie was out with his gang—he never came in before two, three in the morning—Delores steps out with this little guy. All very innocent. Mostly they came to the club where I sing and I could kind of keep an eye on 'em. And Delores, after being cooped up so long, she enjoyed herself and didn't care how sad the little guy was.

"But the trouble was Charlie got back early one night and no Delores and the baby across the hall with this old woman. Well, he raised hail Columbia, and you can't blame him, in a way. Only why doesn't he take it out on me? I told him it was all my fault, and partly his too for neglecting Delores, but Charlie's funny about me, he never does get sore at me any more. He really started to beat Delores up. Well, she's cut it all out, of course—Charlie keeps a ball and chain on her now.

"So, what with one thing and another," said Laurette, lying down again, "I decided to move in with 'em, and now it's all very peaceful and domestic, the nights I'm not working. Charlie even stays home from his club sometimes. But he doesn't say a word. Just sits and glares. Trouble is, there's no future in it. For them, I mean. I'm not worrying about myself. I always seem to fall on my feet." Laurette yawned again and buried her face in the pillow; in a little while she began to snore gently.

While she talked Patricia lay passive, letting the words float away in the darkness as if they had no connection with anyone she knew. But now they began to echo, and the vision Laurette had conjured up was more dismaying than any nightmare. What seemed worse than anything else was Laurette's calm, as if she were lost in a desert without knowing or caring.

Falling asleep, Patricia thought dimly that she wanted nothing to do with Delores and Charlie and the child they had made; but at breakfast a new emotion started in her. Delores looked so tired and pale, with dark smudges under her eyes, and she did not respond when the baby laughed at her; she sat with bent shoulders, indifferently and mechanically helping him to support the bottle at his lips, as if he were only a tiresome automaton with which she'd found herself saddled. And then Charlie came into the kitchen and Delores' whole body seemed to stiffen.

Pity, it was; Patricia pitied Delores, and somehow it made her friendlier than usual, that day, to the patients who sat waiting in the dentists' office. She even smiled at the dentist who called her Miss Frigidaire, and asked him if he'd had a nice Christmas.

"What defrosted you?" he asked, perching for a moment on the edge of her desk. "Stay that way, will you? It's much more becoming." He nodded at her solemnly and withdrew to extract an impacted wisdom tooth.

Patricia hadn't known before that she felt life ought to make a pattern, and a good clear one, so that when you became as old as her grandparents you could look back at all the years behind you and see that they had amounted to something. You did not lose the past. All the vanished moments were you, and she became ashamed of some of her own vanished moments; when the waiting-room was empty, she took up the telephone to call her father at the paper.

She could hear somebody shouting: "Bry! Hey, Bry! Lady on the phone, kid. Hot damn!"

She felt shy when his voice said, "Bryant speaking."

"It's only me, Father. Father, Laurette told me something last night—well, it's too complicated to tell you now, but *make* Charlie let Delores and the baby stay on for a while. It's important, Father. I've been worrying all morning."

"So have I. . . . It's all fixed up, Pat. Charlie dropped down here and I talked everything over. Wish he'd stay too, but as it is we'll kind of have to revise the budget, I guess. No more beer on Sundays for me, hey? Charlie's left already with Laurette, and Laurette's going to try and keep an eye on him. But you cut out the worrying, you hear? That's my business."

He placed the receiver gently on its hook and leaned back in his swivel-chair. If this was what being in love with Vincent was doing for Patricia, maybe it was a good thing.

Norris said to Ack Guion, "You ought to be glad you never had any children. Worry, worry, worry."

Ack grunted. "You're telling me."

"They surprise you sometimes, though. Sometimes they can be a great consolation," said Norris, and then forgot his worries in the noontime rush.

More snow fell that evening, but in the night a sudden current of warm air flowed over Broadfield and the snow became rain, the gutters ran full, the mountains began to dwindle along the sidewalks. By morning the rain had spent itself, the sun came out, and there was a wholly deceptive smell of spring in the air all that day.

Norris returned from work and found his grandson sleeping, his daughter-in-law giving the house a thorough cleaning. She looked more cheerful already and he thought comfortably that everything was going to work out; the bad old year was almost over, the new year was bound to be a good one.

"There's a letter for you," Delores said. "Didn't you see it?"

"Didn't look. Nobody ever writes me letters. Only the Department of Internal Revenue," Norris said, and slit open the envelope. The letter was from Betty Lou; the ink was purple, the paper pale mauve, the writing round and childlike; a faint perfume floated up and he thought of Betty Lou beside him at the concert, being amused by the conductor.

DEAR NORRIS,

Pardon this vile paper and *the purple ink* AND *this perfectly terrible fountain pen, all of which I have borrowed from my sister Myrtle who has a heart of gold but the most* PECULIAR *ideas. I am afraid this will reach you too late to say Merry Xmas but I hope in time to say A Happy New Year to you and Pat and everybody and please say hello to Johnny Wheelwright but as far as I am concerned you can cut the Rourke boy dead. I hope you will write soon, remember your promise, I am feeling homesick for Broadfield already, Muskogee somehow is not what it used to be or maybe I'm the one who has changed. All us girls got here and most of them brought their hubbies along and children too we are going to sit down* EIGHTEEN *to Xmas dinner, imagine! Poor Mamma is failing fast I'm afraid but is remarkably chearful considering, what a darling she is Norris I wish you could see her, her cheeks just as pink (though* I SUSPECT *with a little outside asistance) but somehow I do not feel too chearful myself, I keep thinking of all the dear dead days beyond recall. Isn't it foolish, what good does it do. Don't let any boys break my windows with snowballs, I suppose the snow by now is at least ten feet high, here there isn't a smidgin (Sp.?) I feel embarassed writing a letter to a city editor I see you with a pencil in your hand scowling and correcting all my grammar punctuation etc. I want to thank you again Norris for that lovely concert and everything and hope to see you all again before very long. Hope all is well with you and yours and Pat will make a New Year's Resolution to be kinder to Johnny Wheelwright.* I MISS YOU. *Your's affectionately . . .*

Norris carried the letter up to his room, meaning to answer it right away; he felt guilty because Betty Lou had gone clean out of his mind. But he needed a typewriter, really; a pen felt unnatural in his hand, and with one of his soft pencils he would have written a letter all in headlines. He would write to Betty Lou from the office tomorrow afternoon.

He fell into a dream at his bedroom window, thinking how little he knew of Betty Lou, really. She was hardly an individual yet, only a caricature of herself. But that was the way it always was with people. Those with personality began as caricatures, those without as nonentities, and then little by little the flatness was rounded, the gaps filled in, and you knew a human being.

Even Laura, the first time he had seen her—though love had caught him like a blow between the eyes the moment she ran out on the stage—had been not so much a girl of flesh and blood as an incredible loveliness. And he'd come close to missing that loveliness altogether. It was spring and business was bad for the stock company; tickets were being given away in handfuls at the

Chronicle and because his ticket had cost him nothing he had almost gone to a beer garden that night.

He had no idea what the play was about; the play was only an annoyance when Laura was not on stage. He walked back to his boarding house in a daze, and lay awake all night, and made inexcusable blunders in his work the next day because he could think of nothing but returning to the theater. He returned every night for a week, and at the end of the week, still in a daze, he made his way backstage and thrust himself upon Miss Laura Royce and said he had been commanded to interview her for the paper.

"You mustn't," she whispered, and her freshness and youth shone out through the paint on her face. "The leading lady would scratch my eyes out—*she* hasn't been interviewed—and I need my eyes badly, Mr. Bryant. My living depends upon them." So he began to interview her every night when the performance was over, and presently the interviews turned into Sunday excursions in a hired buggy. They rode sedately out into the country and somewhat less sedately picnicked on the bank of the river, where it flowed wide and peaceful between the wide and peaceful fields. Norris felt at once stiff because of his best suit that didn't fit very well and the high starched collar and the satin cravat with the pearl stickpin, and sophisticated because he was spending Sunday with an actress.

But Laura was not stiff, nor did she seem sophisticated. She lay flat on her back, careless of grass-stains and the proprieties alike, gazing up at the sky, watching petals float past like snow on a breeze which had just blown through an orchard. She smiled, and sighed, and said how good it was to get the smell of grease paint out of her nostrils. What she had looked like then he could still see clearly, but the image of the farm boy turned newspaperman, the boy with whom Laura Royce had fallen in love, was past his power to imagine. He had been straight then, and strong from all his summers on the farm; his dark blond hair had rebelled against the grease he used to make it lie flat; and in the cheap flashy clothes he must still have looked like a hobbledehoy.

Once she smiled up at him and said, "Dear God, Norris, don't look so noble. You frighten me when you look noble."

"I wasn't thinking noble thoughts."

"What were you thinking?"

"How much I wanted to kiss you," he said, and blushed furiously; for despite the four years at State College and a few furtive excursions to the wrong part of town, he was naive with a kind of naïveté (it seemed to him more than a quarter-century later) which no longer exists in the world. One did not make such remarks to ladies.

"Is that so ignoble?" she asked. "Don't you ever put your

thoughts into action?" She sat up; she leaned toward him. "Kiss me, then," she said.

She was, at first, more passionate than he was; her passion shocked him a little, because he had somehow absorbed from his mother the conviction that there was evil in all men but that women were pure, and those who were not pure were very bad indeed. But Laura was not bad, although she was an actress; there could be no evil in anything she did.

All the time it was happening—all the time the audiences in the theater dwindled away to a scattering, all the time spring dwindled away to summer—he could not believe it was happening at all. He had wandered by mistake into a romantic play, and the time would come when he could no longer improvise his lines. It was impossible that she should love him as he loved her.

But they continued to go out together—alone into the country, mostly, but sometimes to beer-gardens, sometimes to band concerts in the park in the mild still evenings of early summer. Beneath their happiness a fire was blazing; the fire became their happiness; and against his highest resolve, without his meaning it to happen, they became lovers when the company entered its final disastrous weeks. She had grown frightened; it was as if she wanted to make sure of something before the world collapsed about her.

He was a clodhopper learning by painful stages how to be a newspaper reporter; she was a young actress whose name nobody knew; it was a place and time when moral standards appeared rigid. But what they were doing had no connection with morals, no point of contact with the world beyond themselves; no sense of guilt ever touched them.

But on their last Sunday excursion together, she turned away from him suddenly and began to weep. "The company's disbanding," she said. "I must go back to New York and begin all over again."

He had never seen her cry before; he thought her tears were because he had ruined her life, and he didn't know what to say to her. He kept pulling the heads off daisies and scattering them on the grass, and finally he said, "I'll always love you. But you won't marry me. Why should you? I have nothing to offer. You're a great actress."

"Oh, darling, I'm not!" Laura laughed sadly. "I can sing a little, I can remember lines, I can register the appropriate emotions in the appropriate spots, but that's all. . . . You haven't *asked* me to marry you."

"Will you?" he said.

She sat in silence, gazing away through the trees; presently she laid her hand on his and said, "Stop destroying the daisies. . . .

I'll have to go back to New York first. So many things to attend to. And I'll have to break the news to my mother."

So she had gone back to New York and her letters came to him every day; the letters and her distance from him made her more real; in September he talked himself into a week's vacation and rode East on the long gritty train journey for the first time in his life; and they were married in New York.

Laura's mother was furious. At first she would hardly speak to Norris, who had put an end to all her elaborate plans, begun twenty years earlier in a little town dropped as by accident on a rise in the endless, oceanic emptiness of Dakota. All that scrimping and saving, all the long hard years after she'd fled the wilderness with Laura, all the scheming and contriving and battering down of doors, all the hard lessons which had been drilled into Laura, all this gone for nothing; so Laura could travel a good part of the way back to Dakota and bury herself in the Middle West, waste her talents as a newspaperman's wife. Her mother was the one who should have had a stage career, said Laura. Mrs. Royce withdrew into a fit of sulks which lasted until she caught a second husband for herself—which lasted, indeed, beyond her second marriage to the day she died.

As for Norris's parents and sister, their outrage was magnificent. Until Charlie was born, two years later, the farm was forbidden to Norris and Laura. But in bearing Charlie, Laura came so near dying that the Bryants decided the Almighty had sufficiently punished her and had forgiven her, since after all she'd survived; and so they forgave her too. Grudgingly, of course.

Norris and Laura were not touched by the outrage either; their happiness in those first years came close to being flawless. The picture darkened because of Laura's unsuspected fragility—it enraged her, she said, since she believed in large families as an only child sometimes will—and later there were stormy periods, times when Norris's early training haunted him and he wondered if they were not being punished after all. But for the most part their life together maintained the quality with which it had begun.

No one but Laura ever saw him in that light. To the rest of the world he was only Norris Bryant, that increasingly shabby, that dull and plodding and humble figure, that failure.

Now that she had been dead for ten years and more, the old incredulity returned to him. It staggered belief that this should have happened to him. He never should have answered her letters from New York, never traveled East to marry her; she would have forgotten him in time and gone on to the career her mother had planned; and he would have married somebody else, the ordinary woman who was all he deserved, and the grief and the pain, the terrible chaos into which his life and his children's lives had fallen, would have been avoided.

Yet he knew that if time could be turned back, he would do what he had done all over again.

He pulled himself together and dropped Betty Lou's letter on his desk; he had been holding the folded paper in his hand all this time.

After dinner that night Patricia went to the movies with Vincent; Joel was off somewhere with Buzz Boonstra; Delores sat by the radio and sewed. Norris wandered about the living room, unable to settle down to a detective story or come to rest at all because he was unused to Delores's presence and felt he ought to do something to entertain her.

"Charlie's going to have the crib and things shipped up, isn't he? Kind of strange, having a baby in the house again, after all these years," Norris said.

"I hope you don't mind too much."

"Hell, no," he said, wishing she would speak above a whisper. "I'm going to see what I can do about rustling up a job for Charlie in Broadfield. Might be something. . . . You'd like that, wouldn't you?"

"Oh, yes," Delores said.

"You'd like living in Broadfield better than living in Detroit."

"Oh, yes, yes, I would. I like Broadfield a whole lot."

"Dreary enough in winter, but in spring and summer and fall—well, there's nowhere else in the world I'd rather live."

"Unh-huh," said Delores.

"Thing about Broadfield—" Oh, hell, Norris said to himself, and took up from the table the first book he laid his hand on. "You can turn the radio up louder if you want," he said. "Won't bother me at all. Paper's a noisy place to work, you know. I can really concentrate better when there's a racket going on. So you have the radio on as loud as you like."

"It's just fine the way it is, thank you," said Delores. "My hearing—I can really hear very well. My eyes are good too. I never did have any trouble with my eyes, and I guess I never will. Just so long as I don't overstrain them."

"Mmmm-hmmm. Fine," Norris said heartily, "fine," and opened the book; it was the one Vincent had given to Patricia.

Norris had never read very much poetry, but Laura, when the mood was on her, recited it by the yard. She liked the English Romantics; she knew all of the *Ode to the West Wind,* all of *The Eve of St. Agnes* by heart.

Norris flipped the book open and came upon the frontispiece, at which Laurette had exclaimed: a tree and a moon (or was it the sun?) and a boy and a girl embracing among what looked like bulrushes. He turned the pages slowly, looking at the other pictures, reading a stanza here and there. It seemed like harmless enough stuff, mostly, and easy to understand; though it didn't make you feel more cheerful. Then he read:

> More than I, if truth were told,
> Have stood and sweated hot and cold,
> And through their reins in ice and fire
> Fear contended with desire. . . .

It was as if the poet had spoken to him directly; a little shaken, he turned the page, skipping a longer poem and then a shorter one; and then the words leaped out at him again:

> If truth in hearts that perish
>   Could move the powers on high,
> I think the love I bear you
>   Should make you not to die.

He sat quite still. Delores had turned the radio on louder after all and there was an audience screaming with laughter; but he felt that he was sitting in the center of a profound silence. He shook himself and read the other stanzas:

> Sure, sure, if stedfast meaning,
>   If single thought could save,
> The world might end tomorrow,
>   You should not see the grave.
>
> This long and sure-set liking,
>   This boundless will to please,
> —Oh, you should live for ever
>   If there were help in these.
>
> But now, since all is idle,
>   To this lost heart be kind,
> Ere to a town you journey
>   Where friends are ill to find.

Norris closed the book. He closed his eyes, for they were suddenly wet with tears.

10

HAVE YOU *ever read much poetry, Betty Lou? In school I had to memorize some terrible stuff and then there was what they crammed down our throats at college, but the only time I ever* seemed to get anything out of it was when I heard it spoken aloud. But the other night I was skimming through a book of poems by A. E. Housman that Vincent gave to Pat for Christmas and there was one that hit me where I live.

I read it all over again later and couldn't figure out why it packed such a wallop the first time. Talking of correcting grammar as you were in your letter, I am not too sure about Mr. Housman's grammar in the poem—"Should make you not to die," he says, which sounds a little peculiar to me. And then the rest of the poem sort of trails away, as if he stopped being inspired—it runs downhill instead of up. But I think maybe you shouldn't look too hard at a poem; if it packs that wallop the first time, that's all you have any right to ask.

Norris paused, lifting his hands from the typewriter, to light a cigarette. It was late on Saturday afternoon and he had the editorial room to himself; in the long run, he'd found, he wanted solitude for his letter to Betty Lou. Also he had been able to prowl from desk to desk until he found a good typewriter with a fresh ribbon in it. He blew smoke over the pale-gray copy paper and began to tap again:

I wasn't planning to talk about poetry, but the lines keep running through my head. What you want is news, and I'm a newspaperman of sorts, so here goes. Nobody has broken any of your windows with snowballs—we've been having a thaw and the snow is almost gone. But your house looks lonesome, especially at night with all the windows dark. I hope your mother gets to feeling better fast, so you can come back sooner than you expected. Our Christmas was a pretty messy occasion, what with one thing and another, and now I have my daughter-in-law and grandson living with me for the time being while Charlie hunts a job in Detroit. I don't know if you ever met Charlie, who is a good boy at heart, although embittered, I'm afraid, from all the hard knocks he's taken.

His wife's name is Delores, which always strikes me as a silly name, and there are times when I think Delores is kind of a silly girl. Not much gray matter, I guess. Charlie must have picked her for her looks, which are Okay. She has taken over all the housework and we are looking so neat these days you wouldn't recognize the old dump. She even gets up and makes my breakfast for me, so I can sleep an extra fifteen or twenty minutes in the morning. I told her she shouldn't bother, but the baby gets her up anyway. But she hardly ever smiles and sometimes I think she resents us all. Afraid Charlie was kind of rough on her and she doesn't want to be sent back to him.

But the baby—I think you're going to like him, Betty Lou. His name is David Norris Bryant and he's going on seven months old. For a while I couldn't believe I was a grandfather—makes me feel like Methuselah—because I hadn't seen him since that trip to Detroit right after he was born. He's dark, like Delores, with quite a lot of fluffy black hair, and dark eyes that look surprised most of the time as if he wasn't used to the idea of being alive yet. He cried almost all day Christmas, but since then he's been behaving pretty well. Just wish Delores would take a little more interest in him. Most of the time he lies and stares at all the new strange things around him, but he's beginning to get up on his hands and knees now and I suppose before so very long he'll be creeping. Well, I'm beginning to think a baby is something no home should be without. Life is full of surprises for him, and even when he's bawling he gets a kick out of it, I think. Makes an old man like me ashamed of himself for feeling so tired and sad and worried all the time, always thinking, as you said, about the dear dead days beyond recall.

Remember the story about the Labyrinth? Well, I've been feeling as though I strayed into a Labyrinth some years back, and lost hold of the thread which would guide me through, and I guess really that's why I have been thinking so often about the past, looking for that thread again. Hope I find it before I meet the Minotaur. This is getting pretty fancy, I'm afraid, and I don't remember the story too well so maybe I shouldn't have brought it up; but sometimes I get a little scared and feel as if there really is going to be a Minotaur or something unpleasant around the next couple of bends.

I hate to say so but I have an idea Charlie's marriage has just about gone on the rocks. It's really why I asked Delores to stay on for a while—thought perhaps a rest from each other would do them both good and it takes a weight off Charlie's mind while he hunts for work. Then there is Pat's great love affair with Vinnie Rourke. She moped and kept snapping my head off worse than ever for several weeks while he wasn't coming around, but now it is all sweetness and light. She is a whole lot more human than she ever seemed before, so maybe some good will come out of it after all. For a while I wanted this to happen because I thought Vinnie was headed toward some kind of success and it's time some member of our family married a success instead of a failure; but the more I see of Vinnie, the better Johnny Wheelwright looks to me. There are more important things, after all, in a marriage than financial success. Well, worrying doesn't do any good. All I can do for the present is let things take their course.

This is turning out to be a regular dirge, and I meant when I started to tell you all the good stories that have been going the rounds this week, but now I can't think of any it wouldn't be illegal to send through the mails. . . .

"Christ sakes, Bry," said Chuck Halsey, who had emerged from the library in his hat and overcoat. "Writing the Great American Novel? You been pounding away for hours."

"So have you."

"Getting a head start on next week's editorials."

"I'm just writing letters," Norris said, and waited until Chuck had gone down the stairs.

Anyway, this letter is longer than any letter should be, so I'll stop. Used up more of the Chronicle's *valuable stationery than I have any right to. Write again soon, Betty Lou, and I hope I'll have something livelier to talk about.*

He hesitated a long time before he tapped out "Yours affectionately," which sounded unmanly and suggested warmer emotions than he felt. But he shrugged in the end—hell, he *did* feel affectionate toward Betty Lou, and while he wrote she had seemed very close and real to him.

Her reply did not come for almost two weeks, and this time it was on white paper with a black border.

Oh, Norris, what a wonderful wonderful letter, what did you MEAN *that night, you'd forgotten how to write letters? It's the nicest letter I ever had from anybody, cross my heart, but you should have copied out all of that poem so I'd know what you were talking about. You are so* BRIGHT *Norris, I'm afraid I'm just an uneducated moron and Eddie Guest is about as intelectual as I can stand.*

But oh Norris, I can't write a real letter now, you can see from this ghastly stationery what happened, poor Mamma caught a cold Christmas Day, the excitement was too much for her I guess, and then Complications developed and she died Jan. 2 she knew us all right up to the end and was laughing when she passed away. It is foolish to feel so sad about it because Mamma although she did keep up her spirits wonderfuly ever since the accident did not get much fun out of life any more, she was always a little thing, so quick and light on her feet, flying around doing a thousand and one things and she hated so much having to lie still most of the time. So as they say it's a blessing really but I cannot yet feel that in my heart.

There are many things to attend to, all my sisters but Myrtle had to go back to their homes, Myrtle lives right here in Muskogee and I am going to stay on and help her settle Mamma's affairs, try to sell the house etc., Myrtle feels it even more than I do because she was so close to Mamma living right alongside of her

*the whole time but at least she has her husband to console her.
Well I hope to be back in Broadfield by the end of Feb. or
March 1 at latest, I can hardly wait. Norris maybe we are wrong
about the Rourke boy, maybe he is all right after all, I mean I
think a boy who is not ashamed of liking poetry and would think
of giving a book of poems to a girl he likes, well there is something
to be said for him after all. I will try to get hold of this A. E.
Housman book and read it myself though I guess it is hopeless in
Muskogee. Love . . .*

When Norris wrote again he closed with "Yours as ever." It
was a stiff short letter of condolence and after he had mailed it he
was afraid it might sound unsympathetic. He did not believe in
letters of condolence anyway, unless they broke straight from the
heart. He couldn't remember the words in any of the letters which
came to him after Laura's death; all he remembered was how he'd
torn up Andy McBain's letter without having read it.

In a few days he wrote to Betty Lou again, sitting at the desk
in his bedroom. Maybe it was because he wrote with a pen that
the letter turned out as stilted as the note of condolence, but more
probably it was because he had begun to sweat at the notion of
Betty Lou's finding a copy of *A Shropshire Lad* in Muskogee after
all and identifying the poem and thinking he thought of it as being addressed from him to her.

He stepped out into the cold evening to mail the letter, and at
the box on the corner ran into Johnny Wheelwright's father. They
turned back together, pacing in silence along the street; the sky
was blown clear and stars were tangled in the cold twigs.

"How's Johnny making out at Northern?" Norris asked presently.

"Pretty well, I think. He likes it better than I expected, and
prison three days a week isn't so bad as prison six or seven. I hope
he isn't trapped there permanently, though. Once you're caught
up into a machine—" Mr. Wheelwright sighed.

"I was wondering," Norris said, "if there might not be another
opening at Northern. My boy Charlie's been looking for work since,
oh, hell, way back in September."

"I'll be glad to speak to Norman Trees." Mr. Wheelwright
paused; they had reached his house.

"Oh, you don't need to do that. Thanks just the same. I can
speak to Norman myself." Norris never felt at ease with Dick
Wheelwright. Dick had gone East to college and been a brilliant
architect and had plenty of money once; he'd resigned his masculine duties to his wife without shame; he remembered Norris's bad
days; and now there was this uncomfortable business of Johnny
and Patricia.

"All right," said Dick after a pause; his voice was remote and Norris thought he'd offended him. "I don't imagine there's much hope, though. When *are* times going to get better, Bry? Think they ever will?"

"Bound to," Norris said absently, "sooner or later. I think Roosevelt's trying hard. We have to give him that much credit, anyway."

"Funny, I voted for Norman Thomas. Futile sort of gesture. I don't think I believe in socialism, even if it could come to pass in the United States. But there's more danger we'll move in a slightly different direction. It wouldn't be just like Germany, nor yet again Italy. It would be one hundred per cent American, but quite as vicious. . . . But I mustn't go climbing on my hobbyhorse," said Mr. Wheelwright. "Have you ever read *Tristram Shandy,* Bry? I've been reading it all over again—lost track of how many times this makes it."

He suddenly put his hand on Norris's sleeve. "Come on in and sit a while. Trude was saying only the other day we hadn't seen you for ages." He moved forward, up his front steps, and Norris followed him. "I'm afraid you're letting yourself in for a theatrical performance, but Tink will be glad of a larger audience," he said, pushing the door open.

Norris had often thought it strange that Dick Wheelwright, who designed such handsome houses, lived in such an ugly one. But you forgot the ugliness once you were inside, and the shabbiness did not seem to matter.

The curtains had been pulled across between the living room and dining room and pinned snugly around the proscenium of Tink's marionette theater. In the darkness of the living room, Mrs. Wheelwright and Dorothy and Johnny were sitting in a row, waiting for the performance to begin.

"Why, Bry, hello there! Come and sit down. How nice," Mrs. Wheelwright said, and Norris thought she meant it. Contentment flowed through him as he sat with the others. The play was *Jack and the Beanstalk;* the lines and the voices, the scenery and the puppets, were all Tink's, said Dorothy, who played the piano between the acts, of which there seemed to be a great many. At last, though, came the final act, laid in the Widow's garden. Presently Jack appeared, sliding down the enormous beanstalk, with money-bags almost as large as he was fixed under either arm.

"Mother, Mother," he cried as he reached the ground, "come quick with the ax! The Giant is hot upon my heels and he will gobble us both up unless we slay him."

Out from behind a corner of the cottage flew the Widow; her uplifted arms held the ax, and with great presence of mind she whisked over to the beanstalk while Jack rested beside a bush, clutching his money-bags. The Widow's chopping was sketchy, but caused a convulsion in the beanstalk, which presently collapsed; the Giant came crashing after, with such violence that he lost his head—it rolled out over the edge of the stage and dropped to the living-room floor.

"Oh, darn," said Tink behind the scenes; but Jack now leaped to his feet, crying, "Mother, we are rich! We are practically millionaires, and with the ill-gotten gold I have stolen from the Giant we can purchase the finest dairy farm in the country."

"Hooray!" shrilled the Widow, bouncing on what was left of the Giant and still flourishing the ax. "Jack, my son, I take it all back. Those *were* magic beans, and I love you dearly, and we shall live happily ever after."

The curtain fell amidst applause, and Tink came out from the dining room, his thin face bright red, his eyes enormous with excitement.

"I'm *exhausted*," he said, and fell into a sofa; but after the living-room lights had been turned on he sat up and accepted a bottle of Coca-Cola from the tray of drinks Johnny had brought in.

"What I want to know," Tink said, "what did you think was best? The scenery or the play or the acting? I have to make up my mind what I ought to be. Of course the puppets are no good, but you need more people to work *real* marionettes."

"I'm worrying just a little," his father said, "about the ethics of the play. Not quite sure I approve of Jack's lust for gold. And the Widow! I wouldn't care to meet that woman on a dark night."

"Well, I had to sort of follow the story. I mean, I only changed it a little here and there."

"Why try to specialize?" Johnny asked.

"Well, I don't know. . . . I had to paint the castle in a hurry and it wasn't quite dry yet. I guess it ran a little, but you could kind of make believe that was moss growing on the stones. Couldn't you?"

"I thought it was moss right along," said Mrs. Wheelwright. "Well, Tink, off to bed with you. Johnny'll help you take the stage apart."

"Couldn't I stay just a *little* later tonight?"

"It's a whole lot later already," said Johnny, beginning to dismantle the stage. "School tomorrow, remember."

"Watch *out*, Johnny! That part isn't *supposed* to come to pieces." Tink sprang forward, knocking over a Coca-Cola bottle. Presently he turned and said to them all, "But didn't you *like* the play?"

"We loved it, Tink," his mother said. "Goodness, I don't see how you did it all without any help."

"Well, Dorothy did help a little. She thought about having the

Giant sort of dripping with gore. It really *looked* like blood, didn't it?"

"Dorothy!" Mrs. Wheelwright laughed a little. "It's your bedtime too. Off with you both."

The stage, the scenery, the puppets were packed away in a large box, which Johnny lifted from the floor. "Come on, kids," he said. "Nice to've seen you, Bry."

He marched away, carrying the box; Tink and Dorothy, after good-night kisses, trailed behind.

"Tink's pretty amazing," Norris said presently. "He's brighter now than Joel is at going-on-fourteen."

"Too high-strung," said Mr. Wheelwright.

"And spoiled." Mrs. Wheelwright sighed. "It's been too easy, right along, to spoil Tink." She sat, large and firm and placid, but looking a little troubled, and sipped her beer. "He worships Johnny. Johnny knows how to make him behave."

"Johnny's the one worked out a way to get Tink to scrub his teeth," said Mr. Wheelwright. "A chart on the bathroom wall, and spaces marked off for days in the week. If every space for a month is filled, Johnny takes Tink to the movies. Sheer bribery, but maybe it'll cut down on future dentist's bills. . . . On the whole I think I approve of Tink, but there are times, Bry—oh, there are times when I wish he was more like Joel."

"Joel's all right," Norris said, trying not to glow. "But what goes on inside his thick skull is more than I know. . . . I do nothing these days but worry about my kids."

"Don't we all?" Mr. Wheelwright smiled and struck a match for his pipe. "Waste of nervous energy."

"They won't ever talk to me. Whatever I find out, I get second- or third-hand. Did Charlie tell me he'd lost his job? He did not. Laurette told Patricia, Patricia told me."

Mrs. Wheelwright set her glass aside. "They're all the same, Bry. Oh, I have long talks with Johnny sometimes, and Dot's a babbling brook, but they never tell me what I *want* to know. In the days when we had a laundress, they confided in her. Now I don't know where they turn."

"Perhaps it isn't quite decent to be so curious. I've given up prying. And if the urge to offer advice gets the best of me, I try indirection." Mr. Wheelwright hesitated, sucking at his pipe. "Been wanting to discuss a delicate situation with you, Bry. Namely, my boy and your girl. Indecency again. Still, a father must relieve his feelings. Any idea what's happened?"

Norris sighed. "Oh, this Rourke boy, he's come along and—just now Pat doesn't seem to be able to *see* anybody else. I'm not sure it's serious. If it is, I don't like it. Always did think Johnny was the right boy for Pat." This became true as soon as he'd said it, and he smiled at the Wheelwrights, thinking how much he liked them.

"I've always had a soft spot for Patricia myself." Mrs. Wheelwright thought for a moment. "She's more like—"

"A nice old-fashioned girl," said her husband. "Maybe that's how Johnny sees her too. But there seems to have been a great rift ever since October. Something went wrong that day."

"Day Rourke came to supper," Norris said.

"I've been trying to get Johnny to go out with other girls. I mean, if Patricia's a lost cause— Well, he's a healthy young male, and now he's turning into a hermit." Mrs. Wheelwright spoke with some constraint. "Goodness, I never used to think Johnny would sit brooding in his room—"

"He's taken up reading," said Johnny's father. "Fairly profound stuff, some of it. Came down the other day and asked if I had a copy of Plato's *Republic*."

Mrs. Wheelwright laughed. "He said he didn't think much of it."

"Well, that puts Plato in his place. What next, I wonder."

"He's been trying *Walden*. And Emerson's essays. Johnny really does a good deal of thinking," said his mother, glowing in her turn. "He worries about the state of the world. He's been reading *Casual Journey*, Andrew McBain's book, and now he's upset about Europe."

"It's always cropping up—Andy's book," Norris said.

"Well, everybody's reading it. I suppose we like to think of him as a local product. Though he doesn't mention Broadfield once," said Mr. Wheelwright.

Mrs. Wheelwright said that she was quite excited about his lecture. "I remember the last time he was here—goodness, must be all of thirteen, fourteen years ago—with the little limp he had from the war. He—"

"Haven't *you* read it, Bry?" Mr. Wheelwright had stood up, and was crouching before a bookcase. "I'll lend it to you. Bought it when it came out. Where is it, now? Johnny was all through with it last week, wasn't he?"

"It's right there somewhere. I tucked it away out of sight. Tink," Mrs. Wheelwright said to Norris, "will read anything, especially if he gets the idea it's something we don't want him to read." She was looking a little flustered.

"Here we are!" Mr. Wheelwright came back across the room and tossed the book to Norris.

Norris stared down at the photograph on the back of the jacket: dramatic lighting, the shadow of the hat-brim dropping down one cheek, the eyes staring into far distances, the lips faintly, quizzically smiling; at once noble and disillusioned looked Andy McBain, and far younger than Norris would have expected—but that might be the photographer's doing. The old pain turned in his heart and he said with an effort, "It's funny a book by a foreign correspondent would be so popular."

"It's good stuff, a lot of it." Mr. Wheelwright sat down again. "Not so good as Sheean, though. I've been reading Sheean in some back numbers of the *Atlantic*. Sheean's from a younger generation, of course—entirely different viewpoint. But they're in on the ground floor, both of them—I'll lay a bet with you, Bry, that their books start a flood. So many of the boys roaming the world now, seeing the wheels within the wheels, or thinking they do—finding things out their papers won't print."

"It's a long book," Norris said, riffling the pages. It gave him a strange feeling; for the first time he had in his hands a book written by someone he knew. He'd never had literary ambitions himself, but he was aware of a sharp envy; something solid, like this, that felt heavy in your hands, a concrete symbol of achievement. . . .

"He takes in a lot of territory. Begins way back with his war experiences, the idea being to show how they laid the groundwork for his philosophy of life. Whatever it is. I came to the last page," said Mr. Wheelwright, "without ever being sure. I'm afraid he's a cynic, or maybe a nihilist."

"Goodness knows," said Mrs. Wheelwright, "he has a high opinion of Andrew White McBain."

"Why not, why not? We've strayed far afield from Johnny and Patricia."

Norris stood up to go. "She ought not to keep him dangling," he said. "I've tried to tell her that before, but maybe I could try your method—indirection. How do you do it, Dick?"

"Wait for the inspiration of the moment. Somehow I dislike the thought of Patricia and Johnny having a good heart-to-heart talk. Until it happens, Johnny can go on hoping, faintly. But he used not to be a hoper—he was a doer. I don't know. It's all pretty baffling." Mr. Wheelwright helped Norris into his overcoat.

"Tell him good night for me, anyway," Norris said. "I'm still on Johnny's side. . . . I've had a nice time."

"So have we, Bry." Mrs. Wheelwright had followed them into the front hall. "You must come again."

"Come over and see me sometime. Come and see my grandson."

Norris departed; and upstairs Johnny went on reading to Tink. He had been reading to Tink for a long time, out of *Roy Blakeley on the Mohawk Trail*, partly in the hope that it would inspire Tink to join the Boy Scouts when he was old enough.

For Johnny worried more and more about his brother. The excitement of the marionette show, in preparation ever since Christmas, had been too much for Tink, who had dissolved into tears for no reason at all when he was halfway through scrubbing his teeth.

"It was a *lousy* show," he wailed, "and they're lousy marionettes, and I'll never be able to make any good ones," and in his despair he took no interest when Johnny blocked in the square on the chart for that night.

"Five more nights and you'll be due for another movie," said Johnny, hoisting Tink up on his shoulders, and carried him into the bedroom. "You're getting heavy, you know it?" He dumped Tink on the bed. "If you'd just start taking a little more exercise, and go outside when you get home from school instead of fooling around with that theater of yours—"

"I hate the winter." Tink continued to sniff, sitting cross-legged on his bed. "I hate the snow; I hate everything about it."

"Don't you like to coast, Tink?" Johnny sat on the edge of the bed.

"A lot of big bums, they're always shoving their sleds out in front of you and then you have a crack-up. You could be killed," Tink said.

"Knock 'em down, Tink. Knock 'em down."

"They're bigger than me."

"I'll have to teach you how to box. And jiu-jitsu. Guess I remember a little about jiu-jitsu from that time at the Y. That way you can take care of guys twice your size."

"I don't want to take care of them. I just want to be left alone."

"Yes, but, Tink—"

Tink, though, had undergone one of his swift changes of mood. "Will you read to me, Johnny?" He stood up on the bed; his eyes blazed.

"Look, Tink, it's half-past nine already—"

"That clock is fast. I keep it fast on purpose. Then when it goes off in the morning I know I can stay in bed another half-hour."

"What a system! You like to kid yourself, Tink, don't you? All right, I'll read to you. But for just ten minutes, see? No more. If you'll lie down and pull the covers over you and concentrate on getting to sleep." Johnny opened up *Roy Blakeley;* he pulled a chair into place beside the floor lamp. "All set?" He began to read.

Roy Blakeley and his friends were not quite like any of the Boy Scouts Johnny had known in Troop 7, but at least they weren't interested in marionettes. While he read, Johnny kept trying to steer his own mind away from the truth, which was that the other kids at school thought Tink was a sissy. Indignation stirred fiercely in Johnny and his voice became louder as he read. It was just that the other kids were jealous of Tink, who was too bright for them. But he ought to be outdoors more; he ought to eat more food;

he ought to learn how to take hard knocks and give them. Would it be possible to teach him a little about boxing, or would that just upset him? There wasn't time to do for Tink all the things that ought to be done—teach him how to throw a baseball like a guy instead of a girl, and how to kick a football, and—

"You aren't reading with any expression," Tink complained.

"Keep your trap shut," Johnny said gently, "or I'll stop reading altogether. You're the actor in the family."

Tink sat up. "Want me to read and show you how?"

"You're supposed to be concentrating on sleep."

"How can I, when Roy Blakeley keeps on being so funny?"

"Shut up, now, or I will stop. It's way over ten minutes already." Johnny read on, and eventually Tink showed signs of becoming drowsy. Johnny read more softly; he slowed his voice down. Tink sighed and closed his eyes; he turned sideways in the bed, tucking a hand beneath his cheek as he always did. Johnny laid the book down; he snapped off the light; he went on tiptoe toward the door.

"Johnny"—plaintively.

"What?"

"You forgot to kiss me good night."

Johnny returned to the end of the bed. "Look, Tink," he said. "Fellows don't kiss each other."

Tink lay quiet and thought about that. "Will you shake my hand?"

"O.K." Johnny grinned in the dark. "Put it there."

Tink's small hand lay still and hot in Johnny's big one for a moment; but suddenly he sat up in bed, his grip became amazingly strong, and he began to twist Johnny's arm. "Jiu-jitsu!" he shouted, bouncing exultantly. "And *you're* more than *four* times my size."

"You're a little—devil." Johnny cuffed him. "Go on, now, go to sleep, or I'll knock you into the middle of next week."

"Then I wouldn't have to do my arithmetic," said Tink, still bouncing.

"I mean it." Johnny strode from the room, clapping the door shut behind him.

"Johnny! . . . Joh*neeeee!*"

Johnny let him wait for a moment; then he pressed his mouth against the crack and said, "What?"

"You forgot to prop the door."

Johnny sighed and opened the door and crouched to adjust the door-stopper. "You're old enough not to be afraid of the dark any more," he said.

"I'm not afraid of the dark. I just like to see the hall light."

"That's going out in another second."

"I'll be asleep in a *split* second."

"I'll hold you to that."

Johnny went down to the living room, where his father was emptying ashtrays. "Mom go to bed already?"

"Mm-hmm. Tink was pretty wild tonight."

"Yeah."

Johnny's father picked up the *Chronicle* and straightened the edges; he folded it neatly and put it down on the sofa. "Bry told me to tell you good night for him."

"Thanks. . . . Bry's a good egg," said Johnny.

"I think so too. He—" Johnny's father adjusted the position of a chair slightly—"he says he's still on your side."

"Oh. Well—guess I'll get along to bed too. Night, Pop."

"Good night, Johnny. . . . Faint hearts and fair ladies, you know."

"Sure."

Johnny went back up the stairs.

11

JOHNNY lay prone in his own bed now, in his own room at the far end of the hall, his chin propped on his hands and Emerson on *Self-Reliance* propped on the pillow before him. He frowned and sighed as he read; there was a crick in his neck and his arm was going to sleep but he would not shut the book or turn out the light until he had finished another page.

Sometimes his mind moved eagerly after the words and sometimes a shiver went down his spine because Emerson's voice rang out like a bugle-call. That odd sad long-faced man with the straight upper lip and the deep lines running down from the big nose, dead this half-century in Concord, Massachusetts; his voice rang out from the page. Sometimes it was like that but more often Johnny had to flog his mind out of inattention. There was too much he did not know, too much discipline his brain had missed; but he read on, plodding through the paragraphs which said nothing to him, waiting for the bugle to sound again.

Live no longer to the expectation of these deceived and deceiving people with whom we converse. Say to them, "O father, O mother, O wife, O brother, O friend, I have lived with you after appearances hitherto. Henceforward I am the truth's. . . . I appeal from your customs. I must be myself. I cannot break myself any longer for you, or you. If you can love me for what I am, we shall be the happier. If you cannot, I will still seek to deserve that you

*should. I will not hide my tastes or aversions. I will so trust that
what is deep is holy, that I will do strongly before the sun and
moon whatever inly rejoices me, and the heart appoints. If you are
noble, I will love you; if you are not, I will not hurt you and myself by hypocritical attentions. If you are true, but not in the same
truth with me, cleave to your companions; I will seek my own. I
do this not selfishly, but humbly and truly. . . ."*

Did Johnny know what Ralph Waldo Emerson was talking
about? Had he missed the clue, buried somewhere three or four
pages back? Was there a whole area of place and time and thought,
his ignorance of which must blind him to Emerson's meaning?
Johnny suspected that this was so, but perhaps it did not matter;
perhaps all that mattered was that the bugle had sounded and
rang in his head for a while after the book was shut and the light
turned out.

All the years when he was growing up he read very little because there was so much living to do. Emerson said books were
for the scholar's idle times, but Johnny had never been a scholar;
and he had turned to books now hoping they might divert his
mind from darker channels, or cast light upon his darkness.

There were marked passages in the book of essays; Johnny's
father too had heard the bugle sounding—"Life only avails, not
the having lived. Power ceases in the instant of repose; it resides
in the moment of transition from a past to a new state, in the
shooting of the gulf, in the darting to an aim." Once that had
rung in his father's head as it now rang in Johnny's, but Johnny
couldn't talk to him about it. Shyness seemed to have increased
between them, and there was no one, now, to whom Johnny could
talk.

He lay on his back with his eyes shut tight, trying not to think
about Patricia or about the other girls he knew. Faint heart never
won fair lady. But it was not faintness of heart; it was anger, it
was jealousy, it was hatred of Vincent Rourke, it was any ignoble
emotion he could find a name for. Possibly it was something else
too, a new delicacy of feeling—the knowledge that in many ways
he must always have been displeasing to her; and although not
to see her was pain, to give her pain would be worse yet. Let her
forget you altogether, let her love Rourke if that would make her
happy; and kill your own hatred, become a civilized being instead
of a savage.

Sooner or later there would be another girl for him. Plenty of
other dames, said Stan Wolenczik, who had long ago sent him
off to Sophie and the little wooden house on Barrett Street. He
lay and thought about those evenings and wondered if they would
ever be repeated: the pretense that this was just like any other

date, the promenade to a shabby beer parlor, the dancing to the coin-in-the-slot phonograph, the promenade (not quite sober now because of beer and lust) back to the little wooden house and up the outside wooden staircase at the side and into Sophie's room. It was a very bare little room, and very clean; that was all he noticed about it the first few times, because there was Sophie, not a bad girl really, hard as nails but very kind and calm and efficient, almost like a nurse, he had strangely thought, so that there was something clinical about the experience; afterwards it would seem there had been as little heat in it as in going to have a tooth pulled. But on later visits he saw her room more clearly and it was her room, not Sophie, which made him think the visits would have to stop. There were four ornaments on the bare walls: an old cover from the *Saturday Evening Post,* a picture of the Sacred Heart, a crucifix, and a photograph of Sophie's father taken after he had been placed in his coffin. Sophie was committing a mortal sin, but would be washed clean again when she had confessed to her priest. Johnny wasn't sure about sin; but there was no desire left in him when he remembered the photograph, the crucifix, the Sacred Heart. It was far worse to do what they had done before these things which were holy, to Sophie, than it would have been in any other place.

So when his lust began again he tried to think of the room, not Sophie; he tried to think of his family and especially Tink; he tried to remember his own days of innocence.

But Ralph Waldo Emerson commanded him not to turn his head backward; and remembering that, Johnny would call up one of the nice girls he knew and maybe they went to the rink and roller-skated, or to the movies, or just sat and had a couple of beers to drink and dropped nickels in the phonograph. Some of the nice girls didn't mind holding hands a little, some of them expected to be kissed and pawed about; but when this happened outside, nothing at all happened inside Johnny. The girl he had his arms around was a wraith; only Patricia was real; and kissing a wraith who believed you were kissing a girl was worse, almost, than going to see Sophie.

So Johnny, more and more, stayed at home in the evening, plodding through the books he might have learned about if he'd gone to college, trying to put his ideas in order, to control the violence in his body, to forget that across the street and five doors down lived Patricia Bryant, who was beautiful as Sophie never would be and was being seen everywhere these days with Vincent Rourke.

But faint heart never won fair lady, and one night in February Johnny forgot the new delicacy of feeling, pitched his books away, and marched from the house, across the street and five doors down, and pushed the bell before he had a chance to think twice about it. I will do strongly before the sun and moon whatever inly rejoices me and the heart appoints.

Patricia wasn't there, though. Nobody was there but Charlie Bryant's wife Delores, and the baby asleep upstairs.

"Won't you sit down anyway?" said Delores. "I was just kind of listening to the radio and working on an old dress I'm making over. My father-in-law, he's to a Father and Son Scout Banquet with Joel, and Patricia—well, maybe she'll be back soon. I was feeling kind of lonesome." Delores continued to stand and so did Johnny; Delores smiled but Johnny wanted to walk out of the house. "That's a nice soft chair," said Delores, with a half-gesture, and sat beside the radio; so Johnny sat down too and wondered what they were going to talk about.

He looked at Delores and thought that life had badly frightened her, and wondered why a dock-walloper like Charlie had ever picked her. But love made no sense anyway, thought Johnny; nine times out of ten you could see no logic in the pairings-off that took place. Why had his mother married his father, even though it had worked out well? Why had Laura married a man like Norris? —She smiled serenely from the picture on the piano. If she had been here now she might have answered some of his questions, thought Johnny. Or was that because she looked like Patricia, and he was still in love with Patricia, worse than ever?

"Do you like this program?" Delores asked.

"H'm? Oh. Oh, sure, yes. It's fine."

"I could switch to something else."

"No, no, it's fine. It's a swell program."

"I like to have the radio going. It gets kind of creepy when everything's quiet," Delores said. "It's a very quiet place to live, Broadfield. Don't you think so?"

"Yeah. Sure. This part of town, anyway."

"Sometimes a whole hour or more goes by and not a single car along the street. Nobody *walks* past, even. All you can hear is the wind blowing and little creaks, sometimes, upstairs. Like somebody was walking around up there. Of course nobody is," said Delores, and went on sewing.

"You always live in Detroit before?" Johnny asked.

Delores nodded. "All my life. I was born there." Her hands paused; her voice was almost awe-struck. "Detroit isn't quiet," she went on. "Oh, way out, of course, where the rich people live. But not where I ever lived. Noise all the time. That's something about a big city; it's noisy all the time. Late at night even."

"I don't like cities," Johnny said. "I like the country."

"I don't like the country at all. It's too quiet. And people who live there, they don't ever have any fun."

"All depends on what you mean by fun, I guess."

"Well, yes, I guess you're right. Life is what you make it," said Delores, and her face glowed with pleasure. "That's what my mother used to say. . . . My mother passed away two years ago."

"Gee, tough, I'm sorry," said Johnny.

"Unh-huh. My father, he passed away so long ago I can't hardly remember. When I was just a little girl. Not that I'm so very old even now. I won't even be twenty until the end of next summer."

"Pat's age," Johnny said absently.

"Sometimes I think I got married too young. It would be different if it wasn't for the baby coming so soon, and Charlie losing his job. I think a girl ought to have some fun before she settles down, but I don't really have any at all, to speak of."

"Well, we're all in the same boat, I guess. These days."

"Yes, that's right. That's really very true. Still and all," said Delores, "a girl does like to have some fun sometimes. I mean Charlie—well, there are some things that Charlie just doesn't seem to understand. Laurette is different. Laurette always has a good time, no matter what. Laurette is really a very wonderful person. I'm just crazy about Laurette," said Delores.

"I never knew her very well."

"Just crazy about her. You should have come over Christmas. She sang that night. Sings real well. She has talent, Laurette has, but she isn't the least bit conceited." Delores bit off a thread. "Patricia is a very nice person too, but she *is* just slightly conceited. If you don't mind me saying so."

"Unh-uh."

"I know it's none of my business," Delores said, sewing rather more quickly after she had rethreaded her needle, "but naturally I know just a little about, well, everything. *You* know. And I wouldn't give Patricia a second thought, if I was you. I guess I'm being fresh?"

Johnny shook his head.

"Well, like I was saying. This Vincent Rourke, he's a terribly cute boy. *Terribly* cute. Not that you aren't too," said Delores, looking at him thoughtfully, "but in a different way. You're an altogether different type. Altogether. So what I started to say, Vincent and Patricia, they're more the same type. Both a little conceited. In my opinion, anyway."

Johnny tried to control the inward savage. "She out with him tonight?" he asked finally, giving in.

Delores nodded. "Oh, my, yes. I don't know what they *do* all the time. I mean, Broadfield is so dead. Even if you had any money. And I guess he doesn't have so much. He told Patricia he was a whole month behind in his room rent."

Johnny could think of nothing to say.

"There!" said Delores suddenly. "Hear it?"

"Hear what?"

"That noise upstairs," said Delores. "Just like somebody was creeping into my room to look at the baby."

Johnny looked at her seriously; he was beginning to have an eerie feeling himself. "You don't believe in ghosts, do you?" he asked, and grinned at her.

"Oh, no! Goodness, no! But sometimes I just make believe. I just make believe," said Delores, "that Charlie's mother is still *here*."

"Scaring yourself on purpose, hey? My kid brother Tink—"

"Oh, it doesn't scare me, exactly. Because she wouldn't hurt you, even if she could come back. Charlie used to talk about her. When I was going steady with him. He talked about his mother all the time. More than he did about *me*."

"She must have been pretty swell, I guess."

"Charlie was crazy about her. So was Charlie's father. Charlie's father thinks about her all the time. It's very sad," Delores said, "but what I think, it's kind of beautiful too. I mean, to have a man as crazy about you as all that. Now you take me, I honestly don't think Charlie would care at all if I died tomorrow."

She sewed in silence for some time; presently she twisted the dial on the radio until she had found a musical program, and hummed under her breath as she sewed, tapping one foot on the floor. Johnny continued to stare at her seriously: what made Delores tick? She wasn't quite a moron. She watched what was going on, and listened to what people said, and put things together in her mind (rather as Johnny tried to) and sometimes she drew the right conclusions. But her small half-stifled voice hardly rose and fell as she talked and was as unemotional when she mentioned Charlie as when she said cities were noisy or life was what you made it.

"Well," she said now, as if there had been no pause in the conversation, "it isn't surprising I get to feeling she's here. The way everybody's always thinking about her." She lifted her eyes to Johnny's. "Listening to every word we say, maybe."

"Aw, no," Johnny said. "That's just—"

"Not that I *really* believe it. But when I get lonely, I like to think it could be so. Nobody ever talks to me very much, you see. So I'm having a wonderful time tonight, talking to you. You're an awful easy kind of person to talk to, Johnny, you know it? Like Laurette says. 'Johnny's a sweet kid,' she says, and it's true."

"Hell," said Johnny, and felt in his pockets for a cigarette; but he had left the pack at home. "Laurette doesn't even know me."

"You'd be surprised, all the things Laurette told me about you."

Johnny got up. "Think Bry would mind if I bummed one of his cigarettes?"

"Goodness, no! But wait, I have some of my own. I guess I'll have one too." Delores began to grope in her sewing-bag, and came up with a battered pack of Luckies. The way she stared at Johnny while he was lighting her cigarette for her embarrassed him vaguely. "You used to play football, didn't you?" she asked.

"Yup." Johnny turned away, dragging on his cigarette.

"Charlie too. But Charlie's starting to get a corporation already. I used to say to him, 'Well, thank goodness in some ways we *don't* always have enough to eat,' I said—kidding, you know—'because I'd hate to think how fat you'd get then,' I used to say. I don't think Charlie has very much of a sense of humor, though."

"You don't mean you—" Johnny turned back again. "Gee, have things been that tough?"

Delores shrugged. "Oh, we didn't starve. But if it hadn't 've been for Laurette, I guess maybe we would have. And now I feel sort of embarrassed, living here. Of course, looking after the house and cooking the meals and all—that's quite a job, really. But I don't have any spending-money of my own. Laurette generally sends something when she writes, but I hate to take any of it, of course."

"Makes me feel like a louse for bumming one of your cigarettes," Johnny said. "I don't smoke much—forgot to bring mine along."

"I don't smoke much either, really. I didn't smoke at all, while the baby was on the way. I don't know if it makes any difference, but I thought I wouldn't take any chances."

"Sure. Good idea." Johnny felt increasingly restless; he couldn't sit down again. Prowling the room, he noticed *Casual Journey* lying open and face down on the table, and absently, automatically, picked it up and closed it. Johnny's father was a great believer in the prevention of cruelty to books.

"Of course, if it wasn't for the baby, I could get a job myself, maybe. I'd like that," said Delores. "It would be more interesting." Johnny felt her looking at him again; she said, "I bet you're a whole lot stronger than Vincent Rourke is."

"Out of condition now." Johnny punched a pillow. "One reason I use my bike so much—good exercise. But this weather a bike's no good to you." He lifted his head; footsteps on the walk outside, footsteps on the porch; Joel and his father returning from the banquet. Relief swept over Johnny; he held his breath, waiting for a current of fresh air to blow into the room.

But when the door opened it was Patricia and Vincent who blew in.

A fist in the solar plexus couldn't have made Johnny feel worse; though he stood motionless he felt that he was reeling. There were words of surprise (polite) and voices explaining things (gaily) and a radio announcer praising a face cream (fervently). But things presently settled into place, and there was Delores sewing away, there was Patricia sitting calmly in a chair, there was Rourke helping himself to one of Bry's cigarettes.

Johnny sat down on the sofa and crossed one leg over the other. In a moment he would think of something to say; meanwhile he could only gaze at Patricia, and this was torment because she looked so radiant—he wanted to lay his hand against her cheek to feel the warmth. He turned his head away from Rourke, who was responsible for the radiance; the inward savage was beating a tom-tom and howling for blood.

Johnny suddenly laughed at himself, and felt much better.

"How nice of you, Johnny, to come in and keep Delores company," Patricia was saying. Her manner was grand beneath the radiance; she was a duchess at a rather vulgar garden party.

"I didn't come to keep Delores company," said Johnny blithely. "I came to see you."

"We went to the movies," said Patricia, somewhat less like a duchess. The truth was she felt very angry with Johnny. "But it wasn't much good, so we walked out in the middle." Lout, she thought, oaf, boor, fool. . . .

"It was, in fact, a stinkeroo," said Vincent. Quite at ease, smiling at some private joke, he leaned against the edge of the table and blew a perfect smoke ring. With his eyes half shut he watched it expand; it hung a long time in the air and its edges gave birth to miniature smoke rings. "But at least we got in free." He cocked his head toward Delores. "You see before you the new movie critic of the *Broadfield Chronicle*."

"You mean you get to go to *all* the shows free?" Delores asked.

"Until Lucinda Craik recovers from bronchitis. Movies, concerts, stage plays if any, lectures, and other cultural activities—all free while Lucinda lies on her bed of pain," said Vincent.

"Do people ever die of bronchitis?" Johnny asked. "It would be swell if Lucinda died and then you could always get in free."

Patricia jerked her head toward Johnny, but Vincent gave him an agreeable smile. "After about two weeks of it, I'll be fed to the teeth. So I hope Lucinda survives. She has a strange and wispy beat—there's nothing you can get your teeth into. Also, the city desk being agin culture on general principles, my copy has a way of being whittled down to a nubbin. Still, it's a nice change from the Board of Education. I was always having to attend meetings on the budget. God," said Vincent softly, and blew another smoke ring.

"Gee, I wish *I* had your job," said Delores.

"The trouble is," Vincent said, "you have to know how to spell."

Delores giggled. "Aren't you fresh! I won a *prize* for spelling once, so there!"

"The poems of Henry Wadsworth Longfellow, I'll bet, bound

in purple plush. But you don't mean you actually used to *go* to school, Delores," said Vincent. "I didn't know they had schools in Detroit."

"Vinnie!" Patricia laughed. "Stop it." She was pleased but uneasy, like the mother of a precocious child. Not that Delores seemed to mind.

"I got real good marks," she was saying. "Always."

"Sucking around the teachers," said Vincent. "I know you. A teacher's pet if I ever saw one."

"I'll bet you were the *women* teachers' pet," Delores said.

"How did you guess?" asked Vincent, and then David let out a sudden wail upstairs, and Delores sighed and tore herself away.

Vincent flipped his cigarette into the fireplace and sat in the chair she had just left; pushing her sewing to the floor, he said, "Too bad I don't get three passes, Johnny, or you could come along too—to the movies and the concerts and the lectures."

"I'm like the city desk," said Johnny. "Agin culture."

"The physical type," said Vincent.

"Just a lousy toolmaker." Johnny established himself more comfortably on the sofa. His finger-nails were blackened and broken; his flannel pants bagged at the knee; his sweater with the block letter on it from high school days was inside out, and torn in several places, and too small for him; his open shirt-collar looked a little dirty; but he sprawled on the sofa, as much at ease as Vincent. He kept grinning, and there was such a glitter in his eyes that Patricia wondered if he hadn't been drinking. Johnny had mostly been humble before, and somehow the change disturbed her.

He looked at her now as if she were alone in the room with him—appraisingly, so that she almost believed he knew what had happened on the way home from the movies.

"How about a date tomorrow night, Pat?" he asked. "Come and do something lowdown for a change. There's a little place I found across the tracks where mostly Negroes go; the music's pretty good. If you like really dirty stuff."

"Harlem in Broadfield?" Vincent asked. "Pat, you've been keeping things from me."

"I'm sorry, Johnny. Vincent and I—"

"Pat is the unofficial assistant temporary culture reporter," said Vincent, rescuing her. "Tomorrow night comes a grand opening at the Broadfield Art Gallery. American Painting Since 1920. Pat is going to tell me what to say about all the pictures."

"Saturday night, then," Johnny said. "Things get really hot across the tracks on Saturday night."

"Saturday is all taken care of too," said Vincent.

"Find yourself another wench and I'll take Pat and we'll make a double date of it," said Johnny. "And if you don't know any other wenches I'll be glad to supply one. You really owe it to yourself to step across the tracks someday. It's a different world."

"Sorry," said Vincent. "It sounds charming, but other plans are afoot."

"Charming," said Johnny. "Ah, yes. You're really a very charming fellow, aren't you? It must be something they teach at Princeton."

"Harvard," said Vincent. "I majored in charm."

"And graduated summa cum laude, I'll bet. Well," said Johnny, and now he did haul himself up out of the sofa, "I'll have to be running along. Toolmakers get to work early in the morning. But keep my little proposition in mind, will you? Maybe Saturday *week* we can all go across the tracks. I'll be looking around for a suitable wench. The kind likes a guy graduated summa cum laude after majoring in charm."

He picked up the sofa pillow against which he'd been leaning, tossed it a little way into the air, drove his fist into it, caught it, and set it neatly in place. "So long, Vincent," he said, and lounged away to the door.

Patricia found herself following him. "Good night, Johnny," she said, and held out her hand; she was a duchess again, bidding the least of the gardeners a gracious farewell.

"Good night, Pat." Johnny held tight to her hand, and his own felt very different from Vincent's; Vincent's hands, Patricia thought suddenly, were soft as a girl's. "Good night," Johnny said again, and the muscles of his face tightened, a look of pain came into his eyes. She saw that, and then he had jerked her toward him, clamped both arms about her, bent his head, and kissed her on the mouth. He kissed her so hard, he held her so tightly, that it hurt; she could feel his heart, under the torn sweater; for a moment she could not breathe. It was all very different from the way Vincent had kissed her, on the way home from the movies, in a shadowy place under the trees—just a delicate brush of the lips, that had been.

Johnny released her; he stepped back and turned to Vincent. "You take any courses in kissing at Harvard?" he asked, and walked out of the house.

Patricia stared at the closed door; she stood still until the inward tremor had ceased. Then she said, "Where in the world can Father and Joel be?" and walked back toward the sofa.

Vincent said nothing. There was a dead look on his face and Patricia thought one of his moods was starting; a feeling of impatience, almost, fluttered in her for a moment, and she sat firmly on the sofa.

"I suppose you're disappointed," Vincent said at last.

"Disappointed?" Johnny had been sitting on the sofa and the sense of his physical presence oppressed her still.

"I was supposed to beat his ears in, wasn't I? Wasn't that the idea?"

"Oh, Vinnie." She drew a breath. "Don't be silly. Forget the whole thing. I—can't stand Johnny."

"He is fairly obnoxious, isn't he?" Vincent's voice sounded less taut; he stood up and moved to the table. "Cigarette?"

"No, thanks."

He was behind her, and she could hear him tapping the cigarette on the box-cover and striking a match. She hoped he would come and sit beside her and kiss her again as he had kissed her under the trees. It had happened so casually—they had been walking up the hill, more and more slowly, laughing about nothing; their arms were linked; then he was holding her hand and they walked more slowly yet and now they had come into the shadows and were not moving at all. One of his hands still held hers, and the other just touched her shoulder, so that she turned and looked up at him; then his face floated toward hers in the dark and then the moment was over and they were strolling on again, arm in arm, laughing again about nothing at all. . . .

But he did not sit down. Behind her back he said, "Andrew McBain's book. You reading it, Pat?"

"Father is."

"It's a good book. I hope they'll let me interview McBain when he comes here to lecture. That's the kind of career I'd like." He moved back into her circle of vision, but returned to the chair by the radio. The mood had lifted, she thought; his eyes were fixed intently on her face—with love?

But he asked, "Didn't your father use to know McBain?"

"I think so. Before my time." Vincent was so strange.

"But you never saw him."

"No."

"Didn't he ever come back here? After the war?"

"I don't know, Vinnie. What difference does it make?"

"Oh—I just—" Vincent lay back and gazed at the ceiling; he seemed to have nothing more to say.

Patricia watched him anxiously. Perhaps the kiss under the trees hadn't meant anything to him; there must have been similar episodes for him—he had glided so easily into the moment and out again. But she couldn't feel casual about it; it was the first hint of physical intimacy in all the times they had been out together.

"Would you like that?" she asked, for the silence had begun to oppress her. The mood, she thought, was coming back after all. "Traveling all over the world for news?"

"You dry up, you shrivel away to nothing, when you stay put."

"I suppose you mean Father."

"I was just thinking about me. It may be different for some men."

Patricia sighed and stood up; looking through the window, she said, "The banquet seems to be going on forever."

"You bored with me, Pat?"

The edge was back on his voice and she turned quickly. "Of course not, only—"

Vincent's lips twisted for a moment. "Only the Butch act isn't one of my specialties," he said. "That's it, isn't it?" He stood up.

"Vinnie, I don't know what—"

"Lusting after Johnny, aren't you? The cave man."

"Vincent—" She was becoming frightened; his face worked so strangely.

"You think I'm— You think what your sweet brother Charlie does, don't you?"

She held her hand out toward him and then began to feel foolish and let it drop; no words came.

"It's all right," Vincent said, deliberately working himself into a fury. "I'm going now. I'll leave you to your dreams of Johnny. You don't have to come to the gallery tomorrow night. If you're sick of me, why don't you say so? God knows it's going to be a dreary occasion and you'll have a lot more fun across the tracks with your cave man, getting drunk with a bunch of niggers."

"Oh, Vinnie," she said, "stop it," and tried to laugh at him. "You aren't jealous, are you?"

"Jealous!" He almost shouted. "Christ! What do you think I am? What the hell do you think I am!"

Wisdom seemed to flow into her, and she moved toward him and took his hand. "Vinnie, don't, please. We've never quarreled and we aren't going to now—and about Johnny, of all people. Don't you know—" she became somewhat breathless but there was no turning back—"don't you know, Vinnie, how I feel about you? I'm in love with you," Patricia said. The words, which she had not expected to say to anybody, ever, astonished her, and she stared at him; his thin soft hand, with the fine bones palpable under the flesh, lay taut and nervous in hers.

It was time for him to say something but he did not say it; she could not bear the silence and went on talking.

"Sit down," she said, and there they were, side by side on the sofa. "I'll never see Johnny Wheelwright again," she told him, and looked at his rigid profile. He bent his head, as if he were about to weep, and she wanted to touch the back of his neck; she wanted to soothe him as she might have soothed a child; but these were new and strange impulses to her and she was too shy to give in to them.

"You're so childish sometimes," she said. "Sometimes you don't seem to be grown up at all." A great flood of tenderness went out from her toward him—surely he must feel it—and she said, "Didn't you hear what I said to you? Vinnie, darling—"

But unease checked her tenderness. This was all the wrong way around; he ought to be saying these things to her. Not once had he said anything about loving her; an hour ago he had kissed her out of silence, and there had been silence after the kiss; there was silence now.

She dropped his hand and moved away from him on the sofa.

"Pat," Vincent said, "listen—"

She could not understand the torment in his face; and what he had been about to say she never learned, because Joel and Norris had returned at last from the banquet. They were stamping the snow off their overshoes, out on the porch, and now the door burst open and they came in, noisy and hilarious, their cheeks red from the cold.

Vincent, who had miraculously pulled himself together, went quite soon; and Joel had gone straight up to bed. But Patricia's face was on fire—she almost put up her hands to hide it—and her father was looking at her so intently that she asked him about the banquet.

He said that it had been fine. "Glad I went. Joel thawed out some on the way home. It's like you said, Pat, the West Point thing—the uniform, chiefly. I think we'll be able to talk him out of it long before the time comes."

"Joel could do worse than the Army." Her father was still hovering at the foot of the stairs. "Good night," she said.

"There's nothing wrong, Pat?"

"No. No, of course not. Johnny was here when we got back from the movies, that's all." Her glance fell on *Casual Journey*. "Vincent was asking about Andrew McBain. If you didn't know him once."

Norris frowned and moved to the table. "Somebody lost my place." He picked the book up.

"How *well* did you know him?" Patricia asked; he was still looking troubled.

"I used to think he was my best friend."

"He never came back here, did he, after the war?"

"Once. Just once." Norris had returned to the foot of the stairs. "He was on his way East from California—he'd come right around the world, Middle East, India, China, Japan, guess he squeezed in the Dutch East Indies and the Philippines too. It's all in the book. Hell of a casual journey that was."

"Did he—see you then?"

"Sure, don't you remember? You must have been around three

or four years old. He was here a week—always dropping in." Norris stared fixedly at a point halfway up the stairs. "Changed a lot, of course, all he'd been through. The war, and then traveling, meeting the big-shots." Norris sighed. "We didn't have an awful lot to say to each other. He'd gone a long way, I was stuck fast in the mud. Guess he tried too hard to be nice about that. I never did like being patronized." Norris paused. "Why the cross-examination, Pat?"

"I don't know. It seems funny, in a way—somebody like that being an old friend of yours."

"Thank you."

"I didn't mean—"

"I know what you meant. It's all right. I didn't care. I wouldn't be in Andy's shoes for the wide world. Good night," said Norris, and went on up.

Patricia began to turn out the lights, and then Delores appeared suddenly; she had been lurking in the dining room, Patricia didn't know for how long.

"Well," she said, "you and your boy friend were having yourselves quite a time. I started to come down, then I thought maybe I better wait in the kitchen till the storm blew over. . . . He's pretty excitable, isn't he?"

Patricia turned without a word and walked upstairs, but she felt curiously heavy; it was an effort to lift her feet from step to step. McBain, and the dark hints dropped by Aunt Maudie and Grandma Bryant, and that last bad quarrel her mother and father had, and the sudden trip to New York—

It was as if a ghost which had been laid a long time ago had suddenly come back into her mind. She ought to forget all about it, she thought; what did it matter, something which had happened years ago if it had happened at all? But she wasn't going to forget. She was going to have to write a letter to Laurette.

12

"I DREW a blank on Andrew White McBain."

"Drew a blank, darling? What in the world do you mean?"

"Hide-in-the-dark. Don't you remember?"

"That dreadful afternoon! My dear, we really must let the dead past bury its dead. Have another cup of tea, and tell me all about the culture beat. I adored your story on the arrowheads in the Public Museum."

"You didn't really read it!"

"Of course I read it. I comb the *Chronicle* feverishly, these days, looking for that haunting je ne sais quoi which only you can give to a story."

"How'd you like the Art Gallery critique?"

"I was *most* impressed. Especially by your initials at the end."

"I should have had a byline on that one. Lucinda always gets a byline."

"You have such an entirely different set of clichés from Lucinda. What Lucinda looks for in pictures is cows—cows, or Indian encampments. Then she can talk about a realistic depiction of pastoral serenity, or of our nation's stirring past. Anything else baffles her. How is she, poor dear?"

"Convalescing, I'm afraid."

"What a shame! Really, you know, you've been handling culture much better than she does. But Lucinda, I suppose, is an institution. I wonder how old she *is*."

"Not more than a hundred and twelve, at the outside."

"Vincent! . . . What will you do when she comes back?"

"Oh, they'll find plenty of work for me. We're still short-handed. Now Ack knows I can handle a story, he keeps me on the run. Even if he does still hate my guts."

"Darling, must you use these expressions? They're so physical."

"Perhaps I'm being coarsened. A crude world, full of profanity and obscenity and brimming cuspidors—"

"*Please,* darling! . . . If it hasn't corrupted Lucinda, why should it corrupt you?"

"Lucinda swears like a trooper. She's as tough as they come."

"I don't believe a word of it. That funny little creature, in her black bombazine? I haven't the faintest idea what black bombazine really is, but it sounds exactly like what Lucinda wears. She certainly must date back to the black bombazine era. Bombazine. I love the word. Look it up for me, Vincent, the next time you're near a dictionary."

. . . So they went on drinking tea in the little room out behind the dining room, while the late afternoon sunlight deepened, rippling like golden water on the cream-colored panels. It was the first time Vincent had visited Carola since the afternoon when it seemed as if the sun might never shine again on Broadfield. Now February was almost over, but the air outside was colder than it had been all winter; a wind charged up the hill and banged at the windows; when a pause came in the conversation, Vincent heard a frozen branch crack somewhere behind the house.

The room was overheated and the tea scalded his throat but still he felt a little cold. Carola was fencing with him; the dead past had not buried its dead; but their relationship was quite different from what it had been before Christmas, even though they hadn't seen each other since, except for the evening at the Art Gallery.

Vincent had taken Patricia with him after all. He must have changed his mind about it twenty times that day, but in the end he went across to the Parker Building and waited in the lobby, watching the elevator disgorge people until at last it disgorged Patricia. He couldn't tell if she was glad or sorry to see him; the little smile might have meant anything.

"Mind if I walk you home?" he asked.

Patricia shook her head; she allowed him to take her arm.

"I'm sorry about last night," said Vincent. "I suppose you're through with me now for good."

"No, I—" Her voice wavered, and he gave her arm a joggle.

"I've been trying to figure out what happened," he said cheerfully. "To both of us. I think it's because it hit us so suddenly. Maybe I'm wrong, Pat, but it never has happened to you before, has it?

"No."

"Well, it hasn't to me either. Not this way. So we've both been a little wrought up. Anyway, I was last night. But it's silly to be wrought up about it. It's silly to—oh, take love too seriously. Being in love is fun, Pat. Or it ought to be. The best kind of happiness there is."

"But you never—" She looked down at her feet as she walked; her arm, linked in his, was rigid as iron.

"It's so new for both of us," Vincent said, "that we're going on as if it were a tragedy. But it isn't, Pat. It's the most marvelous thing that ever happened to me. We're going to be—we're going to learn how to be gay about it." A deep pleasure was growing in him; he was so moved by his own words that they became true, almost. "Aren't we?" he said, and joggled her arm again. "We were laughing last night after the movies. We have to find out how to keep on laughing."

"Yes," she said.

"All right, then. Laugh, Pat! You haven't forgotten how, have you?"

"No," she said, and turned her face toward him; there was a wan smile on it.

"Try a little harder."

"Oh, Vinnie—" Tears threatened, but in the end she contrived a laugh.

"That's better. But not good enough yet."

They had reached the top of the hill and turned into Johnson Avenue. Lights shone through the windows and touched the shape of trees and lay kindly on the hard snow, which looked pure again in the dusk. It was that mysterious moment of a winter evening, just before full darkness comes, when the stillness is portentous: a breath is being held, someone is about to speak the final, illuminating word.

Straight ahead of them stretched the long avenue, the perspective diminishing in two ways; beyond this block of big houses was a block of smaller ones, set closer together, and beyond that block was one of smaller houses yet: Patricia's block.

The houses dwindled as they walked with ringing heels on cement scraped clean of snow, but the magic continued; it was so strong for a little while that Vincent began to wonder if he might not, after all, be falling in love with Patricia. At almost any other moment the thought would have frightened him; but now he believed what he had told her about the gaiety of love—gone were the pretty ladies who hadn't abided by the rules, gone was Anne Bannister, gone Carola Wilmot—and tenderness filled him, and he said, "You're a darling. . . . You'll come with me tonight, won't you?"

"Of course, Vinnie. . . . How much do you think I ought to dress up?"

"Right up. We'll knock their eyes out. It's a formal opening, after all."

"I've never been to one before. You have to be a patron."

"Or the unofficial assistant temporary culture reporter." They had reached Patricia's house.

"Will you come in? Stay to dinner? We can stretch the food."

"I have to go back and get dressed up."

"I don't know how my—I only have one evening dress just now. Betty Lou and I were going to—" Her face was blurred in the darkness. He bent his head and kissed her, gently still, but less so than last night because desire was stirring faintly—like a rumble of thunder beyond a summer horizon, so far and small you can't be sure if it is thunder or not. He was hardly aware of her body, muffled away from him in the overcoat; but her lips were soft and transmitted an eagerness to his.

"You're a darling," he said again, and stepped away from her with a sigh. "I'll stop by around eight-thirty."

He watched her go into the house, and did not move on until after the door had closed.

The feeling of tenderness continued while he ate his dinner in a half-empty tearoom, and while he washed and shaved and made himself splendid in his evening clothes. He needed a new dinner jacket, and damned Uncle Bertrand, who really must be spoken to seriously about the lack of checks. The tide of debts was mounting; sometimes Vincent almost worried. There had been a scene with the landlord of the apartment house, and it would be embarrassing, for instance, to borrow money from Carola.

The trouble was that he had been indolent about financial and legal matters; but it simply did not make sense that a fortune which had been split three ways should still enable Bertrand to live in idleness while Vincent sweated blood for fifteen dollars a week. The next time he wrote, Vincent thought, he would say something pointed to his uncle.

A wind which had come up after nightfall blew viciously against him all the way to the Bryants' house. He still felt pleased with himself, though, warmed by faint intimations of desire. Desire was something which had never troubled him greatly, and the satisfaction of desire had always been incidental, the least important part of the episode, and not to be arrived at too quickly. When desire was over, so was the episode, and it was necessary to look about for someone else and start the long process all over again. It would be a mistake to let desire trap you—think of Johnny Wheelwright.

This would not happen to Vincent. By the time he reached Patricia's house the wind had blown his tenderness away; by the time they arrived at the gallery, his mind felt very cold and clear.

Like the Civic Auditorium, the Broadfield Art Gallery was new, one of the last fruits of the boom years. Modern and severe, it lay like an oblong box beneath trees which had been young when the city was only a river trading-post, and it had an air of drawing itself in and back, away from the gimcrack mansions on either side, and from the Gothic Revival church across the street. Flood-lights now whitened the plain granite façade, and caught the great banner which flapped in the wind, announcing the show.

Cars were parked along the street in either direction; more cars kept turning into the icy driveway, and from them emerged ladies in trailing dresses and high-heeled shoes, who clung to the arms of dark-clothed gentlemen and picked their way fastidiously across the snow. As the gallery doors opened and shut, little bursts of noise shot out into the night. Broadfield was making a gay obeisance to art.

The air inside was dry and hot and smelled of radiators. The crowd was so dense that it was difficult to move and almost impossible, at present, to see the exhibit. Tomorrow and for the rest of the month the gallery visitors would be mainly school children; but tonight was gala.

The rich and mighty predominated; they had turned out in full force and their best clothes, careless of the impending revolution, and they spread themselves about the front room, talking loudly, overshadowing the others in the crowd—the humbler intelligentsia, such as schoolteachers and librarians, and Broadfield's bohemians, the stray women with leathery skins and horn-rimmed glasses, wearing hand-loomed dresses; the stray young men, pallid and bony and also bespectacled with shaggy hair, shaggy tweed jackets, and shaggy pipes clenched between their teeth.

Vincent smiled, although there was no one definite to smile at, and was glad he had dressed for the occasion; it allied him with the rich and mighty, it drew a line between him and the shaggy young men.

"We may as well fight our way around, I suppose," he said to Patricia. "I hope you know something *about* American painting since 1920. I don't."

Patricia merely smiled. She was looking shy and dazzled, but beautiful. Her smooth bare arms, the shape of her breasts beneath the black velvet, must not be regarded too closely—Vincent tried to pilot her through the crush without having to touch her elbow. He thought he knew how Johnny Wheelwright must feel about her; it was strange what a long time it had taken him to feel the same way.

The inner rooms of the gallery were less crowded; here there were people actually looking at the pictures—the women earnestly, the men casually and as it were over their shoulders, so that nobody could accuse them of giving art more than its due. Vincent, with Patricia holding to his arm, drifted a little closer, trying to overhear the comments.

On the whole, conversations had to do with the weather, with business, with politics local and national, with a darling little dinner dress that cost only fifteen ninety-eight, and with Cousin Hattie's foolproof recipe for chocolate cake. And presently, gathering in the sculpture court to drink coffee and nibble iced cup cakes, the rich and mighty and the humbler intelligentsia talked of anything but art, while the stray bohemians stood about in a gloomy intellectual silence.

Vincent, who had been making little checks on his mimeographed catalogue of the exhibit, and jotting vague notes on a wad of folded copy-paper, said to Patricia, "I'm lost. I don't think I'll be able to write a story at all."

"You can say who some of the people here are. And who's presiding at the urns. That's what Lucinda always does."

"But Milly Prentiss had all that on the society page today."

"It doesn't matter. You can say it all over again in your story." Patricia craned her neck; she began to give Vincent names; and then she said, "Anyway, in a little while there'll be a conducted tour, I think. Just copy down some of Mr. Berner's remarks. Lucinda probably does that too."

But before Mr. Lewis Berner, the gallery director, had caught the attention of the assembled art lovers, Carola Wilmot emerged from the throng, wiping her sticky fingers on a handkerchief.

"Vincent! Darling! What a lovely surprise! Ah, you're here in line of duty, I see. And you've dragged poor Patricia along. My dear," she said, clasping Patricia's hand, "you quite take my breath away—spring can't be far behind: you're a harbinger, definitely." She regarded Patricia as if she too were a work of art. "You are becoming the very image of your mother. Not ten minutes ago, when I saw you across the room, I said, 'There is Laura Bryant!' The years fell away from me—it was quite uncanny. And how sweet of you to dress for our silly exhibit. But why do you children insist on wearing black? Spring colors, my dear; you should wear nothing else. . . . I'll see you both later perhaps. And *why* haven't you come around to see me, Vincent? I've been feeling *quite* neglected."

She waved and whirled off.

"My uncle used to know her," Vincent murmured in Patricia's ear. "I had to look her up when I first got here, and now she doesn't seem to want to let go." He had been unprepared for Carola, and Carola, perhaps, for him; she had overdone her little performance.

"Here's Mr. Berner now," Patricia said.

Somebody was rapping on a table; somebody was trying to speak above the hubbub, which gradually diminished; cups were set aside, faces turned toward Mr. Berner. He was a small white-haired man whose dinner-jacket was a shade rusty, whose tie was riding up leftward; he resembled a mild bedraggled bird.

"I *adore* Lewis's little talks," came a loud whisper from the back of the sculpture court; there was a ripple of laughter, and Mr. Berner smiled and bowed.

"Thank you. Thank you. The ordeal begins in the front gallery. Except for the water-colors, we have tried to hang the pictures chronologically, so as to bring out the trends, if any, in the last decade." He bowed again, and moved from the sculpture court out toward the front of the building. Those who followed him were mostly the ladies in evening dresses, some of whom managed to tow their husbands along. The humbler intelligentsia seemed of two minds—eager to learn, reluctant to appear unlearned—and compromised by hovering on the fringes of Mr. Berner's circle. The leathery women, the shaggy young men, went off to pay homage to Marin in solitude.

Vincent's pencil flew now over the wadded copy-paper; and reassured by someone who really knew, the ladies in evening dresses began to let out little gasps of admiration. Their husbands looked bored or sheepish or scornful, and tended more and more to detach themselves from the circle, to withdraw into corners and exchange jokes which were probably not in the best of taste.

Mr. Berner, moving from picture to picture, lectured glibly on. Presently Vincent, who had far more notes than he would be able to use, began to suffer from claustrophobia, and said to Patricia, "You had enough? Come on down to the *Chronicle* with me. I think I'll write the story tonight and get it out of the way."

So they left the hot dry clamorous gallery and walked downhill, toward the place where the road widened and became Main Street, brilliant with rows of lights. It was after ten o'clock. They had to bang on the *Chronicle* door before the night watchman let them in, and climbed in silence to the third floor, where Vincent switched on several lights.

"Make yourself as comfortable as you can," he said. "I'll try not to be too long."

He dropped his overcoat, uncovered his typewriter, sat down in his swivel-chair, and lit a cigarette for inspiration. It pleased him obscurely to be seen at work by Patricia; and once he had written his lead the words came fast. They were Lewis Berner's words, mostly, and he found he hardly needed his scribbled notes. He let the story run on until he had covered three sheets of copy-paper, and pasted the sheets together and read through what he had written and took it up the room and dropped it in Ack Guion's box.

Patricia said, "Where does Father sit?"

"Haven't you ever been up before? Right there, next to Ack."

"It's bigger than I thought. And more impressive. . . . But how can you stand the smell?"

"Used to it, I suppose. I hadn't noticed. Ready?" He helped her into her cloak, and then held her elbows for a moment; he brushed his lips across the back of her neck. "Still love me?"

"Oh—Vinnie."

He switched off the lights. They walked down the stairs slowly, hand in hand, and when the night watchman had let them out again, Vincent said, "You want to drop back to my place for a little while? I have some beer, I think." He was aware of a pulse beating somewhere in his head; he was aware of his heart. He wanted to see her there, that was all, he wanted to see her again with the cloak off. He swung her hand and laughed. "But no etchings," he said.

"It's late, Vincent. I think—"

"It's just after eleven."

"But you have to get up early, and so do I. And if anyone saw me going in—"

"Everybody's in bed and asleep long ago."

Patricia stared down Main Street, empty in the glare of the lights. "No," she said, "I think I'd better not."

"O.K., sweet. Whatever you say."

The excitement still moved in him but he was glad in the end that she had decided against coming. Nothing would have happened, he thought, smiling at Carola across the tea-tray without hearing what she said; nothing beyond the gentlest caresses; but even they could wait. He would be in Broadfield for a long time, and when he was done with Patricia he would have to be done with Broadfield too.

It wasn't that he was caught; not really. He could still escape from what he had started; but there was a fascination in thinking that it was inevitable because then he would know what was going to happen eventually and Patricia would not. He almost pitied her—so innocent and eager, moving ahead so blindly.

What a fool Johnny Wheelwright was, Vincent thought, and set his empty cup down on the tray. Patricia was a pushover, if only Johnny knew. Then he had the uncanny feeling that Carola had been reading his wandering mind; while she poured him a third cup of tea, she said, "Patricia *is* beginning to look more like her mother, you know. There was nothing reminiscent of icebergs about her that night. I do believe she's fallen in love with you, Vincent."

"She has. She's told me so."

"Do you think it's quite nice, do you think it's the gentlemanly thing, to tell *me?*" Carola arched her eyebrow.

"No," said Vincent. "I never said I was a gentleman. I'm only a half-breed. My mother married below her station."

"Tell me all about your mother. *And* your father. Which one do you look like?"

"My father, I suppose. I don't know anything, really, about either of them. If there were any photographs, Aunt Lucy hid them, or destroyed them altogether."

"All very sad for you, my poor child. I suppose, after all, you're entitled to your little glooms. An orphan," said Carola. "I always think of orphans in terms of Oliver Twist, who had, I'm sure, a runny nose. You carry your orphanhood very well. And I don't believe it, about your father. I'm sure he was a nobleman in disguise."

"Just a handsome Mick, with a weakness for good-looking women. That isn't just Aunt Lucy's story; it's Uncle Bertrand's too."

"Well, even that could be rather amusing," said Carola. "I have my guttersnipe moods, you know. . . . What are you planning to do about Patricia's great love?"

"Is it the ladylike thing to ask?"

"Darling, we're being guttersnipes now. The tea is pure humbug. I should have offered you some rum to put in it, though I think myself that rum in tea is filthy. I've been having headaches and one thing and another, and the doctor said alcohol and nicotine should be ruled out for a while. Would you *like* some rum?"

"No, thanks. This is Uncle Bertrand's kind of tea."

"I might have known. But don't let's get led astray. Are you going to settle down and marry Patricia, after all, and eventually become assistant city editor of the *Broadfield Chronicle?*"

"I could marry her without the rest of it having to follow."

"Yes, I suppose you could." Carola studied his face. "Something tells me, though, that you aren't matrimonially inclined. No, the more I see of you, the less do I picture you in an atmosphere of bottles and babies and diapers on the clothesline."

"That wouldn't have to follow either."

"Somehow I feel it would, with Patricia. Once those knots came undone. She's still very young, of course, but she conveys maternity to me. Just as her mother did. Laura Bryant was one of those infuriating women who look ravishing during pregnancy. *And* after. Although I believe she had a hard time. In fact she died of a miscarriage eventually."

"I think the conversation is getting a little morbid," said Vincent.

"Darling, there is nothing morbid about babies. There is something morbid about *not*-babies, if you like. I often wonder what it might have done to me, having a child. Nevil didn't want children, and neither, of course, did Bodo, but Hank—poor Hank," said Carola. "I told him I was past the proper age for childbearing, so eventually he decided that what he needed was a girl in the bloom of her youth. By now, I believe, she's had five. He must be insatiable."

Carola sighed and lay back on her chaise longue; wind swooped up the hill again and rattled the glass in its frame, and Carola played a tune with her fingers on the chair-arm. She asked presently, "What was it you were saying about Andy McBain?"

"I thought you didn't want—"

"I was being a lady, then. I flit from mood to mood, darling, just like you. . . . Patricia didn't turn pale, or clutch at her throat, or fall in a swoon at Andy's name?"

"Patricia wouldn't do that, anyway. But I don't think she was upset at all. Or even interested."

Carola studied the ceiling. "It might all have been so much more amusing if she— Almost like history repeating itself. The triangle, with interesting variations. Patricia for Laura, Johnny for Norris, Vincent Vaughan Rourke for Andrew White McBain."

"You don't mean her mother had an affair with—"

Carola sat up and smiled at him. "One puts two and two together, darling. My answer may be five, or even ten. I'm afraid I have a nasty mind. People have forgotten now, but Norris's marriage really was a scandal, you know. Quite apart from Laura's having been an actress. They lost all discretion. What had been going on between them, months before he married her, was com-

mon knowledge. Or so I've been told. I was a young innocent at
the time, and Norris was quite beyond my mother's ken. But
later, years later in the Players, some of the women who couldn't
abide Laura—" Carola smiled again, dreamily. "It gave me quite
a different feeling about her. She no longer seemed the charming
little bourgeoise. . . .

"Those who said he'd had to marry her were terribly disappointed when Charlie took so long in coming. Elephants, yes;
Laura Bryant, no. So there was never any actual proof. But I suppose I must really subscribe to the theory of once a loose woman,
always a loose woman—just like those dreadful creatures at the
Bryant farm.

"How *was* your Christmas there, by the way? You've never told
me."

Vincent put his cup down on the table. "I got out of it, finally.
Just something I couldn't face. Though I did go around to their
house that night. . . . You were right, long ago. I couldn't marry
Pat—the thought of those in-laws. God!" said Vincent. "You can't
imagine—"

"Oh, yes, I can, darling. Don't go into the sordid details. What
I have been thinking, Vincent, is that if you want to stop this side
of matrimony, you might do a little discreet *un*burying from the
dead past. Once Patricia grasped the notion that she would only
be following in her mother's footsteps—" Carola broke off; she
stood, and went with a sweep of her long skirt to the window, and
jerked the curtain-pull, shutting away the ice-clear evening light.
"I get so bored," she said in the suddenly dim room. "Oh, *God*, I
get bored, Vincent."

But by the time she had switched on a lamp she was smiling
again. She sat on the window-seat and said, "Laura was not so
good as she should have been. That much we know. We know
too that Andy McBain had gone to Chicago before Laura appeared in Broadfield. But when Andy came charging through here
after the war, after that fantastic tour of his, he called every night
on the Bryants. To talk about old times with Norris? I hardly
think so. Laura did have that quality, you know—even after all
those years, after having borne Norris three children; she must
have been in her middle thirties then but she was still lovely. And
with that little common streak. . . . Andy left for New York; a
month later, Laura also left for New York, and was gone for ages.
Norris looked shattered, the children looked frightened, but just
as everybody was becoming quite *sure* of a scandal, Laura returned.
Nine months to the day later, Joel was born. Does Joel have the
faintest resemblance to Norris? I don't think so. . . . Well, two
years and more went by, and Laura was again with child, and that
time everything went wrong."

Carola stood up; she pulled the curtains open again and stood looking out into the garden.

"I shouldn't have come back to Broadfield. I should have hardened my heart and packed my father off to a nursing home." She turned. "These are the little tales I tell myself at night when I can't sleep. This about the Bryants is only one from an endless repertoire—the Broadfield closets are crammed with skeletons, and somehow one hears about them all sooner or later."

She returned to her chaise longue; this time there was no melancholy in her smile.

"Now you know why I can hardly bear to wait until Andy McBain turns up again. I hope he and Norris encounter each other. I hope I'm there when they do. I should also like to see a meeting between Andy and Joel. I keep wondering if Andy knows about Joel's existence. Does he know why Laura died? Does he know that —stretching a point—it's almost as if he'd murdered her? . . .

"Have I shocked you at last, darling?"

Vincent shook his head and smiled. "But it's all so shoddy, really."

"Shoddy," said Carola. "I suppose I am."

"I didn't mean you. Norris Bryant hasn't any right to get himself mixed up in a thing like that. He's too drab. There ought to be something tragic about him."

"Perhaps there is, if we had the eyes to see it. . . . Andy, too, will probably look a bit shoddy, by now. We grow old, we grow old, all of us." Carola sighed. "My facts may be askew, of course. I've had most of them second- or third-hand. While all this was going on, I was otherwise employed. . . . Will you stay to dinner?"

"I can't. I'm dining with the Bryants."

"You'll be seeing them in a new light. I hope you're properly grateful. It might have taken you months to find all this out by yourself." Carola rose; Vincent rose also. "Now, you really must not let such a long time go by before you come to see me again. Flowers are nice, darling, but you can't afford them; and besides, I prefer you in person. You may even come and weep on my shoulder again, if you feel like it."

"That will never happen. I promise."

"I shan't hold you to your promise," said Carola, and escorted him to the door.

13

THE WIND had shifted by the time he reached the Bryants' house and a wall of slaty cloud was blocking off the first stars. Before he left, at half-past ten—it had turned into a domestic evening and they all sat at the dining-room table playing poker for matchsticks —the snow had started again, floating down out of a now windless silence, floating patiently, as if it meant to keep on for a long time. It lay a half-inch deep on streets and sidewalks as he went back to his apartment, muffling his footsteps and the sound of passing automobiles; it cast a spell on the other tenants, who made less noise than usual; and while he sat at his desk, writing a rude letter to Uncle Bertrand, he could hear a train-whistle far away; after that only the silence and the faint whisper of flakes against his window.

February was almost gone, but winter had come to stay.

Poker for matchsticks had bored Vincent, and he had diverted himself by running his eye over Delores, who presently began to giggle and lose track of her cards; Patricia saw what was going on and her distress extended to Norris; and Vincent had decided that it was time to go.

He wondered why he had been so foolish. Anyone could see what a birdbrain Delores was. But while he sat there he had thought of the horrible phrase, going steady; and the bleak shabby golden-oak dining room and the stained-glass chandelier and Norris with his vest open and his shirt sleeves rolled up had oppressed Vincent suddenly; and he hadn't felt less oppressed when he thought of Carola's story.

He finished his letter to Uncle Bertrand and went to bed, but it was two in the morning before he slept. The wind had begun again and he had to keep his window shut against the snow; the radiator bubbled and sang and the air of his room became close and stale.

The snow and the wind continued all that day and the *Chronicle* was filled with stories about the weather—accidents on the highways, trains arriving hours late, a bum found dead of exposure in the railroad yards. The *Chronicle* staff cursed the weather but all the men were pleased obscurely. SNOW BLANKETS MIDWEST: life for the moment had ceased being quite ordinary, and all over the north central states the severity of the weather was bringing the same curious satisfaction to men and women. Who would live in Florida, although there are sometimes hurricanes, and who would live in Southern California, although there is the chance of forest fires and earthquakes?

That night the snow turned to sleet and the sleet stopped falling and the stars came out; and in the morning a sadness touched the *Chronicle* staff; their own part in the big news was over.

Now that the sun had reappeared, so did Lucinda Craik, as brisk as ever and complete with her bag of knitting for periods when all was quiet on the cultural front. She stood at Vincent's desk, very small and bent and old, exactly like a witch—the knitting-bag was large enough to hold a collapsible broomstick and a cat—breathing the scent of peppermint over him, and told him he'd done a good job.

"I'd have stayed in bed longer," she said, "only I was getting scared. Thought you'd take my beat away from me."

Vincent never knew when Lucinda was joking; he smiled with some care and said, "Well, I'm glad you're back. I don't mind if I never see another movie as long as I live."

"I'm glad to *be* back," said Lucinda. Tiny and meager and hunched, she trotted off to her own desk, yanked up her typewriter and blew away the dust, spread things wildly from the drawers and the knitting-bag, and achieved utter confusion in five minutes flat. Then she sat back to hold court for ten minutes more.

Watching the other men gather to pat her on the back and kiss her cheek and otherwise indulge in playfulness, Vincent wondered if she knew or guessed he hadn't been asked to contribute anything toward the flowers they had sent her in the hospital. He felt lonely, suddenly, shut out from an inner circle. Lucinda was the first woman ever hired by the *Chronicle,* and once she had covered society as well as culture, writing about the very pretty weddings of Spanish-American War days. She was a *Chronicle* tradition, more firmly established than Norris or Ack Guion, whom she still looked on as boys.

"Now go on!" she was saying with beldam coyness. "Go on, now, and tend to your business, and let me tend to mine."

Vincent sighed and devoted himself to rewrites. He almost wished she had died after all. He would be sent back to the Board of Education and the YMCA and the YWCA and the Boy Scout Council and the building-and-repair permits and all the other unconsidered trifles which no one else wished to bother about and which never made the front page.

And for the first time in his life he was becoming worried about money. No letter, no check, had come yet from Uncle Bertrand; and if you were to economize, where would you begin? He tried being frugal about meals; he ruled beer and cocktails out of his life; he limited himself to half a pack of cigarettes a day. Still there was nothing left of his pay check by the week's end, and even if he moved out of his apartment, into a room at the Y, he still couldn't exist on his salary alone. Not Vincent Vaughan Rourke, Esq.

He sent a telegram to his uncle finally; and at last, one March afternoon, the letter came to him at the office, with a check for twenty-five dollars.

I suppose you were joking but something seems to have happened to my sense of humour & like the dear Queen, we were not amused.

My pre-1929 indiscretions are water over the dam, Vinnie, as you very well know; since then I have tried to make amends by sharing as much as possible. When I think of the cost of your Harvard education, & the car, & the money—my money—you squandered so blithely on your grand tour, & all the clothes I have given you, not to mention bed & board, when I think of all this I am tempted to cut you off without another penny. If you insist, I can assemble statistics to prove that you have already cost me as much as I lost for you in a wholly unselfish effort to double or triple your capital. Other people have learned to live on $15 a week & so must you. Surely the cost of living is lower in Broadfield than in New York. Besides, there are still your dividends, minute though they are. You must just grit your teeth & hang on until they come. It isn't as if I could deduct you from my income tax—you remain a pure luxury, Vinnie, & I do think you might have the decency to be polite to your poor old uncle, even if gratitude is beyond you. Here is a cheque which I hope may tide you over. I am already contemplating another move, presumably into a packing case on Riverside Drive, & it may interest you to know that I have lately been prevailed upon to work for my living, even as you. Probably you do not recall Cynthia Babcock, who runs one of those little shops just off Third Ave., where she charges the most outrageous prices for the most inane old junk. She has managed to squeeze a place for me because of the flair I have always had for finding rather amusing things in the most unexpected places & acquiring them for a mere song. Even in these heart-rending times, it would seem, there are a few suckers left in N. Y., & no sooner have Cynthia & I fixed up some ancient pot de chambre and made it really amusing than the doorbell tinkles & in comes some moron in mink & buys it. The latest moron became so entranced with us we did over her entire apt. in Biedermeier, acquiring many gray hairs in the process, & that is the only reason I am able to send you this cheque. I do not expect to get rich quick so do not count on anything more. I am sure that Broadfield in winter must be even more ghastly than you say & it is only my pity for your plight that prevents me from being really offended. Saw none other than Anne B. in the Crillon at lunch the other day & she actually smiled so perhaps that breach is about to be healed. It all depends on Tom B., I suppose, who, being unable to kill you, would probably not mind killing me instead. Why Anne does not divorce him I cannot imagine, as their married life must be pure hell & it is well known he flits from one chorus girl to another—his taste, unlike hers, is appalling. Possibly he has some mystic charm which escapes me, but Anne, I may say, was looking like the wrath of God & I suppose she is still eating her heart out over you. What fools women are. Your devoted & long-suffering uncle. . . .

Uncle Bertand's method of hitting back had always been feline; his mention of Anne Bannister must have seemed worth the twenty-five dollars it had cost him. Vincent tore the letter into many pieces and dropped them in the big tin waste-basket, but the memory of his sickness and fear and revulsion remained for a little while.

For Anne had threatened to kill herself. She wanted to divorce Tom and marry Vincent, because she was carrying Vincent's child; and Vincent had turned upon her savagely and accused her of tricking him. He would not marry her in any circumstances, he said—he was not in love with her, he had never even liked her. And then she had gone to pieces and threatened suicide; he had been haunted for at least a week by visions of a suicide note and his own name dragged into the newspapers. Even later, after Uncle Bertrand had come to the rescue, Vincent had been paralyzed with fear; it was still possible that Tom Bannister might find out about the whole dirty business.

Well, he'd never learned the full truth; and now that was a year ago, and Anne and Tom were more than eight hundred miles away. . . . Vincent wiped his sweating palms, and recalled that Uncle Bertrand's letter had not said with whom Anne had been lunching at the Crillon; so it had probably been another unattached young man, a poet or a struggling scene designer. She had insisted that Vincent was a thwarted artist; her love was supposed to be the great fertilizing force which would make self-expression possible.

Christ, thought Vincent, and tore his mind away from the past. Taking up a pencil, he turned his attention to Milly Prentiss's society copy. By now he could correct Milly's copy for grammar and style without having to take in the sense at all. But toward the end an item caught his attention:

Mrs. Betty Lou Hanbury will return Tuesday to her home on Johnson-av. after several months in the South. En route back she will visit with friends in Evanston, Ill.

Vincent carried the item into Milly's office, which had a carpet on the floor and a vase of sooty paper roses on the window-sill, as well as the customary litter.

"Where in the South?" asked Vincent. "Always be definite."

Milly smiled at Vincent and tapped a pencil against her long teeth.

"It's such a minor point, Vinnie," she said, adjusting the hat she always wore at work; it was like something out of a museum. "I know how Ack is about minor points, but Betty Lou told me not to put in an item at all, when she wrote, and she'd kill me if—"

"Why put it in, then?"

"Vinnie, there's a whole empty column still staring me in the face. I *can't* cut out anything. . . . Do you know Betty Lou? Well, you know how she is, then, about coming from Muskogee—"

"Muskogee?"

"Oklahoma. It isn't really the South at all. I knew her for just ages before she broke down and told me. Can't we risk it and try to slip it through the way it is?"

"O.K.," said Vincent, and returned to his desk, where he made certain changes in the item: "after several months in Muskogee, Okla."; delete "back" after "en route"; delete "with" after "visit." Then he sent all the copy down on the elevator and forgot the item.

But Patricia saw it in the *Chronicle* the next day and called her father's attention to it; and it was one of the first things Norris mentioned to Betty Lou when he met her at Union Station on Tuesday.

She came down off the train into a cloud of steam, with the preoccupied and slightly forlorn expression of someone who does not expect to be met, and looked blindly past Norris until he began to tug the suitcases from her.

"Why, Norris! *Norris!*" Betty Lou almost screamed. "You lamb-pie," she said, and flung her arms about him and kissed him full on the mouth. Then she stood back, laughing breathlessly, and said, "Oh, shoot! Now I've gone and embarrassed you. But, Norris, I never dreamed— You ought to be at work. And how did you know when I was—?"

"Read all about it in the *Chronicle,* and took a chance on the train. Things are quiet at the office today. Ack gave me an hour off."

"It's the loveliest thing that ever happened to me. A brass band couldn't have been nicer. Now look, I can carry *one* of those bags."

"Unh-uh." Norris marched away toward the taxis.

"You mean that terrible Milly went and put something in after I *told* her, on pain of death, not to say a *word*—" Betty Lou came trotting after him.

"Not only that," said Norris, surrendering the suitcases to the cab-driver. "Milly told all. The cat is out of the bag, Betty Lou. All Broadfield knows about Muskogee now."

"Norris, she didn't!" Betty Lou's mouth fell open. "Just wait till I lay my hands on her!"

"Hop in, Betty Lou, hop in." Norris handed her into the cab and climbed after her. "As a matter of fact I don't think the Muskogee part of it was Milly's doing," he said when he'd given the driver the address. "Vincent edits the society copy and I kind of think—"

"I always did say he was a snake-in-the-grass. . . . Oh, well. It serves me right, I guess, for being such a base deceiver all these years. The girls'll never let me hear the last of it. I could boil that boy in oil."

She sat on the edge of the seat, holding to the window-strap, and peered through the glass as the taxi slewed out of the station yard, into the cobbled street, and bounced along between cheap hotels and grubby warehouses and old disreputable office buildings. Norris thought she was more flustered than he had seen her before; she pulled her gloves off and put them on again; she kept adjusting her hat, which had a foolish little veil on it; she glanced at him and then away.

"Feel like I've been gone for centuries," she said. "Everything ought to look different. All the old buildings torn down and new ones built in their place. My, will you look at all the snow! Filthy," Betty Lou said happily, "just as filthy as it can be. Oh, Norris, I'm so glad to be back."

"Broadfield hasn't been the same without you."

She sighed and said, "Poor Mamma. . . . I hate funerals," and gazed straight ahead, at a hearse, at a funeral procession moving through the streets of Muskogee. Then she suddenly snatched off her hat. "I must look perfectly ghastly. This *hat!* It's like being shut up inside the Iron Maiden. I'll have a headache for weeks." She sat back and patted Norris's hand. "I just can't get over it, you coming to meet me. All the way from Chicago I kept feeling sorrier for myself, thinking nobody would be at the station to say 'Welcome home.'"

"Guess I haven't said it yet." Norris coughed. "Kind of figured maybe none of the bosom friends would think of it."

"Oh, them!" Betty Lou sniffed. "Not that I won't be glad to see them all. . . . I declare, I *never* thought there'd be so much snow left."

"Didn't you read about our great blizzard?" Norris felt as shy as a boy; there was a change in Betty Lou, and he kept being surprised at how glad he was to see her.

"I never looked at a paper the whole time I was there. Norris, why didn't you write to me again? Just those two little-bitty notes, after that one wonderful letter. I kept waiting— Will you listen to me complain! I'm the limit!"

She sat quite still then, as the taxi skidded up the hill past the Moose Temple, past St. Ignatius Church, past the Hotel Wheeler and a parking lot and the VanderVeen Funeral Manse. Her animation died; her smile died too.

"Norris, what do you think?" She did not look at him. "I found that book of poems right there in Myrtle's house. Myrtle's husband, he's a regular bookworm, and there it was the whole time. *A Shropshire Lad,* by A. E. Housman. Well, I read it right straight through."

Betty Lou paused; she held the hat absently on her lap and there was an odd silence inside the cab.

"I wish I'd known Laura, Norris. Oh, I can just tell, from the photograph, and what you said about her, I can just tell how lovely she must have been." Betty Lou turned her head at last. "I guess maybe I'm speaking out of turn, but all the way up on the train I—I kept thinking how I'd say this to you, Norris. Maybe I should have waited, but then I might not have said it at all, ever."

She laid her gloved hand down on his. "Norris, we're *good* friends now, aren't we? We can *talk* to each other. Really talk. What I've been thinking, ever since your letter came—maybe you ought to talk more about Laura. Instead of keeping it all shut up inside of you—year after year. Norris, you can talk to me, if you want to." She lifted her hand, turning to the window again. "That's what I wanted to say. I just had to, and I'm sorry if it was tactless."

"It wasn't. Of course not." Norris didn't know when he had felt so ashamed of himself.

"But you did start to tell me about that poem in your letter, and when I read it, I— Oh, shoot!" said Betty Lou. She jammed the hat back on her head and sat with her hands folded in her lap, like a little girl at school. So she sat while the snowy streets, the black bare trees, the gray and brown and yellow and dull-red houses slid past. He wanted to say something to her but he couldn't think what; and maybe silence was better after all.

When they reached her house there was a slight scuffle about paying for the cab, which Norris won; then, carrying her suitcases, he followed her up the walk, up the front steps, and into the small cluttered front parlor.

"You started the furnace for me," she said. "And look at all the flowers! And everything so spick-and-span—not a *smidgen* of dust. Oh, Norris!" She looked momentarily tremulous. "Watch out," she said, "or I'll kiss you all over again."

"You'll have to kiss Pat and Delores and Joel and Johnny too, then. It was a co-operative enterprise," Norris told her.

"Well, I will, soon as I get a chance."

"Johnny's the one kept your walks shoveled off, Pat thought of the flowers, Delores did the dusting, Joel started the furnace. I was just kind of a kibitzer, really."

"Home," said Betty Lou, and began to pick up one knickknack after another. "Funny, Norris—Broadfield really is home now. I never realized." She sighed; she dropped her coat and sat down on the curly-backed sofa. "You can stay a few minutes, can't you? I'm too excited to unpack or anything just yet."

Norris looked at his watch. "I ought to be getting back. But you'll come over to dinner tonight, Betty Lou. Roast beef. Delores has found a really good butcher."

"I'd love to. Only let me bring dessert. I'm just in the mood, *just* in the mood, for pie crusts. . . . Oh, there's so much to catch up with. I'm dying to see that baby. How is he, Norris? How's everybody?"

"The baby's fine. He can crawl now. Mile a minute on the carpets, but he skids on the bare floor."

"And the rest of you?" Betty Lou studied him anxiously. "Norris, you're worried."

"No more than usual. We won't go into that now." Norris found himself staring at a wedding picture of Betty Lou and Samuel Hanbury. Betty Lou really did look like ·a child in this—round-faced, dimpled, eager, and a little awed by her own finery and the importance suddenly conferred on her. Samuel was a small man, not much taller than his bride; he stood very stiff, with a wooden face and a small mustache and hair parted in the middle and slicked back carefully, vintage of 1912 or so. Norris didn't think he altogether liked Samuel, who looked pompous and overpossessive; probably he hadn't really appreciated Betty Lou.

"Plenty of time for that later," Norris added, looking away from the picture. "Were you *married* in Muskogee, Betty Lou?"

"That terrible old picture!" She laughed. "Muskogee was the only place I'd ever been at all, really, until Sam was transferred to Broadfield. Oh, we lived a couple years in Tulsa, he was a Tulsa boy originally, but—" Betty Lou stood up and made a face at the picture. "We look like a pair of dummies." She laid it face down on the table. "What is it, Norris? Hasn't Charlie found a job yet?"

"Not yet."

"I wish there was something I could do."

"Isn't anything anybody can do, I guess. Went to see Norman Trees a couple of weeks ago, and heard a lecture on the NRA, but there's nothing doing there. Something may open up on the paper. Charlie could sell space, if they'd give him a chance, but they're overstaffed as it is."

"I was just thinking, Norris—" Betty Lou stood behind the sofa and ran a finger along the carved curlicues. "If it's a question of *money*—Sam being in the insurance business and all, he saw to it I'd never have anything to worry about and my money was in a good bank and I have so much more than I need, really, and—"

"You're pretty swell, Betty Lou. But Charlie won't take that kind of help from anybody. Even Laurette has to—"

"I was thinking about you more, really. With Delores and the baby. If you ever have any trouble making ends meet—"

"Oh, hell, *we* manage. But I'm damn grateful, Betty Lou. You're—" Norris took up his hat. "No, I don't worry about Charlie as much as I ought to, I guess. Out of sight, out of mind. It's Pat and Vincent, chiefly." He nodded at her and turned toward the door.

"Now, Norris, I'm just not going to let you get away before you tell me."

Norris smiled at her, spinning his hat. "It's taken me a long time to make up my mind about Vinnie. And I still can't figure him out. . . . He came to dinner, couple or three weeks ago, and started some kind of funny business with Delores. I should have thrown him out of the house, I suppose, but I thought maybe I was imagining things. So damn cheap. But Pat noticed too. Well, he hasn't been around since. Or called her up, even."

"Good riddance," said Betty Lou.

"Sure, but I don't think we've seen the last of him. . . . Too bad he's doing such a good job on the paper. Ack relies on him now. Still doesn't like him worth a damn, but he admitted the other day that Vinnie does more work and does it better than the two men we let go last summer. . . . I have a hard time being polite to him, when I think what he's done to Pat."

Betty Lou went to the windows and let the shades all the way up. Looking into the street, she said, "What about Johnny?"

"Oh, he still comes around sometimes. But Delores is the only one pays any attention to him. If I didn't know Johnny better I'd think it was Delores he really came to see."

"Maybe he's trying to make Pat jealous," Betty Lou said hopefully.

Norris shook his head. "I can't see Johnny doing a thing like that. He's such a decent kid, clear through. Sometimes I think they're a little crazy, all three of them. I wish you could see Pat. She floats around like the lily maid of Astolat, looking sad and noble. And she's always forgiving me for something I haven't done. 'Oh, it's quite all right,' she keeps saying. 'I don't mind at *all*, Father.' And I honestly don't know what the hell she's talking about. . . .

"If it came to the point where Vincent wanted to marry her," Norris said with a sigh, "I don't know what I'd do. I wake up in the night, sometimes, and get scared they'll elope."

"Well, it doesn't look like they're fixing to do that in any hurry. Norris, you've been in the thick of it so long, maybe you can't see the wood for the trees. But here I am, all fresh from Muskogee, and it might be I could size the whole situation up and maybe have an inspiration."

"I don't know. I hate to drag you into it."

"I'd be awful mad if you didn't drag me into it." Betty Lou had been moving toward him, and now, absently, she began to button his overcoat. "You run along and quit worrying. I'll unpack and pull myself together and get going on that pie."

Norris smiled down at her. "You're getting the buttons in the wrong holes," he said, and caught her gently by both arms. "God, I'm glad you're back, Betty Lou."

"Run along," she said again, and gave him a little push toward the door. "I'll come in tonight and wave my magic wand and everything'll be all fixed up. Just like that."

She didn't exactly wave a magic wand, and whatever was wrong in Norris's house went right on being wrong after she had left; but she had made them all laugh and that was more than anyone else had done most of the time she was in Muskogee. David was just being put to bed when she arrived and she began by making him laugh—a portent, Norris thought, since David was mostly a solemn baby. Success with David went to her head and at dinner she described her train journey with wild exaggerations: the near loss of her suitcases in St. Louis, the fat shoe salesman who tried to get her drunk in the club car, the elderly lady who looked like the most conventional of grandmothers and was an ardent Rosicrucian. . . .

What made Norris happiest was the end of the coolness between Betty Lou and Patricia. "You come on over as soon as you can," Betty Lou told her before she left. "Mamma had trunks and trunks of the loveliest silks and brocades and stuff and I want you to tell me what to do with my share."

When Vincent turned up again, a few days later, and took Patricia off to the movies, Norris worried less than he might have; it was as if he had resigned at least so much of his troubles to Betty Lou, who might be foolish in some ways but had wisdom too; and so delicate a problem was probably best left in a woman's hands. Laura would have known what to do; so might Betty Lou.

Unreasonably comforted, Norris felt a long tension relaxing. When he came home from work in the afternoon he sat and watched his grandson, who continued to study the world with grave attention, and who, after long periods of thinking things over, would make new experiments. One afternoon he caught hold of the bars of his play-pen and hauled himself to his feet. He stood there, clutching the bars, gazing at Norris wide-eyed and open-mouthed; he let out a yell of triumph; that was too much for him and he sat down hard and became thoughtful again.

Norris felt like cheering, and then he began to feel sad. The eagerness with which babies hurled themselves toward new experience—David was pulling himself up again, grunting with conceit—their passion to rush away from infancy, made him want to put out his hand and stay his grandson's progress: don't be in such a hurry, hold on to innocence as long as you can.

David swayed, clutching the bars; he began to bounce; carried away, he let go with one hand and flourished it at Norris—and this time he fell harder, smack on top of a wooden giraffe. Triumph fled from his face; rage came, a vast indignation; he opened his mouth and sucked his breath in until Norris was afraid he was going to explode; and the air was torn by his yell of grief.

"See?" said Norris, restraining himself; he sat where he was and let his grandson yell. But he felt a little guilty. The giraffe was his present to David, who was too young for anything but soft toys.

Worrying about your offspring, or your offsprings' offspring: a waste of nervous energy, said Dick Wheelwright. But it seemed to Norris that you ought to be able to learn from your own mistakes, and transmit a wisdom you had not had yourself. What he had allowed to happen to David's father must never happen to David.

Yet think of Laura, who had emerged from a distorting youth as whole and sane as anyone he had known—strengthened, not twisted, by the forces which had beaten against her. The original stuff of which you were made mattered too; the flaws in his children were his bequest to them; and what had he ever done to mend them?

He went upstairs and wrote a note to Charlie; and the next evening he wrote another; and presently he fell into the habit of writing to Charlie every night before he went to bed. He had begun by discussing the prospects for a job, and with accounts of David's progress; but after a while what he wrote about was mainly Charlie's mother. If Laura could be made real for Charlie, Charlie might walk straight again; and it was easier, as always, to say things in a letter than to Charlie's sullen face.

The more Norris wrote about Laura, the more he remembered; his letters grew longer, night after night, until often he filled three or four pages with his cramped stiff handwriting. It never occurred to him that the picture he was building up, bit by bit, was not of a human being, but of a symbol, without life or warmth or humor. It wasn't the way he saw Laura in his own mind; but it was how she seemed in his letters to Charlie.

One night there came a tapping at his half-open door, and Patricia slid into the room. She too held a letter in her hand; she leaned against the end of his bed and said, "Father, I've been wanting to—tell you something."

Norris felt suddenly sick; she was going to marry Vincent.

But that wasn't it at all.

"About Charlie," said Patricia, running her fingers along the sheet of notepaper. "Father, what have you been doing to him?"

Norris stared at her blankly. "Doing to him, Pat?"

"Laurette's all upset. She's written to me twice now." Patricia's face looked hot; she stared past Norris at an old calendar on the wall. "She says you're writing to Charlie every day and it's almost driving him crazy."

"But, Pat—" He felt breathless and sick all over again.

"If you want to know what Laurette says," Patricia told him loudly, "she says, 'For God's sake tell Pop to lay off Charlie, will you? Charlie has enough on his mind without Pop weeping on his shoulder every day.' "

"But— Oh, Christ!" Norris said. "That wasn't it! That wasn't the idea at all. I've just been—" He gazed at the litter on his desk. "Charlie's so far away. I wanted to help him. I wanted— Weeping on his shoulder! Hell and damnation," said Norris, "that wasn't what I was doing."

"You don't have to shout about it." Patricia's voice rose too. "Leave us alone. Aren't you ever going to learn? You've got to leave us alone. You can't help. Nothing you can do will help."

Norris tore the unfinished letter across and dropped the scraps in his waste-basket; to make his hands stop shaking he began to collect pens, pencils, rubber bands, envelopes, old bills and canceled checks, and to arrange them neatly in their proper drawers or pigeon-holes. "I'm a god-damned fool, all right," he said. Whenever he thought he had found solid ground, someone came along and kicked it out from under him; he pressed his hands against his eyes and told himself that Patricia did not know, she could not have any idea, how much she had wounded him. "But, Pat," he said, "Charlie needs help. We have to do *something.*" He swung his chair around and looked at her, timidly, almost. Her face was set and rigid; her hand was clenched over Laurette's letter.

"For ten years," Norris said, "I've been letting you all go to hell in your own way. I know that was wrong, Pat. Is this wrong too?"

"Sometimes I think it's families that are wrong. Parents and children—" Patricia studied the calendar; her voice had grown sad. "We all get too— We grow in, instead of out."

Norris sat rocking his chair back on its springs. "Maybe you're right," he said finally. "If it wasn't so terrible, it would be funny. I try to make up for my past mistakes—to grow out—it's what I've been trying to do. But I just make worse mistakes than ever. Such a blind damn fool." He sighed. "Only I'd still like to get Charlie a job. I want him back in Broadfield. . . . You think that would be all right, don't you?"

"I don't know. I don't think they ought to live here with us."

"There's David. David's the one I'm thinking about, really. I want him to have a decent chance, Pat. And the way things are now, between Charlie and Delores— And I don't know about Delores herself. You have to be so wise to bring up a child. But if

Charlie came back and got a job and they could afford a house of their own— It's much too soon to give up hope. Isn't it, Pat?"

"I don't know what I think." Patricia sat down on the edge of the bed. "Why do people have to go messing around with other people's lives? Why can't they just—"

"You're my children. David's my grandson. You're all part of me, Pat; I'm part of you. How can we leave one another alone? Messing around," said Norris. "God, is that how it looks to you? It's the way things are, Pat; it's the way the human race works. Wait till you have children of your own."

"It's why I think families are wrong."

"Can you figure out a better system? Oh, I know the wisest of us make mistakes. Even your mother. . . . We make mistakes, but some of the things we do turn out right, Pat. More by luck than foresight, maybe, but we have to take the chance. Wasn't it better to take a chance with Charlie than let him go all alone, down into—"

"There's Laurette."

"Laurette's young; she has her own life to live. I can't leave her saddled with Charlie. Pat, there must be something I can do." He stood and leaned on the end of the bed, looking down at her. "Don't you ever feel any sense of responsibility? Don't you ever want to help somebody else?"

Patricia sat there playing with Laurette's letter. "It doesn't work out. It never works out. You have to let people go their own way."

Norris smiled faintly. "You're very positive—after nineteen years of living. After fifty-three years, I'm not positive about anything any more." He paused; he tried to find the words he wanted. "But I think you're wrong, Pat. We haven't grown up, it seems to me, until we see that—we *are* our brother's keeper. We make a bad job of it; half the time we forget, or try to pretend it isn't so. But we have to keep on trying. It's one of the things life is about. We're alone, we'll always be alone in most ways, all of us. But there are bridges," Norris said. "There are a few little bridges we can build. And it isn't normal to want isolation."

Presently he said, "I don't know; I guess I'm talking nonsense. But my instincts—I can't deny them. I have to try to do what I can for my children, and their children. If I go on making mistakes, I'll have to make them. But I can't cut myself off from you."

After Patricia had gone he returned to his desk and cleared away the rest of the litter. She couldn't be in love with Vincent Rourke after all—not seriously, not deeply; if she had been she would have recognized the truth after which he was fumbling. But her face had stayed unresponsive, quite blank except for a shadow of embarrassment. They all became embarrassed when he fumbled after the truth; as if it were not quite decent to expose your inmost beliefs. It was permissible to talk about the weather and what you had for dinner last night, but faith and love and all the discoveries you had made after so much effort and heartache must be hidden like shameful secrets. Faith and love—the words had been rubbed over too much, passed through too many hands, until they were soiled and common coinage.

He thought of all the words he had written down about Laura and sent to Charlie, and what did they amount to but page on page of sentimental maundering? Weeping on Charlie's shoulder, asking his son for pity; how could his letters have been taken that way when he had meant them so differently? *I think the love I bear you should make you not to die;* but he had recognized and accepted Laura's death. All he had wanted to do was to clarify— for Charlie as for himself—the part of Laura that could not die; to rediscover the gift she had come, unconsciously perhaps, to bestow.

But now, since all is idle . . .

No, he did not believe that yet. That was something he would never believe.

PART TWO

The Minotaur

. . . The grown-up is alive with his filial, brotherly feelings for others, and his love flows outward. . . . Love becomes the mainspring of our psychological energy and the cornerstone of that edifice which represents our social, esthetic, and spiritual life. Love becomes the master drive which keeps permanent vigil, holding back and trying to neutralize the aggressive, antisocial drives coming from within as well as the aggressive impulses aroused by the impacts of reality coming from without. Love is the source and substance of our conscience.

—Gregory Zilboorg, M.D.,
Mind, Medicine and Man

14

Since Christmas, Charlie had moved a good deal further down the long hill into nether darkness. It was a relief at first not to have his wife and child to worry about—the wife who no longer cared for him, the child that filled him with despair because his love was turned to guilt, the world seeming to deny Charlie Bryant the right to have begotten a child at all. For a few weeks he walked the streets of Detroit again, he entered the tall office buildings of Detroit, with a faint renewal of hope.

The trouble was that Charlie remained tired, and in his weariness the hope could not flourish long; not when the faces continued to look at him blankly, the flat voices to say, "Sorry, nothing doing; no, we were looking for somebody with experience; no college degree?—I'm afraid you aren't just the type we had in mind; no sense hanging around, mister, we're letting people go, not hiring them."

They were seeing only how threadbare his overcoat was, how run-down at the heels his shoes. He found it increasingly difficult to push through a revolving door and ascend in a shining elevator and cross the carpet to the receptionist who sat behind her desk, and looked at him as if he were dirt, as if he smelled bad, before she turned back to her magazine, flipping the pages over with long varnished nails.

Presently he forgot about the office jobs and made the rounds of the big plants; and now there was no pretense at politeness. For a man who'd never worked with his hands, had no skills, had not worked in any way for five months, for six, for going on seven, for such a man to seek a job amounted to a seditious act. It was worse at the smaller plants, and at the plants so obscure he wouldn't have known they existed if he hadn't gone through the classified telephone directory.

He forgot the factories too and looked for work in restaurants and lunch-wagons; maybe he could be a chauffeur, and if he didn't look the part, then what was wrong with driving a taxi or a truck? He answered advertisements for janitors in shabby apartment houses, but men who had stoked furnaces and tinkered with plumbing and emptied garbage pails for years were always ahead of him.

Each blank face that glanced at him as if he were a shadow,

each flat tired voice that rose into anger because he had the gall to draw breath, shoved him further out of the world of the living, into the half-world of the drifters, the floaters, the derelicts who perhaps had never worked and surely would never work again.

When he began to see himself like that something failed inside him, and he stopped trying to find a job. He hated to leave the apartment for which Laurette was paying, because he had begun to feel tiny and defenseless on the streets, prey to the wind and snow, the blown smoke and grit, the unending clangor of automobiles and trucks and street-cars, of no more account than torn paper eddying along the gutters.

But here, in the warm stale air that smelled of bacon grease and dead cigarettes and unwashed beer glasses, in the gray light seeping through the windows, sunk in lethargy beside the radio that alternately soothed him with music and urged him to go forth and buy all the necessities and luxuries and trash for which he would never again have the money, here where no one could see him he began to feel like Charlie Bryant again: a human being who had hoped once, who had worked once, whose body had been quick, whose mind alert, who had run thirty yards to make a touchdown for Broadfield Central High School, who had knocked a boy out for calling his father a souse, who had sent the ball hurtling down the alley for a ten-strike, who had laughed and been drunk and sung songs and known good fellowship, who had fallen in love and lain with his beloved and gotten her with child, who had gone out into the country on summer Sundays and felt the warmth of the sun and the coldness of amber water on his flesh, and smelled the trampled grass and seen the shadow of a cloud move across the wheatfields and heard the sound of locusts in the burning air.

It was easier to sit and dream than to do anything else, and he no longer attended meetings of his club; his dues were in arrears and he thought even his own bunch had begun to despise him. He went to bed early on the daybed in the living room and came only half awake when Laurette passed on tiptoe through to the bedroom. He slept heavily, and again came only half awake in the morning when Laurette rose and made breakfast and went off to the beauty parlor—thrusting himself back into sleep, sleeping as long as he could so that when sleep was no longer possible there would not be too many hours for him to fritter away.

For days at a time he went without shaving or dressing. In his old flannel bathrobe he puttered about the apartment, warming over the coffee Laurette had left and drinking cup after cup of it as if that could clear away the thickness inside his skull; frying bacon and eggs, stolidly dulling his hunger with half a loaf of bread; washing the dishes at last when no clean ones were left on the shelves; making half-hearted efforts to clean the apartment, poking among the dust and dirty laundry and yellowing newspapers and brimming ashtrays and the books Laurette brought him from a rental library, which he never seemed to get around to reading.

Laurette let him go on like that for almost a month before she said one evening, "Jesus, Charlie, you look horrible. Charlie, for God's sake, you've got to snap out of it," said Laurette before she went off to her night club. "When your good suit comes back from the cleaner's," she said the next morning, shaking him awake, "you take a shower and shave and get dressed and go get yourself a haircut. Go out and take a walk, at least. Go out to Belle Isle and sit in the sun a while—it's warm today," said Laurette. "And buy yourself a drink on the way home, have a meal in a restaurant and take in a movie, why don't you? Here's five bucks, Charlie," said Laurette, opening her pocketbook. "That ought to cover everything; you ought to be able to buy yourself a good time on five bucks. It's all a question of morale," Laurette told him. "You've got to get your morale back, Charlie; you've just got to."

This happened several times and occasionally she pulled him out of the lethargy; obedient as a child he did what she'd told him to. But when he emerged too far from the lethargy he became sick with shame, and if the shame did not turn to hatred it turned to fear. He had not yet reached the point of wanting to die altogether, but he might if something didn't happen soon.

What happened was that his father's letters started coming, and Charlie was glad of them at first because they made the days seem not quite empty. The buzzer would sound three times, the postman's signal, and down the four flights of stairs he would go, his unshaven face still bloated with sleep, his bathrobe gaping across a hairy chest, and unlock the box and take out the letter and climb up again and read it slowly, and think about writing some kind of answer, and instead fall asleep in the chair by the radio.

At first it seemed as if his father were throwing him a life-line and if only he caught hold and hung on, he might be tugged back into the world. But when the fifth or sixth letter came he began to feel persecuted; and then he wondered if his father were not going insane; and then he fell into a rage one day and sat where he was at the postman's ring, and tossed the letter aside unopened when Laurette brought it in with her at six o'clock that evening.

Laurette said nothing. She stood and looked at him, her arms full of parcels, before she went into the little kitchen. Charlie was hardly aware of her when she returned to the living room and began to set the table.

She settled herself for a while and read the evening paper through, and then finished her preparations for dinner. Charlie emerged a little way and saw that she was lighting two candles and switching off the lamps; she brought in a small steak and a dish of peas and two artichokes; she brought in a half-gallon jug of cheap red wine and filled the water-glasses from it.

"Come on, Charlie, sit down," she said. "We're celebrating to-night."

"Celebrating what?" asked Charlie from his lethargy.

"It's Mom's birthday," said Laurette. "She'd have been forty-eight years old."

"That's a hell of a thing to celebrate." Charlie tried to focus on the food and wine and swaying candle flames. "Wasting money on steak and artichokes and dago red," he said.

"I just felt like celebrating. Such lousy weather," said Laurette, cutting the steak in half, dipping a spoon into the peas. "Artichokes and wine and candles—they make a meal into something extra. Mom was crazy about artichokes, I remember. And remember how she used to make wine? Out of raisins and dried apricots?" Laurette smiled and raised her glass. "Here's to you, Charlie," she said, sipping. "Jesus but it's sour! Still, it's a pretty color."

"Don't drink too much," Charlie said. "You won't be able to sing."

"I'm not working tonight. You got enough melted butter there?"

"Yeah. Artichokes are pretty silly, aren't they?"

"That's why they're fun."

Charlie ate hungrily for a while, and said, "You're a damn good cook, Laurette, you know it?" There was no kick in the wine, but it was dissolving the thickness in his skull and starting an inward warmth—he lifted the jug from the floor and refilled Laurette's glass and his own.

"So was Mom. And Pop's quite a chef too these days. He's had plenty of practice now, the poor guy. Guess Pat hardly ever does lift a hand around the house. Specially now Delores is there. Doesn't Delores ever write to you?"

"Nope," said Charlie. "I don't write to her either."

"Well, you should." Laurette bit reflectively at an artichoke leaf. "She writes to me sometimes."

"I've seen the letters."

"You read Pop's letter yet?"

"Nope. Not going to either."

Laurette disposed of the artichoke heart and shoved the littered plate to one side; leaning her elbows on the table she said, "Look, Charlie, I don't want you to get the wrong idea. Long as my luck's in and yours is out, I want to keep on helping. But honest to God, you'll have to pull yourself together and *do* something. For your own sake, kiddo. You'll go screwy if you don't watch out."

There was enough cheap red wine in Charlie so that he could

smile at her. "I'm screwy already. Been that way a long time."

"*Aw*, no! You're still fundamentally sound. But I been thinking things over for weeks now, and the trouble is, you're in a rut. Not making any bones about it, Charlie, I don't think you ever will get a job in Detroit. Even if prosperity does come on around that corner." Laurette reached out and nipped a long dribble of wax from one of the candles. "It's a state of mind. To land a job, you have to *know* you're going to land it. It's kind of like they say about dogs, they can smell people who are scared of them. When you know inside you're licked, the guy who does the hiring knows it too. So what I was thinking, you ought to pull up stakes and go somewheres else. Not back to Broadfield, maybe. Just someplace you could get a fresh start." Laurette looked up at him. "I could loan you the money, Charlie."

Charlie shook his head. "Oh, hell, I know I'm living on your charity, and Delores and the kid are living on Pop's, but I couldn't—" His shame rose up again and stuck in his throat.

"You got to cut out thinking like that. Family solidarity, kiddo, all for one and one for all. My God, if things were the other way around, I'd sure expect you to give me a helping hand, and I wouldn't be ashamed to catch ahold of it, either. . . . I guess that's what Pop's been writing about, isn't it? Trying to get you back home?"

Charlie stood up and carried the plates into the kitchen.

"There's ice cream in the top freezing tray," Laurette called.

"Maybe you would stand a better chance in Broadfield," she went on when he returned. "Working on a paper like that, Pop has a lot of contacts."

"Broadfield is still dead and buried. . . . Naw, he doesn't say so much about me going back there. Not any more. All he writes about is Mom, and how she went around campaigning for Cox and the League of Nations, and how she got into a fight over some colored kid was sent to reform school for messing around with a white girl, and how she and some other women got together and tried to start cleaning up the slums, and—" Charlie broke off; he finished his ice cream, he filled his glass with wine again. "What the hell's he driving at? What's he trying to do to me?"

"Well, you know how upset he was, the way you talked Christmas. You ought to write and tell him you don't belong to that club any more."

"Bunch of bastards," Charlie said.

"O.K., tell him that. Make him feel good."

"He didn't use to be like that. Hell," said Charlie, "I liked him better when he was hitting the bottle all the time."

"Aw, no, Charlie! Thank God those days are gone forever. No, Pop means well, but he— It's funny, I was saying to Pat, I don't remember any of those things about Mom. Though I guess I do remember what a pacifist she was. Those last years before she died she wouldn't ever go to a parade, even. Seems now like maybe she was wrong. You read that book by Andrew McBain I brought from the library? I kind of skimmed through some of it on the street-car the other day, and he thinks the world is heading straight into another war. Bigger than the last."

"I don't seem to read anything but the newspapers," Charlie said.

"Well, I better take the book back, if you aren't going to read it. Must be fifty cents due on it already." Laurette bent toward the candle with a cigarette between her lips. "You remember McBain at all?"

"Remember him?"

"Reason I took the book out—I had kind of a queer letter from Pat a while ago—"

"Jesus, how many more of us?"

"Yeah, I know. Like a disease. Pat wanted to know did I remember anything about McBain, the time he passed through Broadfield after the war. I must've been around nine then—I know it was before Joel was born. But I don't seem to remember McBain at all. That face on the back of the book doesn't look familiar, but he'd have been a whole lot younger-looking then, of course. Thirty-eight or -nine. Far as I know I never saw him."

"Anyway, what's it to Pat?"

"She has some screwy idea—" Laurette paused. "She's full of screwy ideas, that kid. I tried to talk some sense to her when I was home, but I don't know— Well, she has it all figured out that McBain's visit and that time Mom went to New York are connected up. If you see what I mean."

Charlie stared at Laurette. "That's a hell of a thing for Pat to think about her own—"

"Sure, I know, but it isn't her fault. And I do remember how shot Pop was all the time Mom was in New York. Well, seems like it's been preying on Pat's mind and she thought I might be able to straighten it all out for her. I don't know what to tell her, Charlie."

"Tell her she has a dirty mind."

"But it isn't that. She's really worried. She was such a little kid when Mom died, she doesn't remember her the way you and I do. She doesn't know Mom was as good as they come."

"Tell her that," said Charlie.

"Yeah, maybe I will. Only now she has me wondering too."

"For Christ's sake, Laurette—!"

"Oh, I know it's foolish. But Mom was human. And she started out to be an actress, and I guess life got pretty dull sometimes.

156

That's why she did so many different things, maybe, to keep from getting bored. Not that they weren't crazy about each other, her and Pop, and he was a swell guy, I guess, up until the time she died. But this McBain—well, if he's anything like his picture he must be a smoothie right now, and back then he must have been— Oh, God, I don't know," said Laurette. "Maybe I ought to write and tell Pat there's nothing at all to what she thinks."

"Well, there isn't," said Charlie. "There couldn't be."

"They did have that terrible fight, Mom and Pop, just before she lit out for New York. I woke up one night, I remember, it must have been two or three in the morning, and, boy, they were going at it hammer and tongs in their room. I could hear Mom pacing up and down the way she did when she got excited. 'Dear God, Norris!' she said. The only way Mom ever cussed. 'Dear God!' I remember her saying that but what else she said I haven't the faintest idea. . . . Charlie, you don't suppose Mom really did take kind of a passing fancy to this McBain guy, do you?"

"Cut it out, will you?" With three tumblersful of wine inside him, Charlie had begun to feel, not drunk exactly, but alive again, and vulnerable to pain.

Laurette shrugged. "O.K., skip it." She dropped the end of her cigarette in the melted ice cream on her plate, where it went out with a tiny hiss. "Let's just stack the dishes and go see a picture."

She did not refer again to her letter from Patricia, nor to Charlie's from his father; but what Norris's letters had started, Laurette's speculations kept going, and Charlie began to spend more and more of his half-dreaming hours in thinking about his mother. It was a kind of rebellion against the picture Norris had tried to draw, the picture Laurette had begun to suggest. Charlie did not want to think of his mother as a symbol of truth and justice, but neither did he want to think of her as a human being, subject to human frailty.

While the last weeks of March ran out, Charlie mooned about the apartment, sunk in lethargy still, but no longer thinking exclusively of himself. There was no order in the memories he'd kept of Laura Bryant; the brief scattered pictures came up haphazard as he groped for them.

There was a spring morning when he woke to the sound of rain, and she had been going to take him and Laurette out to Morison Park for the first picnic of the season. Rain before seven, sun before eleven, she told them; but at eleven the rain was coming down as hard as ever and they went up into the attic, all three, where they could hear the rain striking the shingles just above their heads. They ate their picnic lunch up there and then she read aloud to them from a book called *The King of the Golden River*. It was one of his earliest memories; he must have been a very small boy indeed to feel solaced by a picnic in the attic and a fairy story for having missed a picnic in Morison Park, where there were swings and see-saws and a round pond to sail toy boats on. Yet now he remembered how the attic, the smell of camphor and dust and old clothes and stacks of magazines, the sound of the rain, the sound of his mother's voice reading *The King of the Golden River*, had blended into a magic which blotted out his disappointment. By the time she finished reading, the rain had stopped too; he followed her into the back yard and she stretched up her arms to cut bunches of lilac—he remembered the water-drops showering down on her upturned face, on her hands, and how she turned to him laughing and said, Smell, Charlie! Isn't it wonderful, after the rain?—thrusting the wet flower-heads, the green shining heart-shaped leaves, against his face. Always, always, even when he was much older, a young roughneck tearing his clothes, getting into fights, falling out of a tree and breaking his arm, she had been able to make him look at something quite ordinary and he saw it was not ordinary at all.

One night while the broken arm was healing he could not sleep, and she sat on the edge of his bed and told him a long story about someone (her own parents, or her grandparents?) crossing the plains in a covered wagon to Dakota Territory. It was a gory and exciting tale, with Indians in it, and maybe it was mostly made up; but it was the kind of story Charlie had wanted just then and presently he forgot his arm and went peacefully to sleep, still hearing her voice talking of scalps and war-whoops as he drifted farther from her, and farther, and lost her altogether.

It was the actress in her, perhaps, that made her turn the episodes of daily living into drama; she sat at the dining-room table and described an argument with Mr. Baumgartner the butcher over a joint of tainted meat, acting the parts, acting Mr. Baumgartner best of all as he whacked his cleaver down into the chopping-block and bowed and took her arm and dragged her into the great refrigerator; as he pointed to all the carcasses and parts of carcasses hanging on hooks and told her to choose whatever piece of meat she wanted, a whole steer even, and he would let her have it for nothing. . . . Dear God, said Laura, I was so overcome by all those corpses I swore then and there I'd become a vegetarian—I pointed to the first thing I saw, and fled, and that's why we're having calves' liver tonight.

People who ordinarily seemed dull and stupid changed when they were in the same room with Charlie's mother; as if they had come alive after having been half dead. The times when Norris had to entertain the *Chronicle* men and their wives, about which she groaned beforehand, turned hilarious because of Laura. She made them play parlor-games, which more often than not are torture because people will not shed their inhibitions; but the stiffest of the reporters, the shyest of their wives, revealed unsuspected talents and even Charlie had enjoyed charades when his mother conducted them.

He remembered how he had felt when Patricia was born; she was born at home and Charlie who was six then and Laurette who was almost five were sent out to the farm for a few days. They stayed longer than had been intended because something had gone wrong. Laura was a very sick woman, said Grandma Bryant, and Aunt Maudie said Laura should never have had any more children. So there was the strangest mixture for Charlie of happiness at being on the farm, swimming in the river and riding a plow-horse and high-diving into the hay, and terror at being away from his mother. When Uncle Homer took them back into town at last, Charlie was almost afraid to enter the house, but his mother's voice came down the stairs: Charlie, Laurette, come up and see your baby sister. Their baby sister lay small and wrinkled and hideous in a crib beside Laura's bed, and Charlie turned away; she hadn't been worth all that pother. His mother, reclining on the many pillows propped behind her, looked very pale and tired, but somehow radiant too, somehow triumphant. A boy of six had no words for the way she looked, but he recognized an almost miraculous quality about her, and flung himself toward her, ashamed of his sudden tears but powerless to check them. . . . No, Norris, she said, it's all right, it's perfectly all right, let him stay a little while. . . .

By the time Joel was born Charlie was twelve years old and knew all about how babies came. His father had started to tell him, looking solemn and ill at ease, and got stuck halfway through his explanation and sent Charlie out to buy an ice-cream cone. Charlie had not enjoyed the cone much because he felt there must be something pretty peculiar that his father had left unsaid; but when, a few days later, his mother told him what he needed to know there was no embarrassment on her face, and what did not seem peculiar to Laura Bryant could not seem peculiar to Charlie. But his fear when the time came for her to go to the hospital was worse because it was comprehending.

She lay in the hospital almost a month, and even after she came home again she seemed more exhausted than ever before, to Charlie. She rose late each morning and took naps in the afternoon and went to bed right after supper. And squalling Joel did not seem worth the trouble either.

In all those years Charlie knew he loved his mother and almost hated his father. Norris was always getting angry with him, sometimes for real sins but more often for things that were not really Charlie's fault. But Laura even understood about the eternal squabbles between Charlie and Laurette; she even forgave Charlie for getting into fights with other boys so often and coming home with a swollen eyesocket or a bloody nose. Animal spirits, Norris, it's sheer animal spirits. He takes after my father, I suppose. You want him a real *boy*, don't you? Laura said.—You wouldn't want your son a mollycoddle. (And yet Charlie, knowing she hated him to fight, tried to avoid fighting any more.)

Always it was her admiration and praise he sought; he did not care what his father thought of him. Laura must have known that, and that perhaps was why she praised him so sparingly. Don't you go getting a swelled head, me lad, she said if he boasted of some exploit; but he knew how, when she believed her children out of hearing, she urged Norris to praise him; so that his father's grudging words rang false and only embarrassed Charlie. . . .

He would have lingered there, back in the years which still seemed good; but the trouble with dwelling on the past is that each memory calls up another and you cannot be selective about them. So he remembered the day they had driven out to the big lake in the old Overland touring car for a spring picnic. It was late May but a cold wind blew out of the north, and the waves, said Laura, were like ocean breakers. It was much too cold for swimming; they sat in a sheltered hollow among the dunes where the sun blazed down on them and the voice of the waves was muffled; and when they had finished eating, Charlie's mother went to the rim of the hollow and stood gazing at the great sweep of burnished blue water and burnished blue sky, and turned with the wind blowing her skirt out and said, By the way, everybody, I have an important announcement to make. By next Christmas there's going to be another Bryant, and what shall it be, all of you, a boy or a girl?—The time has come to decide. So what had begun as a gay day ended as a grim one. Norris said nothing; he would not look at his wife, he would not speak even when the time came for them to clear away the rubbish and pack up the picnic basket and climb into the car to start home. On the way they had two flat tires, and that improved nobody's temper, even though flats were taken as a matter of course then.

The first half of that day was the last time Charlie could remember having been purely happy with his own family; his mother's announcement had cast a permanent shadow over the house on Johnson Avenue. Soon it became evident that Laura was very ill indeed; at the end of June she was taken again to the hospital and there wasn't, after all, going to be another Bryant before Christmas.

Charlie thought later that he had known she was going to die. He was fifteen years old, almost a man to look at, shaving twice a week, with a deep voice coming from a deep chest, playing football on the Central High School team; it had been years since he'd decided he was an atheist, but he began to pray—silently, inside his head, at any hour of the day when there was a chance to concentrate. His whole being was fixed upon the one object, that his mother should live; but he could see in his father's face, after visits to the hospital, that nothing could help, not prayers, not the blood Norris gave to Laura.

The telephone ringing in the early morning dragged Charlie from an obscure, tormenting dream; by the time he had shaken sleep off and gone to the door in his bare feet he could hear his father downstairs, saying, Yes, I'll be right over. The voice was high and metallic, not like Norris's voice at all. Pop, what is it? Charlie said, peering down the dark stairs, is Mom—? His father could not have heard him, or possibly Charlie had not spoken above a whisper; Norris had pulled pants and a coat over his pajamas and gone out to the car and driven away without saying a word to his children.

Charlie went downstairs and waited in the living room, motionless at the window as night gradually dissolved and the trees heavy with leaves and the houses across the way emerged and became definite. A voice inside him told him that his mother was dead already and another voice denied this fiercely; the argument went on and on as the day brightened. The sun was up by the time the car came back along the street and drew in at the curb and Norris climbed out slowly.

Like a somnambulist, his hair tousled and the pajama-jacket showing beneath his coat, Norris moved up the front walk; his white face was lifted a little, his eyes looked blind, his hands stretched out before him as if he were feeling his way. Charlie heard his footsteps on the porch; the screen-door jerked open and clapped shut again. Then Norris stood at the foot of the stairs and gazed at Charlie, blindly still. I have to call Ack, he said, I have to call Mamma and Papa. He blinked at Charlie and ran his hands through his hair and went to the telephone; all his movements were slow and weighted, like those of a diver walking the ocean floor; and his voice was slow and weighted also, numb with unbelief, as he said into the telephone that his wife was dead.

Later that day, Charlie and Laurette and Patricia and Joel rode out to the farm in Uncle Homer's tin lizzie. None of them wept— Charlie and Laurette were too old, Patricia perhaps was too young, Joel certainly was. Uncle Homer said there was a new calf on the farm, and a litter of collie pups, and that was all Joel could think about.

Charlie felt right away the queerness in the air at the farm; it was a subdued triumph, shared by all but Grandpa Bryant, who looked sadly at Charlie and said, She's in a better world now, Charlie, that's what you have to remember; she's happier now than she ever was on this earth. . . . Charlie went away from his grandfather and the others. He spent most of that day and of the days that followed by himself, beyond the farm, sitting on top of a sandy hill, where he smoked forbidden cigarettes and looked out between the scrub-oaks at a countryside whose wide calm seemed to deny death.

None of Laura's children went to the funeral. There had been an argument among the grownups; Grandma Bryant and Aunt Maudie wanted to rub the children's faces in the fact of death, but Grandpa Bryant sided with Norris, who lost his temper and swore at the others, saying Laura had not wanted a funeral at all. Funerals were barbarous, said Norris; let Laura's children always think of her quick with life; and so much he managed to win from them.

All four children spent the rest of the summer on the farm, and when fall came there was another argument. Aunt Maudie said Norris was not fit to provide for his children, and what was the use of a high school education anyway for such as Charlie and Laurette? They might just as well quit school and stay on the farm, where there was plenty of work; Patricia could go to the country schoolhouse, and so could Joel when the time came. But Charlie and Laurette stood out against Aunt Maudie, and went back into town to live with their father.

Norris's drinking was still only tentative, that fall, and Laurette and Charlie convinced each other that there was nothing seriously wrong. He would wander away after dinner and be gone only a couple of hours, and return only slightly fuddled; they almost liked him better that way because he smiled more and was less inclined to lose his temper. He would sit with his legs crossed and his hands folded and ask them quite genially about what they were doing in school now; and when he mounted the stairs to bed his unsteadiness was hardly perceptible.

Even when the habit increased upon him he remained fairly discreet. It was true that he was staying out later than he had at first; occasionally he brought strange companions back to the house with him and they played half-drunken games of poker in the dining room, on into the small hours; but there was still a privacy about all of this and it could be regarded as a family secret.

It was not until the end of the first winter that the real binges began, and these were confined to week-ends. Late on Saturday afternoon Norris would come weaving along the street, his hat on the back of his head, his overcoat flapping open, singing *The Star-Spangled Banner* into the wind, pausing to address remarks to the trees, leaning on gateposts to leer at the neighbors who watched his progress through their windows. He would lurch up to his room and sleep until dinner-time, and sit silent at table, avoiding his children's eyes; and after dinner the drinking started in earnest. By now he was drinking alone; he sat behind his locked door, in a complete silence—there was never any sound but the clink of the bottle sometimes, knocking against the edge of his glass, and finally his drunken snores. On Sundays he stayed in bed until late afternoon, sleeping it off. When Laurette and Charlie heard him stirring they would knock on his door until he let them in, and help him down the stairs, and pour coffee into him and force him to eat something. They would devise ways of keeping him occupied, so that he would go sober to bed and rise sober next morning and arrive sober at the *Chronicle*. They learned very fast; it became an accepted part of their lives.

They did not then have any but casual friends; there was no place in the close, warped, family intimacy for outsiders. Charlie had begun to feel an odd fierce loyalty toward his father, overlaying his disgust and shame, partly because of the way Grandma Bryant and Aunt Maudie talked; and there were fights now with boys who told Charlie they'd seen his old man coming pie-eyed out of a beer flat.

Charlie had passed his sixteenth birthday and Laurette would soon be fifteen; they were too young to cope with the situation but they did what they could. When they found bottles hidden away they emptied them down the sink, but Norris was always able to buy more. They went together to consult Dr. Cousins, but Dr. Cousins looked at them coldly out of his pale blue eyes and said that as long as Norris's health held up there was nothing he could do. I am a physician, not a preacher, he said.

Charlie went one night to talk to Ack Guion, who said, Christ, Charlie, I've done my best already; don't think *I* haven't read the riot act to him. He's a hell of a good newspaperman and I hate to see him killing himself. But as long as he gets to work sober, and does a good job, there's no way I can put the fear of God into him. All we can do, just hang on and hope he snaps out of it finally.—Hell, Charlie, I know how he feels. Your mother was a damn fine woman and I could get drunk myself when I think what's happened. . . .

So it seemed there was nothing anyone could do, as long as Norris maintained sobriety when sobriety was strictly necessary; and presently the situation seemed normal and it was hard to remember when life had been otherwise.

In the end, of course, he killed the habit; but before that happened there had been the automobile accident and Charlie's attempt at suicide and all the occasions when Norris went roaring drunk out to the farm. And by the time everyone knew the reform was permanent, Norris seemed an old man to Charlie, and a complete stranger, who couldn't ever have had anything to do with

Laura Bryant. As soon as he had his high school diploma, and the promise of a job from a Central High alumnus in Detroit who'd admired the way Charlie played football, Charlie left home. He was glad to go; he was glad to be living in a place where there was nothing to remind him of the past. For a few months he was lonely and then he met people and finally he met Delores, and married her, and believed the past was quite dead. . . .

Mooning about the apartment in the last cold days of March, Charlie tried to thrust his mind backward again; but Laurette's mention of McBain had been working like a slow poison—across even the clearest images a tarnish had crept, and now he found himself looking at what he had hoped to ignore; he remembered far more than Laurette did about McBain.

The other figures clustered around his mother thinned and blew away like smoke, isolating McBain—a tall man, with a shock of dark hair just beginning to turn white, and a lean bony face; he walked with a slight limp and there was something about his clothes and the way he wore them which set him apart from Charlie's father or any of the other men on the *Chronicle*.

Charlie liked him at first. McBain was full of stories and told them to Charlie unexpurgated. He lay back in one chair with his feet propped on another, chain-smoking and talking in a quick eager voice, living over his experiences and making Charlie live them over too. Sometimes he leaned forward, sometimes he interrupted himself to laugh, sometimes in his excitement he stood up and went limping about the room, slapping his hand down for emphasis on the edge of the table or the back of a chair. For a while Charlie had the notion that he was the one McBain came to see; he was a good listener, better than Laurette, better than Norris, whose attention wandered.

All this came back to him vividly, and looking again at those scenes he knew that McBain of course hadn't been talking to him but all the time to Laura Bryant. Their eyes stayed fixed on each other, and a change of expression in McBain's face would be repeated in Laura's—so that when the time came to laugh, for instance, she would laugh almost before he did.

And then when his vein of reminiscences was exhausted for the moment, and Laura instead began to talk, it was different from her other conversations, and Laura herself seemed different—no longer Charlie's mother or Norris's wife, not a resident of Broadfield, but a citizen of the world like McBain. What they talked about then was over Charlie's head and he became as bored as Laurette and drifted from the room, out into the back yard, where he began to pitch stones at a knothole in the fence. His father joined him presently and said Andy had turned into kind of a windbag, hadn't he?

Before McBain's last visit to their house—he couldn't have come more than six times altogether—Charlie had begun to resent him, though he did not know why then. The discomfort was so acute that Charlie pushed it deep and forgot about it; it had never been connected with that time, only a little later, when his mother went off to New York and stayed so long it seemed as if she might never be coming back.

But now it was connected indissolubly with that time; and it did no good to tell himself that it did not matter, it could not possibly matter, whatever the reason for Laura's flight, since all these things lay far in the past and Laura had been dead for ten years and nine months. He wanted to rub the tarnish from the brightness which had always surrounded his mother, and could not, while the poison worked in his mind.

Lethargy was no longer possible and he began to clean the apartment. Under a pile of newspapers he found the last letter from his father, opened it, and read it. It was just like the others; he tossed it aside impatiently and went on working to the sound of the radio tuned up to full volume, as if noise could drown out his thoughts. But in an indirect fashion the letters, after all, must have had some of the intended effect on Charlie. He looked at the way his life had been going, ever since his mother's death— moving inexorably as it now seemed into this blind alley; he looked at all the things he had done as she might have looked at them, and felt sick at heart; he was dying in the trap he had built for himself.

He went out and walked the windy streets and when he returned to the apartment he knew that Laurette was right and that he would have to leave Detroit.

It was only a few days later that Charlie's father called him long-distance and said there was a part-time job for him, driving a *Chronicle* delivery-truck.

15

CHARLIE said he could bum a ride to Broadfield, but Laurette said that might take a week and forced the money for a bus-ticket on him. A small elderly woman sat next to Charlie and said what a long hard winter it had been; but Charlie only grunted and looked through the window, so she sighed presently and resigned herself to a silent journey.

For a while he felt nothing at all. He was still so lost in the past that the present seemed more like a dream than what had been going on inside his own head; but when the last outflung tatters of the city were left behind, and its smoke was only a far smudge on the sky, and the bus rolled heavily along the open highway, his spirits lightened.

There was a watery sunlight, not strong enough to cast shadows, and the bare tired fields, with here and there a patch of dirty snow still showing, blurred in Charlie's gaze and became a long monotony; despite all the sleep he'd been getting he slept again, his head tipping sideways toward the window, his mouth falling open, his hands lying slack on his knees; he wakened briefly when there was a pause in one town or another, and slept again as the bus rolled onward in a slow purposeful devouring of the miles.

In late afternoon, when Broadfield was just beyond the horizon, he came awake for good. Seeing familiar landmarks slip by—a certain hill, a certain farmhouse, a certain bridge across the yet-frozen river—he felt hopeful and melancholy at the same time: there was going to be a future for him after all but in a sense he was retreating to the past and would become Norris Bryant's boy Charlie again.

The bus toiled up a series of low hills that rose beyond the river valley, and roared down into hollows again, and toiled up and ran along the level plateau outside the city, where farmhouses gave way to isolated suburban developments—half empty of life, most of them were, and had been for several years. The weather had washed away the lettering on the billboards advertising choice sites; there were broken windows in the elegant imitations of Colonial charm and Elizabethan whimsy; and the once-smooth lawns were a tangle of sodden dead weeds.

It was Joel who greeted Charlie, when he pushed the front door open, and snatched the suitcase from him and carried it up the stairs—into his room, not Charlie's old one.

"Hey," said Charlie, leaning in the doorway, "what's the big idea?"

Joel turned. "You're going to be in here with me a while, Pop said. I hope you don't snore as loud as Delores says. Maybe you'll have to put a clothespin on your nose." Joel grinned and thumped his fist on a cot brought down from the attic. "You want to trade beds with me, Charlie? The springs in this one are not so hot."

"Naw, the cot's all right." Norris Bryant's boy Charlie for sure, he thought, taking off his overcoat; just another kid like Joel. "Where's Delores?" he asked, dropping his hat on Joel's head, and tried to stifle the anger which had started in him.

"Kitchen. Getting dinner."

"She could've—" Charlie snapped open the latches on his suitcase. "Where's everybody else, for that matter?" He began to toss dirty shirts and underwear on the floor.

"Pop's over flirting with his girl friend," said Joel, "and Pat's prob'ly out somewhere flirting with her boy friend. He got his car out of storage the other day and now he drives her home every night, the way he used to in the fall."

"Johnny?" Charlie took a clean shirt from the suitcase and laid it on the cot; he began to get undressed.

"Vinnie," said Joel, watching him candidly. "Hey, you think I'll ever get that much hair on my chest? You really look like a truck-driver, Charlie, you know it?"

"Who the hell's Vinnie?"

"He was here Christmas night. He brought Pat that book."

"Christ," said Charlie, "not the pansy who works on the paper?"

Joel took Charlie's hat off and tossed it upward; it dropped neatly on the hook of the brass lighting-fixture in the ceiling. "What's a pansy, Charlie?"

"None of your business. Where's a towel? I need a shower."

"In the bathroom. So many people living here now, we stuck labels around for everybody. You ought to take more exercise, Charlie. You're getting a belly on you like an old man."

"Fresh little punk, aren't you?" Charlie said.

"I'm developing my physique. You want to feel my biceps?"

"Nope," said Charlie, and departed for the bathroom.

By the time he had finished his shower and dressed again his anger was worse; he walked down into the kitchen, but as he descended the back stairs Delores had gone up the front ones with David. Standing in the steamy kitchen Charlie could hear her cooing at his son.

He climbed up again and stood on the threshold of his own room. Delores, bending by the crib to pin the covers over David, stopped cooing; her back looked suddenly rigid, but she did not turn. Charlie sucked his breath in. "Welcome home, Charlie dear," he said. "It's delightful to be married."

Delores still did not turn.

"You deaf?" Charlie asked.

Delores straightened and turned; her face had a pinched look and her eyes avoided his. "Hush up, Charlie. He's almost asleep, and you'll get him all upset."

"He isn't the only one who's going to be upset. For Christ's sake, Delores—"

"Hush *up!*" Delores moved toward him; with a little flare of spirit she gave him a shove into the hall, but he caught roughly at her arms and pulled her after him.

"You're going to kiss me, anyway," he said, but it was like kissing a dead woman; her body remained slack in his arms, her lips were stiff and dry against his, and he could feel the intensity with which she was keeping her teeth clenched. He let her go and said, "Will you tell me what the hell this is all about?"

Delores shut the bedroom door and glanced along the hall. "Later, Charlie," she whispered. "Joel—"

"No, right now. Who the hell cares what Joel thinks? It's all in the family. This nice little, tight little, cozy little goddam family." Watch it, he said to himself. "You been messing around with some other guy again?" he asked, but he managed to keep his voice down. "Is that what it is?"

Delores pressed her back against the wall; she tried to slide past him toward the head of the stairs; but he put his arms out, one on either side of her, and pinned her against the brown oatmeal paper. He stared down at her, seeing her breath coming more rapidly, her neat little breasts rising and falling under the dress. "Don't, Charlie," she whispered. "Don't start that again."

"It's true, isn't it?" Now that he had seen her fear he couldn't control his rage. "You can't leave 'em alone. The minute you're away from me—"

"Stop it, Charlie! Oh, God," Delores said, pushing at his chest; but he stood where he was, rock-like and implacable. "I haven't even been out of the house, hardly, since I came here. I haven't even been to the movies more than a couple of times. I—"

"But you were still too busy to write me a letter. Just one letter. I could have rotted in Detroit. You little bitch," Charlie said. "Who is he? Who's the bastard this time?"

Delores's mouth began to tremble. "Charlie, if you're going to be like this, I can't stand it, I just can't stand it, that's all, I'll have to go away, you'll drive me crazy, you'll—"

Charlie twisted her arm. "Who is he, I said?"

"Charlie, Charlie, Charlie—" Delores's voice rose into a scream, and then broke off short; she writhed away from him and fled toward the bathroom and locked herself in.

Charlie leaned against the wall and wiped his sweating forehead; now that the devil was out of him he felt sick, and too weak to move from where he stood. The front door opened and slammed shut, and Norris's voice came up the stairs. "Charlie? You home?"

"Yeah. I'm home." Charlie continued to stand there while his father climbed the stairs. He could hardly hold out his hand to be shaken; he could not look into his father's face.

"You all right, Charlie?" Norris asked anxiously.

"Yeah, I'm all right. . . . When do I start work?"

"Tomorrow, I guess. You better come up to the editorial room in the morning, and I'll take you down and introduce you to the gang. They're a nice gang, Charlie. . . . You'll be able to drive the truck, won't you? I had to kind of lie about it for you—said you were a truck-driver from away back."

"Anyway, I look the part. That's what Joel said."

Norris smiled uncertainly. "Come on downstairs. We're going to have a drink, just this once, to celebrate."

"Celebrate," said Charlie. "That's a hot one." But his father had not heard, and went away to the kitchen to mix the drinks. Charlie stood by the living-room table, turning the pages of the *Chronicle* without seeing what was printed on any of them. Now that Delores was denied him, he wanted her almost as badly as he had before they were married.

Norris came in with a tray. There were five glasses on it, besides the red glass cocktail shaker. "We'll kind of get a head start on the others," he said, and began to fill two glasses.

Charlie shoved the newspaper away. "What others?"

"Delores and Pat and Vinnie Rourke. Vinnie's coming in to dinner. I wanted to get Betty Lou over too, but she says she's feeling kind of peaked. Getting over a bad cold."

"That the girl friend Joel meant?"

Norris grinned and handed Charlie a glass. "Maybe Joel needs to be taken down a peg. . . . Don't know how this'll be, Charlie. I'm out of practice. Here's to you, anyway."

Charlie watched his father sip; he did not drink himself. "Seems like an awful lot has been going on around here since Christmas," he said. "Will you tell me what the hell's the matter with Delores?"

Norris turned his head away; he sat down with great care, but even so the liquid went sliding back and forth in his glass. "If you'll just keep calm, Charlie—"

"Calm! *Jesus,* Pop—"

"And try to cut down on the swearing." Norris sipped again; he set his glass on the arm of the chair, and ran his tongue over his teeth. "Delores hasn't been any too well lately, Charlie. Maybe I should have written and kind of paved the way. Sorry I wasn't here when you got in, but I didn't know it was so late. Betty Lou gets talking, and—"

"What do you mean, Delores isn't any too well?"

Norris rubbed both hands back through his hair. "When she heard you were going to be here again, she came and had a little talk with me. We talked over a lot of things. Seems Delores—" Norris stopped; he stared hopelessly at the wall. "Well, I decided it might help if you'd be willing to bunk with Joel for a while."

"Help who?" asked Charlie. "For Christ's sake, Pop—"

"I asked you to go easy on the cussing."

Charlie held his breath for a moment. "All right. But willing— I wasn't consulted."

"I know, Charlie. It's tough on you," Norris said, "but if you'll just be patient I think things'll work out. We have to do what's best for everybody—you and Delores and the baby too. It isn't easy to know what's right." Norris took a sip from his glass and set it down again. "From what Delores told me, seems like you weren't as—considerate—as you might have been. Try to look at it from her point of view. Took her quite a while to get over what you did, and as soon as she heard you were coming back, she got scared all over again."

"Because she's been messing around with some other guy. Why don't you tell me the truth?"

Norris's face tightened. "Now, Charlie, you know that isn't so. She's so busy all the time, looking after the baby and taking care of the house—she hardly ever has a chance to go out. She hasn't seen any other boys except Vinnie when he calls for Pat, and Johnny Wheelwright a couple times—"

"Is that who it is? Is it Johnny Wheelwright?"

Norris stood up, almost knocking over his cocktail glass. "Charlie, you'll have to quit thinking like that."

"How can I? Hell, back in Detroit she was having herself a time with some lousy little Kike Laurette introduced her to, and now she—"

"Charlie, she told me all about that, and there was nothing to it. Anyway, it's water over the dam. She made a mistake and she's sorry for it. Why can't you have a little faith in her?"

"Because she's an easy lay, that's why. I know what Delores is. I'm married to her, for Christ's sake. That's where I made my big mistake, marrying her. Jesus, what a goddam fool! I could kick myself around the block." Charlie picked up his glass and drained it; he continued to stand where he was, clutching the glass in one hand; he could have broken it easily.

Norris went walking up and down the room. When he came to a pause, he said, "I guess I know how you're feeling, Charlie, after what you've been through. Right now you just aren't yourself. You don't mean the things you've said, and we'll forget you ever said them." He turned away and absently refilled his glass.

"I'd hate to see your marriage go on the rocks. You loved each other once, you and Delores. I remember the letter you wrote when you got engaged. I remember the wedding. You must still feel the same way, underneath. You'll have to make an effort, both of you," Norris said. "Try to salvage something out of it. If the times hadn't been so tough, maybe none of this would have happened. . . .

"Well," he said, "the bunch of us here, all working together— Joel's taking over a delivery route, by the way, starting next week— all working together, we'll pull through the hard times. Sooner or later you'll find a real job, and then you and Delores and David can move into a place of your own, and go ahead from there and —and make something decent out of your lives. That's the thing to think about, Charlie. Forget Detroit. Think how things'll be a year from now, five or ten years from now—" He broke off, suddenly tired out; and his face took on a remote look, as if he were trying to see the future himself.

All Norris's words did was to make Charlie feel sorry for him; for what Norris had been saying had two meanings—he was also trying to convince himself about his own dead wife, thought Charlie. He said, "Pretty optimistic, aren't you? Mind if I have another drink?"

"Go ahead." Norris sat down again.

Charlie sipped in silence and presently Joel came up from the cellar, red in the face and breathing hard, to ask if dinner wasn't ready yet.

Norris turned his head. "What's happened to Delores?"

"She was screaming a while ago," Joel said. "I heard her. I was way down in the cellar, but I heard her screaming."

Norris looked at Joel, and then at Charlie.

"Oh, sure, I know," Charlie said. "I didn't lose any time. Looks like you have a tough case on your hands, Pop." He stared through the window; beyond the porch he could just see the trees along the street. "I don't know what happens to me," he said.

"Maybe I'd better go up and—" Norris had grown distraught again. "We can't go on this way, Charlie."

"I know, I know, I know. . . . Here's Pat and her boy friend," Charlie said, and withdrew into silence.

No one said very much that evening. Delores did not come downstairs; in the end Norris took her dinner up to her on a tray. Vincent Rourke tried to make conversation, and Patricia tried to help him; but each time silence closed over what they said, it closed more solidly, and as soon as the dishes had been washed, Vincent departed. Charlie, left alone in the living room, tried to read a detective story he took from the bookcase; but one thing and another kept getting between his eyes and the page.

There was Delores, shrinking from him in the upstairs hall; there was his mother listening to Andrew McBain; there was Patricia, looking across the table at Vincent with somewhat the same expression. . . . Charlie put the book aside, crossed the room to the piano, and stood there staring at his mother's photograph; it was astonishing how closely Patricia had come to resemble her.

Patricia was as much of a cipher to Charlie as Joel was; since his mother's death they might have been anybody's children. But it was not quite the same now. The bunch of us here, all working together, we'll pull through the hard times; solidarity, family solidarity, kiddo. An odd tenderness stirred in Charlie; each of them, save possibly Joel, who had been so very young then, had an image of Laura Bryant to cling to, and maybe that would effect the miracle his father hoped for.

Charlie wandered back to his chair again. He was unused to

tenderness, and Andrew McBain came back into his thoughts, and Vincent Rourke, and somehow they were becoming confused with each other, so that first it seemed as if Vincent were telling Laura Bryant about his trip across the world, and then as if McBain were smiling at Patricia. . . .

Presently Charlie joined Joel in the cellar and had a workout on the punching-bag; maybe that was all he needed, a violent outlet for the violence inside him; when he went to bed he was able to fall asleep without thinking once about his wife, lying alone in the room across the hall.

For a while he took a workout in the cellar every night. If he remained too long in the living room, where Norris sat reading and Delores darning socks, the violence would begin again; for the trouble with the job was that it didn't take enough out of him. He helped bundle the papers and load the trucks, he distributed copies still damp from the presses to the various departments in the *Chronicle* building, and he drove his own truck out to dump the papers at the distribution points where delivery boys gathered each afternoon with their bicycles. He found that the men he worked with liked him, mostly because they liked his father. Bry was a kind of legend around the place—it was the same in the advertising department and the composing room and the press room. But Charlie's job was hardly a job at all; it filled only a few hours of each day; and to keep himself occupied he studied seed catalogues and visited nurseries and decided to start a vegetable garden in the back yard.

The garden had fallen into complete neglect since Laura's death. The lilac bush from which she had cut bunches of flowers after the rain was dead, choked by the forsythia, which had moved forward from the back fence to meet the advancing lawn and blotted out the flower-beds; and the lawn itself was all dead weeds and crab-grass. Frost had struck deep into the soil, which would be soggy for weeks to come. Charlie would have to be patient about this, too, but he labored with spade and pickax, and physical weariness made patience easier. He worked even in the rain, and as his muscles got back their old resiliency the last of his lethargy left him—he was more filled with energy than he had been since football days in high school.

Norris began to take an interest in the garden too. He and Charlie spread the seed-catalogues about the dining-room table after dinner, and sat there drawing up lists and making plans and discarding them and making new ones; while they waited for the spring sunlight, a new kinship grew between them.

"We'll have to plan on a few flowers too, I guess," Norris said once. "Your mother liked growing flowers, and Betty Lou has a green thumb; she could give us some good advice."

But all the time Charlie worked, and when he lay wakeful at night in the cot in Joel's room, a troublesome small tune went through his head: he would have to talk to Patricia and find out what she knew about Andrew White McBain, who was coming to lecture in Broadfield at the end of May.

April was turning out cold and rainy, as it almost always did in Broadfield; there were even a few flurries of snow. But spring came slowly onward, the lawns began to show green, the beds of myrtle planted between street and sidewalk shook off the grit the melting snow had left behind and put forth new leaves; buds were swelling on the trees, whose twigs cast thickening shadows; and in the third week of the month there were two fine days in a row, so warm that Charlie rolled up his shirt sleeves before he started raking the soil smooth.

In the evening of the second day he felt restless, and to forget his need for Delores borrowed Joel's bicycle and went for a long ride in the dusk, out beyond the edge of the city to the pastures and orchards that stretched away into the northeast, and then around by Rush Lake where Joel went sailing in summer with Buzz Boonstra, and back past the amusement park which would soon be open for the season. The air was so warm that people sat gossiping on their front porches in the dark, and along the streets, arm in arm beneath the budding trees, strolled boys and girls; the gentle, dreaming, loving time of year had not really come yet, but this was a foretaste, and Charlie was sorry for himself because he was excluded from it. He no longer felt any anger against his wife; it was as if he had sweated it out of him, as if it had run away into the earth. Now he was able to pity her; but he wanted her, he needed her badly, and he hoped he would soon find a way to talk to her again.

Pedaling through the soft dark, he wondered what he could say to convince her that he was different now, even from the way he had been when they first started going around together—as long ago as that, it now occurred to him, she'd given in mostly through fear. He wondered if he really wanted her back. There would be another woman for him someday, perhaps, stronger and wiser than Delores, a little more like his mother.

He pedaled faster, looking straight ahead, trying to ignore the strolling couples under the trees; now that he was in good health again he wanted urgently to have his arm around a girl, any girl at all; though not Delores, maybe, even if she would have him.

The City Hall clock was striking ten when he pushed the bicycle up the rutted gravel driveway. He walked in at the back door, and through the quiet, empty house, and out to the front porch, where he sat alone on the top step, smoking a cigarette.

Music sounded somewhere far down the street; through the

open windows of Betty Lou's house voices floated. Norris was in there with her; Charlie could hear him laughing. It would be strange if his father did get married again, Charlie thought, wondering what it felt like to be going on fifty-four years old. His father wasn't exactly an old goat, but Betty Lou was an attractive woman for her age.

Charlie began to feel lonelier than ever. Maybe even Joel was out with a girl—he was getting to that age.

There was no point in sitting there, but Charlie lit a second cigarette from the stub of the first, and stayed on; he would wait until his father came back from Betty Lou's, and maybe he would even kid him. He would never forgive Norris for the bad years, but it was easier to overlook them now; their joint plans for the garden, and the way the men at the *Chronicle* talked about him, were having an effect. Charlie even felt a little different about the letters Norris had written him, and wished he'd kept them. Between their lines must lie the truth about his mother and Andrew McBain.

But long before his father came back, Delores appeared, drifting listlessly out of the shadows and up the front walk; she was almost on Charlie before she saw him, and then she stopped dead; he saw her hands flutter and could hear the breath she drew.

"Hi, Delores," he said.

"Hello, Charlie. . . . I just went out for a walk around the block."

He flipped the second cigarette away. "I didn't ask you where you went. . . . You leave the baby all alone?"

"Well, your father's right next door. And it was only for a few minutes."

"I been sitting here more than half an hour," said Charlie.

"Well—I did stop in for a coke at the drugstore."

"Just around the block, hey? Never mind," Charlie said, "I'm not bawling you out, for Pete's sake. Sit down. Have a cigarette."

"I don't smoke at all any more, hardly," Delores said. She came up the steps, but did not sit down; she stood there taut, just inside the front door. Though his back was toward her, Charlie knew how tense she was; but he tried to ignore what the knowledge did to him.

"How long is this going to go on, Delores?" he asked.

After a pause, she said, "I don't know what you mean, exactly."

"The hell you don't," said Charlie softly; he kept his hands in front of him so that she could not see they were clenched. "That's nice perfume you're using," he went on presently. "You smell like the spring."

"It's just—Laurette gave it to me."

"Well, it's nice." Charlie turned half around; she had on a light dress which glimmered through the dark; she stood so still it seemed she couldn't be breathing at all. "You ever going to be my wife again," he asked, "or are you through with me for good?"

"I don't know, Charlie," she whispered. "I just don't know."

He turned back and stared into the street. "You could give me a chance, couldn't you? I know what a bastard I've been, Delores. Right from the start. Hell, before we were married, even." He considered his past actions. "I guess I know why it was. The girls around here, the girls I knew in high school—well, they wouldn't look at me. Partly because of Pop; partly, I guess, because I wasn't anything much to look at anyway. But I—I liked girls a lot," Charlie said. "I wanted a girl of my own the worst way, but I couldn't ever have one, not the kind I wanted. I even tried to kill myself, once, over a girl. So I kind of got the idea that the only thing to do, you had to be rough about it. You had to go out and grab what you wanted, before somebody else grabbed it. That's how it was with you. I guess I scared you, but the funny thing is, Delores, I was really the one who was scared. Scared you'd pick some other guy. That's why I kept 'em away from you. Maybe you don't even know some of the things I did, keeping other guys away from you, trying to keep you for myself. And even after we were married I was still scared. I couldn't believe it, that you were my wife. A good-looking girl like you. And so young."

He paused again, watching a car pass along the street; the music had stopped but he could still hear Betty Lou's voice and his father's laughter. It was true that beneath his arrogance there had been a terrible humility; Delores had known too much for so young a girl but he'd told himself she was as good as he deserved.

"You didn't have to marry me," Charlie said. "But we can still—fix things up, Delores. If we try. Both of us. God knows I've been trying." He sighed and said, "I'm willing to keep on this way a while longer, Delores, if you'll—try to feel different too. People *can* change; even in a short time, they can. Like Pop said to me—maybe he said it to you too—the whole thing might have been different if the times had been better. You don't know what it does to a guy, taking it on the chin as long as I had to. I'm not trying to make excuses for acting like a bastard; there couldn't be any excuse for that, maybe. But what I'm trying to tell you, Delores—I'm not a bastard clear through. I don't think I am. Will you give me a chance?"

He sat and looked out at the street, waiting for her to answer; he could not bear to turn his head, for fear of seeing her still tense and frightened in the doorway. But no answer came.

"Haven't you been listening to me, Delores?" he asked, and turned his head at last; but she was not there and there was no way of knowing how long he had been addressing his remarks into emptiness.

It felt worse for a while than anything else that had happened to him.

16

THEY SAT on in the car for a few minutes, after Vincent had driven it in against the curb, as they did almost every evening now; her left shoulder lightly touched his right, and his hand lay warm over hers on the leather seat.

"Have fun?" he asked.

"No. Did you?"

"Worst evening I ever spent," said Vincent.

"I don't know why we keep it up," Patricia said.

"Neither do I."

"Just habit?"

"An evil habit," said Vincent.

"Like taking dope."

"*You're* a dope," he said.

"And so are you," said Patricia, and then he put his arms around her and kissed her on the mouth. It had become an almost unvarying formula; this was now the way all their good evenings ended. After the bad ones, when he was bored with life or his work on the *Chronicle* or chafing because there had been no check from Uncle Bertrand, their partings were sad, or stiff and strained, or he would become conscience-stricken and start berating himself; and this she hated most. But tonight had been a good one.

After he had released her he climbed out ceremoniously, walked around and opened her door, held his arms out and swung her down to the curb; then he kissed her again, a little breathlessly, and then he linked his arm in hers and they moved together up the front walk.

But tonight was going to end differently after all, because Charlie was sitting on the porch steps, smoking a cigarette. Patricia would have sailed on, but Vincent checked her abruptly. There was a pause, and then Vincent's constrained voice: "Hi, there, Charlie."

"Good evening, Mr. Rourke. You keep young ladies out pretty late of a mild spring evening."

"Not too late to tire the faithful watch-dog, it seems." Vincent turned to Patricia and squeezed her hand, too hard, so that she noticed the tremor in his voice. "Same time tomorrow night, Pat?"

"I can't, tomorrow night," she said, mostly because the tremor had angered her; he had been afraid of Johnny and now he was afraid of Charlie. "Betty Lou and I—"

"God rest her merry. Sunday, then? If it's a nice day Sunday, we might even take a trip. Sooner or later I'll have to set eyes on the big lake, and you really ought to be along to see how I empathize to *that*."

"All right, Vincent. If it's a nice day."

"It won't be," said Charlie. "On Sunday there's going to be a blizzard. I have a confidential report."

"We'll hope you've been misinformed. So long, Fido. Good night, Pat," Vincent said, and went quickly back to his car and drove away.

Charlie stood up as Patricia passed him, and followed her into the house. After he had locked the front door, he said, "He's just as cute as he can be, isn't he?"

Patricia ignored him. She crossed the living room and picked up the *Chronicle;* Vincent had interviewed a Republican Congressman that morning, before the Congressman addressed a convention of paper manufacturers in the Civic Auditorium, and his story was on the front page, with a byline.

"Everybody in?" Patricia asked Charlie, who was leaning against the piano with his hands in his pockets, staring at her face.

"Yup. I sat out there like a reception committee. First Delores, then Joel, then Pop, then you and Vinnie-boy. God, Pat, doesn't he ever make you want to throw up?"

Patricia said nothing.

"Just between you and me," Charlie said, "I hate that boy's guts."

Patricia wanted to walk past him to the stairs, but she had a feeling that he would reach out and catch hold of her arm; and she did not want to be touched by Charlie.

"But there's no accounting for tastes, as they say," Charlie went on. He pulled out the piano-bench and sat down. "Talk to me, Pat. I'm feeling lonely."

"It's late. Anyway—there's nothing to talk about."

"There's Andrew McBain," said Charlie.

She felt his gaze like a physical force.

"You wrote to Laurette," said Charlie. "She told me. What's it all about? You think Mom used to mess around with the guy?"

Patricia stared down at the *Chronicle:* SOLON SCORES NEW DEAL. The fat smug face of the solon stared up at her.

"I remember McBain pretty well," said Charlie. "In a lot of ways Vinnie-boy reminds me of McBain. A pair of bastards. McBain thought he had a way with the ladies. So does Vinnie-boy."

"I'm going to bed." Patricia moved forward.

"Not for a few minutes. I want to get this thing straightened out. You were pretty young when Mom died, but I was fifteen years old and I was kind of crazy about her. If you want to know what I think, it's a dirty lie about her and McBain, and I think you ought to be ashamed, sticking your snoot into something that was over and done with years ago."

"I'm not." Patricia wished she could stop looking at Charlie; he was trying to talk lightly, but his face was set, his eyes were tormented, and she didn't want to think of him as having emotions at all. "I don't believe it either, Charlie."

"Then why'd you write to Laurette?"

"I can't seem to get it out of my mind. Everybody—talks about it. They know more about it than we do."

"Who, for instance?"

"Oh—Aunt Maudie, and Grandma Bryant. They were always— They said Mother was an evil woman. And then there's Vincent—"

"*Vincent,* for Christ's sake! What the hell does he know about it?"

"What Carola Wilmot told him. She used to know Mother."

"Yeah, I know."

"And Vincent knows her. She has him in to cocktails, and tells him all the old scandals. You know what she's like."

"Rich-bitch. Yeah, I know what Carola's like."

"I think Carola must have told him McBain wanted Mother to run away with him, and that's why she went to New York that time."

"People are pretty swell, aren't they?" Charlie said. "Jesus!" he said, and slammed his fist on the piano-bench. "You'd think they could let her rest in peace. But hell no, they have to go mauling her over, making her just as cheap and lousy as they are. One thing they can't stand, that now and then there's somebody decent in the world. *Christ,* Pat, why do you go around with a guy like that? Somebody who never even knew Mom, but he'll sit and listen to Rich-Bitch Wilmot tell dirty stories about her."

"It isn't like that, Charlie. Even if Mother—did go to New York—to see McBain," Patricia said, "I don't think we ought to think there was anything—"

"But you think it just the same, don't you?"

"I don't know," said Patricia.

"Mom went to New York other times, before that."

"To visit her mother. To go to her mother's funeral. There was no reason at all for her to go that last time, unless it was to—see him. She'd just had a fight with Father. Laurette said so."

"Hell, they were always having spats. That happens in any marriage," Charlie said, "and Mom had a temper, so did Pop. She came back again, didn't she? Everything was jake, then. They went and had themselves another baby."

"Yes," said Patricia.

"They didn't lose any time, did they? God, I'd like to go around

178

and knock Rich-Bitch Wilmot's teeth down her throat. How many more people in this town think the same thing, I wonder."

"It doesn't matter what other people think. As long as we know—"

"Yeah, but we don't *know*." Charlie rubbed a hand over his face. "You start playing in the mud, and it sticks to you, you can't wash it off. . . . Mom liked McBain all right, but she must have seen through him. Mustn't she, Pat? She was so damn wise. She always knew what people were like; they couldn't fool her. That's why I know Pop must have been quite a guy in his day. Goddam it, she couldn't have really fallen for McBain. Not after she'd lived with Pop all those years, and had three kids, and—"

"Charlie, it's so foolish to start—brooding about it—after all these years."

"Yeah, sure, but *you* brood, don't you? Just like me. I make myself sick, but I can't stop. I've got to know, I've got to really *know* it was all right, between Mom and Pop. It's the only thing pulls me through, Pat, remembering how swell she was." He sat with his fists clenched on his knees. "You think I could—ask Pop about it?"

"No," Patricia said urgently, "no, Charlie, you mustn't do that! Father—he's so innocent in some ways. I don't know, I think people must have been more innocent then, when he was growing up, they didn't know so much about—everything. He couldn't ever have dreamed there was anything like—what we've been thinking. Leave him alone, Charlie. We mustn't start *him* thinking—"

"God," said Charlie, standing up, "if I really did think Mom had fallen for a bastard like McBain, I'd—"

"Don't think it."

"There ought to be some way to prove it. I'd like to prove it to everybody. Rich-Bitch Wilmot, and Aunt Maudie, and— Oh, hell," said Charlie, "I'm going to bed."

It took Patricia a long time to get to sleep that night. She kept trying to remember what Vincent had actually said about McBain.

It had been a raw night and a thin cold rain was falling, but they sat longer than usual in his car, parked beneath the trees on Johnson Avenue, and he began by talking about his poverty. At the end of March he had given up his apartment and moved into the cheapest room he could find, in an old frame house on Eustis Court. It was cheaper than the Y would have been; and having his car to drive was more important, he said, than living in a respectable neighborhood. Knowing him much better now, she thought he rather gloried in the sordidness of the rooming-house—he saw himself playing a romantic rôle. This amused Patricia and made her feel very tender toward him.

"Well," he said finally, "the way things are going, it'll be years and years, Pat, before I can afford a wife. Because I don't see any sense in getting married before you can have a decent home and all that goes with it." His hand dropped down on hers. "I'm old-fashioned in some ways. I'd want to support my wife in style."

It was the first time he'd mentioned marriage; she held the thought away from her, not yet knowing if she really wanted to marry Vincent. Except when he became moody or stopped coming to see her, she liked things as they were now; they were playing at being in love; they were gay about it, as he'd said they must be. And if he had been less difficult, she would have loved him less, perhaps.

"So," Vincent went on, still holding her hand, "that's why I haven't said anything about getting engaged. Young couples in love ought to be subsidized by the government—maybe they will be soon. But I wouldn't want you to feel—tied down to me, Pat. In case somebody came along you liked better. A millionaire, if there are any left."

"You wouldn't want to feel tied down either, would you?" It was impossible, sometimes, not to flick him gently; and usually it only amused him, as it did now.

"Stop reading me like a book," he said, moving a little closer to her. "Sometimes you scare me, darling, the way you see through me." He slid his free arm about her shoulders and kissed her. "Still love me?"

It happened now that when he touched her she stopped seeing clearly; she forgot his faults and the power he had to wound her; what she saw was the glory which suddenly surrounded Vincent.

When he lifted his lips from hers, he kept his arm about her, and the motion of his hand was so gentle and subtle she hardly noticed it at first; all she felt was that she had only now found out what it was like to be really alive.

"I don't know yet," Vincent said, "how you feel about a lot of things. Grownups do a lot of harm to children—they make them think that so many good things aren't good at all. I went through a time like that myself. My Aunt Lucy— But I've told you all about her. I got over it, of course, but it was quite a struggle. But don't you think it's foolish, Pat, to wait and wait for marriage, when two people feel about each other the way we do?"

His hand was more urgent now, and his voice also, and she couldn't speak; but his urgency was gentle still, not like Johnny Wheelwright's, long ago.

"Don't you?" Vincent said, and bent his head again; this time he kissed her in a way Johnny never had, and she felt as if she were drowning. But just before she went under he let her go and moved away from her.

"Maybe you don't think it's foolish to wait, after all," he said.

"I don't know, Vinnie." She spoke with difficulty. "You get me—all mixed up," said Patricia with a sigh, and tried to laugh. "I don't think this is being very gay about it."

"I'm gay. I'm as blithe as a lark."

"Yes, but—"

"It's all tied up in your mind with sin, and going to hell when you die, isn't it? Oh, I know the things they told you, your aunt and your grandmother. But that's just because they have dirty minds. You don't think your mother was a sinner, do you? You don't think she went to hell."

Patricia turned her head; his was only a silhouette against the raindrops glittering on the car window. "My mother," she said. "Vinnie, I've never talked to you about my mother, have I?"

"No. But I know a lot about her. She was a famous person in Broadfield, really. Everybody knows about her. Everybody's still talking about her—except you. Maybe you're suffering from a psychic trauma."

"What's that?"

"Jargon, darling, just jargon. Though I think maybe it's true, in a way. You were pretty badly hurt, weren't you, when she died? And living out on that god-awful farm with those god-awful relatives. And your father trying to drink himself to death. Oh, God, darling, I know how it was; your childhood was just as horrible as mine. . . . But if you could only see your mother the way she really must have been," Vincent said, so tenderly Patricia felt he was seeing her himself, "a wonderful woman, a lovely one. But a *woman*, darling, that's the point. A passionate woman. That's why she didn't wait to get married to your father, don't you see? It's why they—"

But he must have sensed her stiffening; he reached out and took her hand once more. "I haven't hurt you all over again, have I? You knew that about your mother, didn't you?"

"No, I—"

"God, I thought surely your dear Aunt Maudie would have told you. With diagrams, if necessary."

"But, Vincent—you don't know anything about it. Did Carola Wilmot—?"

"Carola was devoted to your mother, darling. I guess everybody was who knew her; they couldn't help themselves. Even Andrew McBain, though I suppose he'd had a thousand love affairs before he ever came back to Broadfield. He was mad about your mother. Didn't you even know that?"

"No. And it isn't true."

"That isn't very nice of you, darling, to think your mother wasn't attractive."

"I didn't mean that."

"What did you mean then?"

"Vincent, you don't think—Carola didn't tell you my mother—had an affair with him?"

"Would you think less of your mother if she had?"

Patricia sat in silence; she freed her hand from his. "I—don't know that either."

"Because that would be really foolish. Foolish and wicked. Anybody as wonderful as your mother must have been—whatever she did was all right. Can't you see that, Pat? Oh, darling, you shouldn't have let them warp your mind. *I'm* not the one who's getting you all mixed up. They're the ones—still, after all this time. Darling, it's high time you said to hell with everything they ever told you or made you think. Wake up, Pat, wake up—the nightmare was over long ago."

But she still wasn't sure; lying in bed at three o'clock, at four o'clock, on that April morning, she still was not sure whom to blame for her confusion. Because she had resisted him that night, and climbed out of the car finally without another word, she had been afraid he would neglect her again. But that had not happened; they kept going out together every night, and the relationship was back on a plane of gaiety and teasing, and of excitement that disguised itself as play.

There was truth in some of the things Vincent had said, she thought; but there remained a suspicion that truth was something which did not interest him. He was not good, as Johnny Wheelwright was good. He was unhappy and selfish and cruel and shallow; these faults she knew, and she could find worse ones if she looked; but it was Vincent she loved, not Johnny. If she had not fallen in love with his looks, probably she wouldn't have fallen in love with him at all; but now she felt she would love him still, if he lost his looks tomorrow. It seemed that it was his weakness that made her love him most—it made her feel so strong that she believed in time she could make him strong too, by giving him without stint everything she had in her to give.

Patricia slept at last; but almost immediately, it seemed, the alarm clock went off and another Saturday had begun. Joel was singing under the bathroom shower; David was shouting downstairs; Delores was rattling pans in the kitchen.

Patricia did not feel tired that day, but abnormally keyed up. The procession of patients passed in a blur through the reception-room; she could think only of Vincent, and wished she hadn't lied to him about the date with Betty Lou. But when the telephone rang and it was his voice at the other end of the wire, her mood altered and she spoke almost coldly.

"You haven't changed your mind about tonight?"

"I can't, Vinnie. I promised Betty Lou."

"O.K., Miss Adamant. But about tomorrow. I had a personal consultation with the weather man, and the weather man says fair and warmer—he says it will be a balmy Sabbath, and just the day for a trip to the lake. So there's a project afoot. Carola wants to go down to open her cottage, and she's asked us both to come. We'll have to work hard but there will be a reward in the shape of an extra-special meal *and* some wine from her father's fabulous cellar. We'll take my car and put the top down and all get a nice sunburn. We'll be starting around eleven, Carola says. I'll pick you up first."

"But, Vinnie—"

"What do you mean, 'but, Vinnie'? Don't you think it sounds like fun?"

Patricia hesitated. "No, I don't."

"But, darling—" His voice hesitated too. "Don't tell me you're jealous! You sweet dope! Carola's old enough to be my great-grandmother."

"No, but, Vinnie, I don't think she really wants me along. She doesn't like me."

"She's crazy about you. She was crazy about your mother, now she's crazy about you. Oh, now, come on, darling, it'll be loads of fun. Carola's swell. She's one of the most amusing women I ever knew."

"I suppose you've known lots of amusing women, haven't you?"

"By God, you really are jealous!" He laughed.

"No, but I just don't like her, Vinnie, she— We won't go if it rains, will we?"

"Don't start *praying* for rain, for *God's* sake. Give my love to Betty Lou. See you tomorrow about a quarter of eleven."

Checking through a list of unpaid bills, Patricia found she was paying no attention to her work—she kept turning her head to look through the Venetian blind, hoping the sunlight would have grown a little dim.

When she left the building in the middle of the afternoon, vague clouds were drifting up out of the west; and she woke in the night to the sound of rain, and went to sleep again comforted. She didn't know why she disliked Carola; it had nothing to do with what Charlie had said. But she remembered how Carola had stared at her in the Art Gallery, and made fun of the black evening dress. And she didn't want Vincent to like women of Carola's sort; he'd known too many of them and they had done him no good.

But the rain drummed steadily on the roof, and she floated off into sleep and peace; when Joel came banging at her door she had to force her way up from such profound depths that it took her a long time to notice that the rain had stopped and the sun was flooding her room.

"Phone-call for you, Pat," Joel was shouting outside the door. "There's somebody on the *phone*."

Still not much more than half awake, she stumbled down the stairs and took up the receiver.

"Hi, Pat. Hope I didn't wake you up." It was Johnny.

"You didn't, but Joel did." The sight of the sun had brought back her dismay, but Johnny's voice drove it off again. "What time is it?"

"Eight o'clock. It isn't really so early. Take a look at the weather, Pat; this is the day we've all been waiting for. I'm going on a bicycle picnic, and it would be more fun if you'd come too."

"Oh, Johnny, I said I'd— When are you starting?"

"Soon as possible. I guess you haven't had breakfast."

"And I'm not dressed yet, of course. But I could be ready in half an hour." Her spirits soared. "Could you wait that long?"

"You bet I could. I'll bring the food, so don't worry about that. And I'll come around and pump up your tires for you. Hey, you think your bike needs greasing?"

"It probably does," said Patricia, "but that doesn't matter. Oh, Johnny, I'm so glad you called. It's a perfect day!"

"That's what I thought. See you in half an hour." Johnny hung up, and went whistling into the kitchen, where his father was cutting bread for sandwiches. "She's coming, Pop; she's coming. You can make a double portion."

"I was planning on it. Had a feeling in my bones, Johnny. . . . I don't know which is brighter—your face or the Sabbath morn."

"I feel pretty swell."

"Well—don't let your hopes go too high."

"No. . . . Hey, throw me the knife. I can spread the butter. I wonder what Pat likes in her sandwiches."

"Didn't you ever find that out? Anyway, she'll have to take what we've got." Mr. Wheelwright dipped into a jar of peanut butter. "You can still change your mind, you know, and come to the lake with us."

"Nope. This is going to be an important day in my life," Johnny said. "I adopted a new policy a couple of months ago, and I think it's starting to work. I wish you could have heard her voice on the phone. She *wants* to come."

"Mmmm," said his father, spreading the peanut butter.

"Course, if you really *need* me at the cottage—"

"We'll do nicely without you."

"Think you'll be able to rent it this summer?"

"There haven't been any nibbles. But I live in hope."

"Try not to rent it before the end of June. We ought to have a couple parties out there first."

"Using buttons for money."

"Everybody could chip in." Johnny licked blackberry jam from a spoon and went to the sink to wash the spoon off. "Thing is, it's the best cottage anywhere along there for a party. We could have just one, Pop, don't you think? Starting in May I'm going to be on full time at the plant; have so much money I won't know what to do with it."

"Just come to me, Johnny. My head is full of ideas for things to do with money. Well, yes, I suppose we might manage one party. . . . Tell me about your new policy with Patricia. If you want to."

Johnny spread his elbows on the kitchen table and stared at the sky beyond the window; it had never looked so blue to him. "Well, in a way," he said, "it all started with Ralph Waldo Emerson."

"Which would probably surprise Ralph Waldo."

"Yeah. But something he said—well, I didn't interpret it the right way, maybe, but always before when I was with Pat, I was ashamed of the kind of guy I was. I kept trying to be somebody different—the kind of guy I thought she might like. But it didn't work. Because I couldn't be anything except the kind of guy I was born. I'm not perfect; hell, there are an awful lot of things wrong with me, but I guess nobody's perfect, so I decided just to go ahead and be myself, kind of. Faults and all. Then I went over there one night, gee, it was a long time ago now, and Pat came in with this guy she's been going around with, and I got a really good look at him, and— Well," said Johnny, absently eating a sandwich, "maybe I'm conceited—"

"And maybe it would be better not to speak with your mouth full. You've had breakfast; that was for your lunch."

"Yeah," said Johnny with his mouth full. "As I was saying. Maybe I'm conceited, and I guess he's better-looking than I am, but you know, Pop, there's nothing to that guy, nothing at all. He's just looks. He thinks he's pretty bright, but I was kind of bright myself that night. And then I—" Johnny swallowed the rest of the sandwich. "Well, I'll skip the sordid details, but I think maybe I made him look like a fool. Pat didn't like what I did very much, but she was sore at him too. So I made him look like a fool, and I walked out of the house, and then I thought I'd give her plenty of time to let it sink in. The significance of what happened that night. He'd be a lousy husband for her, that guy, a lousy husband for anybody. He isn't exactly a fairy, I don't think, but he's something pretty peculiar just the same. No guts," said Johnny, "no guts at all."

He stood up and went to the drawer where the wax-paper was kept, and tossed the box across to his father.

"Well, she keeps right on going out with him," he said. "Every so often I drop in, to check up, kind of. I check up with Delores, and Pat is still going around with him. But she'll see through him, sooner or later. I think maybe today is the day. Up to that night," Johnny said, "I was always kind of, well, humble with her. But that's all over. Like me the way I am, or the hell with you; that's the way it's going to be between me and Patricia from now on."

Mr. Wheelwright wrapped the sandwiches with great care and snapped rubber bands around them. "And if she still says the hell with *you?*"

"I don't think she will. She sounded so damn relieved on the phone. As if she'd been scared it was him calling, only it turned out to be me. . . . Lemonade all fixed? Well, I guess I'll be getting along. Have to grease her bike for her. That's something else about that guy. I'll bet he never got his hands dirty in his life."

Mr. Wheelwright gave the big brown-paper bag to Johnny; he stuck the thermos bottle under Johnny's arm; then he punched him gently on the shoulder. "Good luck," he said. "Fortune and victory sit on thy helm. *That*'s William Shakespeare."

Johnny whistled loudly, pushing his laden bicycle along the sidewalk and across the street and up the Bryants' driveway. Joel was kneeling outside the garage, with Patricia's bicycle strewn in pieces all about him; his hands were black with grease and so was most of his face.

"Hey," Johnny said, "I was going to do that."

"You work all week. Anyway, I thought I ought to get started on it. What's the time, Johnny?"

"Half-past eight."

"Well, there's plenty of time. Vincent won't be here till eleven."

"Vincent?"

"He was going to take Pat to the big lake today," Joel said, working busily, "but she's running out on him."

"Oh, yeah. I know." Johnny felt better than ever. Fortune and victory sit on thy helm; wonderful words, glorious words—when there was time to read again, he would have to look into William Shakespeare.

"The reason she goes around with Vincent is, Vincent has a car," said Joel. "She didn't go around with him so much when the car was in storage. Girls sure are funny."

"They're nice too, Joel. Wait till you have one of your own."

"I have three right now, but they sure are funny."

"Three, huh?"

"Yah. I'm going to wait a while before I make up my mind."

"Who are they? Or is that a secret?"

"Naw, it's no secret. They're Buzz Boonstra's sisters. Two of them are twins and that makes it even harder to pick. The other one isn't a twin and I think maybe I like her best, only she's funny too and she's about a year older than me. She's brighter than I am at school too. The twins are younger, and they're kind of dumb. That's what I like about them," said Joel.

"Don't you have any rivals?"

Joel picked up a wrench and put the back wheel in place and tightened the bolts. "Nothing to worry about. They all like me better than any other kid in school, Buzz's sisters do, so I can take my time about picking. Course, I might pick somebody who isn't even related to Buzz, finally. The trouble with the Boonstras is, they're so darn religious. Always going to church and prayer-meetings and stuff. It's all right to pray, I guess, but not if you do it all the time. And they don't smoke or drink or even go to the movies."

"Kind of cramps your style on dates, doesn't it?"

"Well, it's economical, anyway." The bicycle was now reassembled; Joel rose, wiping his hands on a rag. "There," he said, "all set."

"Thanks a lot, Joel."

"Anything to oblige," Joel said, wiping excess grease from the bicycle. He stood it up and spun the back wheel. "The thing is, Johnny, I don't like Vincent. He gave Pat a Christmas present. A book of poetry."

"Yeah. . . . Look," Johnny said, "if *you* want to go down to the lake today, with my folks, I know they'd be glad to have you."

"Naw, I'm going to work on Buzz's boat. Thanks just the same though."

They walked in through the kitchen doorway together, and Patricia called down the back stairs, "Johnny? Be there in a minute."

When she came, descending from the shadows into a swath of sunlight, he didn't know if he was going to be able to follow his new policy after all—a fist in the solar plexus again.

"Gee, Pat—" he said; the spring morning had become hers, she was the source of warmth and light. Fortune and victory sit on thy helm, Johnny said to himself again, wobbling down the driveway after her. The wind blew her skirt out; the shadows flickered over her; already she was beginning to seem unreal and unattainable; but he rode up alongside of her and put out his hand, saying, "Slow down a minute. Where are we going?"

"You decide, Johnny."

They began by heading northward because that way lay some good steep hills for coasting; they pedaled fast and mostly in silence until the city was left behind, as if they were in flight from something: Vincent Rourke, perhaps. For the first time that year Johnny noticed a faint shimmer of color on the trees; when they passed a swampy bottom-land he could hear the voices of the peepers, high and cold and silvery; the wind blew cool on his face but the sunlight struck through the crystal air, scorching the back of his neck, burning his shoulders through the thin white shirt. There would be other days like this, many of them between now and the end of October, and all of them would seem miraculous; but this was the first of its kind after the winter, and he wanted to shout as he rode.

At the end of a long, slow climb they paused for a few minutes to get their breath back and ease the strain out of their legs.

Patricia asked, "Is this the first time you've been out this year?"

"Naw. Been out every Sunday, now, since the end of March. I need all the fresh air I can gulp, Sundays, to get the taste of the plant out of my mouth. Start working there full time soon. Don't know if I'll be able to take it or not. I don't think I ever knew how wonderful silence was before. I never noticed how quiet it is, on a morning like this, all around Broadfield, until I started working in the plant."

They stood there, holding the bicycles, and listened: a few bird-calls and wind in last year's dry grass, and nothing else at all for a moment until the chime of church bells floated across the fields, and then the noise of a train hooting for a grade crossing—a sound which filled you with yearning in fall or winter, but today was the voice of joy itself.

"See what I mean?" said Johnny.

They rode on again and left the concrete highway for a back road, deeply rutted still from the frosts and thaws of winter and the farm trucks which had churned the mud, but dry enough, and even a little dusty. The wind stirred the dust like thin smoke, saffron-colored, and the sunlight made that seem miraculous too.

Presently they dismounted and pushed the bicycles along a sandy track; it wound upward among small trees and emerged into meadowland which rose to a knoll—they could look back across the route they had followed, all the way back to the city, lying smokeless in the morning air, spreading over its hills and hollows. Now the church bells were so distant they were hardly audible.

"We might as well stay here, I guess," Johnny said. "God, but it's a perfect day."

Patricia stood quite still, gazing at Broadfield. "I'm trying to remember a poem," she said, "a poem we read in high school. The only poem by Wordsworth I ever liked."

"The Westminster Bridge one?" Johnny asked.

"Yes." Patricia looked surprised. "I didn't know you—"

Johnny grinned. "I've turned into a bookworm lately." He sighed; he stretched his arms out, almost unconsciously, as if he could embrace the whole shining day; his happiness was too great, it pulled him apart, needing some form of expression.

"I tried to read a long one, a long poem by Wordsworth called

The Prelude," Johnny said after a while, "but I got kind of bogged down. It begins with the time he was a boy, and how he felt about nature. What nature did to him. . . . Let's sit down," Johnny said. "I guess the ground is dry enough."

Patricia sat on the grass, and Johnny stretched himself out near her; the sun blazed on his back.

"Nature was pretty important to a lot of those old guys," he said. "Emerson, for instance, and Thoreau, and Whitman. In *Walden* there's a whole lot about the way a mudbank, even, looks in early spring, when the thaw starts." He propped himself on his elbows; with his hands he spread apart the dead grass so that he could see the new green blades springing upward. "I guess it's pretty important to me too. Always has been. Nature," said Johnny. "But what I've been trying to figure out— So many people who like nature, they want to be left alone with it. Alone in the fields or the woods or on top of a mountain, or on the shore. As if having somebody else around, another human being, spoiled it a little. But it doesn't for me. It makes it better," Johnny said, pressing his palms against the cold new grass. "We're part of nature, aren't we? We're the most important part. In our own eyes, anyway. You stand on top of a mountain all by yourself, there's something missing; you need somebody to share it with."

He rolled over; he stared through half-shut eyes at the dazzling sky, and presently he had to shadow his face with his fingers. "Emerson and Thoreau, they were the ones who wanted to be alone. There's something in Emerson: 'You cannot freely admire a noble landscape if laborers are digging in the field hard by. The poet finds something ridiculous in his delight until he is out of the sight of men.' Well, maybe the trouble with me is, I'm not a poet. But Whitman didn't feel that way, I think; he liked to be where people were. . . . So when I go out riding all by myself, I don't have such a good time, Pat."

He found that without knowing it he had been leading up to what he meant to say to her, but now he couldn't go on; so he just lay there, sprawled in the sun, shielding his eyes with his hands. It was part of the miracle of this day that he had been able to say as much already.

"Johnny," Patricia said sadly, "Johnny, isn't there anybody else? Isn't there anybody else at all except me, who'd go riding with you, who'd feel the way you do about—everything?"

"It doesn't seem that way, Pat," he said, staring into the sun.

"I keep wondering why you— I've been so horrible to you, Johnny, always. You're so kind and good," Patricia said, "but I've never been anything but horrible to you."

"You're crazy, Pat. You—"

"No, it's true. . . . Johnny," she said, "I'm not the right one, I never will be. You'll have to find somebody else."

He lay quiet beside her. His happiness had turned into an almost insufferable ache of longing for her, but it was happiness still; happiness has a dark as well as a bright surface, and when the dark surface turns upward it is not necessarily despair.

"It's so foolish, Johnny, to let one single person become as—important to you as all that. Especially somebody who'd always—let you down, finally."

"You wouldn't let me down, Pat."

"But I would, Johnny. I always have. I always will. I'm letting you down right now. I didn't come with you today because I wanted to, not really; I came to get away from somebody else. I have to tell you, Johnny. I have to tell you how things are."

"Vincent?" he said. "Was that who you wanted to get away from?"

"No, not even Vincent. We were going to the lake with Carola Wilmot. I'm scared of her, Johnny. I didn't want to spend the day with her, having her look at Vincent and me and thinking I don't know what about us. So you see, I've been horrible to him, and now I'm being horrible to you."

Johnny pushed himself up and sat with his arms clasped around his knees, gazing away at the city. Fortune and victory sit on thy helm; I will do strongly before the sun and moon whatever inly rejoices me, and the heart appoints: whatever the heart appoints—the brave words, the ringing words, ran through his head, and the dark face of happiness still was not despair.

"You really crazy about Vincent?" he said at last.

"Yes, Johnny."

"Poor Pat," he said. "Oh, you poor kid." He touched her hand; he sat there holding her hand in his, bending the fingers gently; he stooped his head and kissed her hand, and then let it go and looked away from her again. "*He*'ll let you down, Pat. I'm not trying to—make you feel different about me. If it doesn't happen, it just doesn't happen, that's all. But he'll let you down finally. I know it."

"Do you think I don't know it too?" She almost laughed, he thought. "Empty," she said, "he likes to feel empty. He likes desert places—that's the kind of nature he likes, to be all alone, driving across the desert at eighty miles an hour. . . . I used to think I'd never fall in love. I thought it was a lie, Johnny, about falling in love. I don't know why it couldn't have happened with you, instead of Vincent."

"Maybe you're just mixed up."

"I've always been mixed up. All my life. But some things have been coming clear, the last few weeks. Being in love makes you more mixed up in some ways, but it makes other things clear. I can see him so clearly now, I can see you so clearly too, and he's nothing besides you, Johnny, I know that. But I can't get him out of my mind."

She gazed intently across the fields toward the roofs and spires and tall yellow chimneys of the city, as if she thought an answer to what bewildered her might be spread in great letters across the sky; but the sky was quite empty.

"I never knew you before, Johnny," she went on presently. "The boy I thought of as Johnny Wheelwright—it wasn't you, it was nobody like you. You make me so ashamed," Patricia said. "I think you're the best person I've ever known."

"Hell," said Johnny softly, though the bright surface was uppermost again, "if you think that, Pat, then I guess you still don't know me very well." He smiled at her, but her gaze was still fixed on the sky above Broadfield. "If anybody'd overheard what you were saying, just now," he said, "they'd think *I* was the guy you were in love with. Pat, are you so sure—are you so damn sure?"

Now she did look at him; she looked into his face for a long time, as she had been looking at the sky, but her eyes seemed dazzled by the brightness of the day. He knew the time had not come yet, but he knew that it would come. He might hasten its coming, if he took her in his arms as he wanted to, and drove away the last of her old fears, and blotted out the last thought of Vincent Rourke; he could do that, he knew, but it was better to wait a little longer.

He saw how tremulous she was looking, and out of his new and enormous confidence said, "Don't cry, Pat. This is no day for crying. I'm not crying, am I? No, don't turn your head away, look at me—look at me again; I'm happier than I've ever been before. Can't you see that?"

He could sit still no longer. He jumped up, and caught both of her hands, and pulled her to her feet. This place which had become glorious to him was a sad one for her, and he said, "We'll ride on. There are better views than this around Broadfield. We'll find the best view of all before we stop and have lunch."

She followed him docilely back to the road. They came to another paved highway, and there was another long hill to climb, another long swift descent on the far side; and by then the color had come back into her face and when he looked across at her she laughed; for at least a little while she had forgotten Vincent Rourke, who was having a bad time of it with Carola Wilmot.

All the way to the lake Carola twitted him about Patricia, and his anger smoldered. Nothing to him the warmth of the sun and the tide of clear air; nothing the high blue sky, the new-plowed fields, the color trembling elusively where trees were massed together. He kept thinking how all the faces had been set against

him, when he ran whistling up the front steps of the Bryants'
house. They were out on the front porch, reading the Sunday
papers, Norris and Charlie, Delores and Joel, and the baby in his
coop was beating a wooden spoon on a saucepan. Vincent thought
absurdly that even the baby had a smug gloating look when Norris
said Patricia wasn't there but had changed her mind and gone
bicycling with Johnny Wheelwright.

"Oh," said Vincent. The way they looked at him made him
feel naked. "Well, it was all pretty vague, anyway. See you tomorrow, Bry," he said, and turned back to his car, whistling still, but
raging inwardly, and shaking too, so much that he clashed the
gears when he drove away along Johnson Avenue. They hated him,
he thought; they actually hated him; and it enraged him that he
should mind.

And then all the way to the lake, from the beginning to the end
of that journey across a monotonous and shabby landscape, Carola
teased him; she was in high spirits, and he supposed she was glad
to have him to herself.

Her cottage was perched among trees on the summit of the high
dunes which rose along that part of the lake shore; it had the
shoddy look of summer cottages anywhere, and a blind look too
this morning, under the glare of the sun, since heavy shutters were
bolted over all the windows.

Carola sat in the car and gazed at her property. "It is so much
work," she said, "as you are about to discover, darling. Didn't I
warn you to wear old clothes?" She was wearing a thin jersey and
denim slacks, and had a bandanna tied over her head; she climbed
down and crossed to a shed, unlocked the door, vanished inside,
and emerged presently with her arms full of tools. "Come along,
darling," she said, "there's no time to lose. And you'd better take
off that nice white shirt. We're about to *grovel* in filth." She looked
astonishingly energetic, and astonishingly inelegant.

They began by taking the shutters down from all the windows
and carrying them away and stacking them in the shed. Then there
was sand to be shoveled off the slatted boardwalk leading to the
brink of the dunes where a flight of wooden steps would be set up;
there was more sand to be swept off the wide front porch; there
was furniture to be shifted from the dark dank interior; there were
screens to be put up.

"We might just as well do as much as we can now," said Carola,
"and then I won't have to pay old Collins for more than a half-
day's work. It's such *energizing* weather."

"I'm glad you think so," said Vincent.

"Never mind, darling, we'll rest soon."

Their labors, however, continued into the afternoon; Carola
seemed inexhaustible, but Vincent, running with sweat, was ready

to drop in his tracks long before she said, "Now I think we might knock off and have a cocktail and a cigarette. Bring the hamper, darling, and those jugs of water. I'm afraid you aren't going to be able to *wash* until you get back to town, unless you want to try the lake, which is doubtless still icy."

They sat on the porch, both of them dirty and disheveled and Vincent still in his undershirt, sipping the Martinis Carola had poured from a thermos bottle, and staring out at the lake.

"I suppose perhaps it has been a little overrated," Carola said. "After you've said how large it is and duly noted that it goes on and on to the horizon, there isn't much more to say or note. I think I should part with the cottage without a pang, if I could sell it. Or even rent it for the season. But owning a cottage by the lake is a kind of tradition with all of us. These little traditions which keep me tied *down* here—what a bore they really are. Still, I must say I love to get *thoroughly* dirty and *thoroughly* messy and just sort of let myself go, on my first trip down each year. It's part of the tradition, of course. Are you ready for another cocktail, darling? Yes, I see you are."

After she had refilled his glass she said, "Poor Vincent! If you could *see* how you look! I do believe this must be the first time in your life you've ever lifted a finger. But you may keep on glowering; you've been an angel, and I've treated you very badly."

She leaned back and swung gently in the hammock, her glance flickering over him with a mild irony. "I suppose you're no good at all with machinery. We'll have to leave the pump to old Collins, I'm afraid. It's a pity, because I'm sure he's a saboteur. I inspect it carefully, and it looks perfectly all right to me, and the next thing I know, old Collins says it needs seven different new parts, each one more expensive than the last. If only I'd thought of it in time, I'd have asked Johnny to come along too. *He* could have made the pump work, *and* switched on the electricity. We are cut off from civilization, darling; even the telephone is disconnected. So we shall both have to remain filthy and unglamourous. . . ."

"Dirt," she said, "does something *most* extraordinary to you, Vincent. You look like the guttersnipe you say your father was. No, it really is not becoming to you. Johnny Wheelwright, on the other hand, crawling out from beneath a car all dripping with grease, is somehow rather charming. . . . I shan't look at you any more," said Carola, "but I think you ought to be glad that Patricia didn't come. She would have stopped loving you instantly. Those endearing young charms—quite, quite gone. As they will be gone for good, my dear, by the time you're thirty or thirty-five—I predict that you will run to fat. Never mind, Vincent; there are times when I can't help resenting your extreme youth. Are you beginning to feel hungry?"

The sad monkey had packed as good a meal as Carola had promised, and the Rhine wine she poured from the tall thin bottle was clear and pale and clean-tasting; the wine and the Martinis dissolved Vincent's anger, and presently he forgot his aching muscles.

"The least you can do now," he said, wiping remnants of cold chicken off his fingers, "is ask me out here for week-ends sometimes."

"For services rendered? I shall be charmed, darling. Shall I ask Patricia too? Can you see me as a chaperon?"

"Patricia thinks you don't like her. As a matter of fact," Vincent said, suddenly feeling quite cheerful, "I'll bet that's the real reason she went off with Johnny instead today."

"Vincent, you cut me to the quick. Won't you have some more chicken? Some more wine, then? There's another bottle." Carola groped in the hamper. "What makes you think Patricia doesn't like me?"

"I said she thought you—"

"I do so dislike having people dislike me. And far too many people in Broadfield do. Simply, you know, because I've had three husbands, not one of whom was really a prize specimen. Still, they are consumed with envy. If Nevil hadn't been killed in the war and had come back and taken to drink and to beating me, my popularity would have known no bounds. The fact that Norris Bryant drank *after* Laura's death has somehow had a retroactive effect; people have far more pity for her than she's entitled to." Carola sighed, and swung gently in the hammock, and sipped her wine.

"I haven't ever told you about Nevil, have I? . . . The one great love of my life. We went to London in 1910, *en famille*—I was twenty then, I was to be given a grand tour of the continent, but in London I met Nevil. He was one of those tall blond rather pretty Englishmen, and icy on occasion, but also *most* charming. Dear me, what an innocent I was. Perhaps I still am, because I still like to think my father's fortune was not the chief attraction. So Nevil became part of the grand tour and by the time we reached Florence we had decided to get married. We brought him back to Broadfield, along with the other souvenirs and objets d'art. I still think Nevil was the nicest, even though he wasn't much of a success in the plant—that was before Father had retired, of course.

"Well, then the war came and I'm afraid Nevil was rather glad to escape into it. Doing and dying without reasoning why was much more his sort of thing than being an ornament to Broadfield society. Well, he was killed at Ypres," said Carola, gazing out at the lake, "and to save my sanity I managed to go overseas for the Red Cross. I can't think now what charm I saw in Bodo, whom

I met in Paris. He was small and rather nasty, but he had a bewitching accent, and we were married the day after Armistice was declared. All very usual, the life we led, in Paris and on the Riviera mostly; it lasted less than a year, and then I began to float lonely as a cloud about Paris. Your Uncle Bertrand fits into the picture somewhere along in those years—my dear, the crowd *he* went around with!

"Then Hank Wendover turned up, still in uniform. I hadn't known Hank very well before, but he was such a contrast to Nevil and Bodo, and of course to your Uncle Bertrand and his little set. I'd never expected to feel nostalgic about Broadfield, but that was how Hank made me feel; I literally hurled myself into his strong arms, and presently back we came, but he was the most ungodly bore, poor darling, and that was why I began to dabble in local culture. It was then that I really got to know Laura Bryant—I didn't know her for more than two or three years before she died, but it seems to have been a long time, as I look back upon it. What I did not know then was the real reason for my jealousy of her. God knows I didn't envy her Norris and that litter of off-spring—but she was content, Vincent, she seemed to have solved a mystery which remains a mystery to me to this day. She was content, at least, until Andy McBain came along. And even after her little escapade. . . . It is all very baffling," said Carola, "and I see that I'm boring you to distraction."

"Not at all," said Vincent. "I'm fascinated."

"Darling, I've *seen* you stifling yawns. Shall we take a stroll along the beach, before you lapse into a coma?"

They walked as far as the Wheelwrights' cottage, and then retreated stealthily, because it was swarming with Wheelwrights and Carola said she simply did not feel in the mood.

"Besides, they'd put you right back to work again, darling," she said. "If you don't want to swim, we might as well pack up, I suppose, and wend our homeward way. I'm afraid the day has been a complete fiasco for you."

"Not at all," said Vincent again.

"You say that just like Noel Coward."

"I used to practice. Uncle Bertrand had some records of *Private Lives.*"

"You make me pine for New York—for anywhere but here," said Carola, looking with sudden disfavor on the lake, and began to climb the steep cliff of sand toward her cottage.

By the time they had packed the tools away, and put what was left of the lunch back in the hamper, and spread tarpaulins over the porch furniture, and locked the cottage up again, it was five o'clock in the afternoon. They returned to Broadfield through a golden light which redeemed the landscape—the occasional shoddy farmhouses, the small villages like squatters' colonies, and the telephone poles marching beside the road in a somewhat tipsy procession, their wires looping up and down monotonously, mile after mile. The country was striped with long rich shadows, the plowed fields looked dark and luscious, and the grass appeared greener than it had that morning; color was now clotted on the trees.

Out of a long silence Carola said, "It occurs to me that I've never really gotten over Nevil. He was so fair," she said, "so dazzlingly fair. . . . I am wearing my heart on my sleeve today, darling; please don't make fun of me."

She said nothing more, but sat with her head averted, looking off into the south, until they came into the western outskirts of the city. They swept past Morison Park, where couples were strolling and children playing in the dusk, their voices ringing high and clear above the sounds of traffic; past the empty factory district, across the bridge, across the railroad tracks, across Broadfield Avenue, and up Warner Street hill toward Carola's house.

"You must come in and have another drink," she said, "all dirty as you are. It's a mistake to drink during the day; I think I must have a mild hangover."

But there was a black coupé parked in the driveway before her house, and she sat staring at it for several moments after Vincent had pulled up behind.

"It's Dr. Laplace's car," she said. "I wonder if— My father had a bad night last night, and I shouldn't have deserted him today. If he's taken a turn for the worse—"

The fact was that Carola's father had just died, so Vincent didn't have anything more to drink that day after all.

17

THE DEATH of Alexander Wilmot was the biggest news on the city side next day, and Norris himself wrote the obituary notice, which appeared on the front page with a one-column cut of Mr. Wilmot as he had looked some fifteen years earlier. The *Chronicle* had more time to collect material than the *Morning Bugle* had had, and printed tributes from industrial magnates and the mayor and the judge of circuit court and other leading citizens who had known Alexander well, it seemed, and loved him well. As Ack Guion said privately, the old bastard had kicked the bucket at last, or, as the mayor said for publication, yet one more of the old guard had passed on with banners flying.

One sentence in the obituary notice kept running through Norris's head: "He is survived by a daughter, Mrs. Carola Wilmot of this city." So often, when an old man died in Broadfield, the names of the survivors filled a long paragraph.

Norris had called Carola on the telephone to check some of the details in the story, and to ask her how she wanted her own name to appear. "The whole business is so disgusting," she said, "and so degrading. Need there be a story at all, Norris? Father would have hated it." Norris said firmly that this was one of the times when the press must override personal feelings, Alexander Wilmot having been part of the history of Broadfield and his death an event. "About your name—" "Put whatever you think best," said Carola, and hung up. He hadn't expected her to sound grief-stricken; he supposed that as soon as she decently could she would dispose of Alexander's property and depart for New York or even for Europe, and never again be seen in Broadfield.

She had never really belonged in Broadfield anyway, as Norris remarked to Betty Lou when he went to see her that night. Ever since her return from Muskogee, the habit of dropping in to talk things over with Betty Lou had grown upon him; now that April was ending he found himself climbing the steps of her porch almost every night. Often she did most of the talking, but there were other evenings when she sat and rocked on the front porch, or swung in the string hammock beneath her sour-cherry tree in the back yard, and listened to whatever he had on his mind to say. Many of her comments were irrelevant, but sometimes she surprised him by neatly and cleanly hitting the nail on the head. He found her soothing and reassuring, and remembering what he had written to her about having wandered into a labyrinth and fearing to meet a Minotaur, he began to think the tangle of dark corridors had been all in his own mind. The walls were toppling, the shadows retreating, and life was opening out again; the muddle of the years since Laura's death was about to be left behind.

So he thought, moving placidly through those days of early spring—in a dream again, but a different kind of dream from the old one because this time he was not afraid of what he might find upon waking.

Broadfield in spring was a city in a dream, anyway. There were processions of days which seemed to have been left over from last November, but between these spells it was really spring and the city took on a grace that astonished the heart. Out of such ordinary materials as leaves and shadows, greening lawns and blossoming shrubs, clear warm days and starry nights, a miracle was being woven: the slattern had become a queen, resting proudly on her hills and valleys, surveying her shining river, casting her smoke like pennons into the sky. It was hard to believe that any other city in the world had so many trees and such tall ones; that the sunlight fell so benignly on any other city; that the sky above any other city could be so blue or the clouds so white; that the buildings of any other city, which had seemed hideous a month ago, could so deceive you into thinking them right and beautiful—the very bricks and mortar and wood and stone had gone a little mad with spring. And from all the great wide meadows that surrounded the city, from the new-plowed fields and budding orchards, from the lakes and streams and woodlands, warm scented winds came rushing like messengers of life, to blow along the streets, push windows open, play a game with scraps of paper, flap the flags, strike into the remotest corners and stir up the old stagnation and drive men and women forth into the sun with the children and the shouting birds.

Not for many years had Norris been so acutely aware of spring; it was like being a boy again, and he forgot to feel guilty about taking so much of Betty Lou's time. She was a necessity to him; but he would not let himself believe yet that he was necessary to her. For she seemed younger to him sometimes than his own children—her life had never been touched by such darkness as he had cast into theirs.

April was gone before he emerged far enough from his dream to see that for them the darkness still went on.

Patricia was spending some evenings with Johnny, but more often she sat listless on the front porch, gazing out into the dusk. She would be there when Norris strolled across to Betty Lou's house, and there still when he returned. Sometimes Charlie was with her, and whatever it was they had been saying to each other would break off as Norris approached. He would stand at the top of the steps, peering at them through the screens, and they would look steadfastly away from him until he said "Good night" and went on into the house.

Charlie was still working hard in the garden, and on afternoons when Norris came back early from the paper he worked there too; but the intimacy which had begun over seed-catalogues and ground-plans had somehow languished and died. Charlie kneeled in silence, pulling out weeds, and when Norris glanced across at him the old sullen look was back on his face; or perhaps it was more a look of bewilderment. Norris wondered if he ought not to have another talk with Delores, and a great weariness suddenly assailed him; Delores seemed hardly worth the effort.

In the end he wrote to Laurette. As well as he could he told her what the trouble was, and asked if she couldn't come to Broadfield for a week-end soon. Charlie had done his share now, Norris wrote, and it was time for Delores to do hers, and maybe Laurette would know better what to say to her. "If the marriage was a mistake to begin with, and can't be put right, Charlie will have to face the fact sooner or later. Maybe he's trying to face it now, and you might help to pull him through a bad time. I know how close to each other you and Charlie are, Laurette, and how much you want to help him."

The silence and strangeness which had fallen on Charlie and Patricia seemed to have fallen on Delores too. She did the housework industriously enough; but how indifferent she was growing toward her child Norris did not know until Betty Lou, with some hesitation, told him one night that three times in the last week she'd heard the baby's wails and gone over and found him dirty and Delores nowhere in sight; and had changed and comforted him herself.

"I just hated to tell you, Norris," she said, staring up into her sour-cherry tree, "because it sounds like I was criticizing Delores. Well, that's what I am doing, I guess. I waited over there, I stayed with David until she got back, and I gave her a piece of my mind. I said if she didn't want to take him with her when she went shopping or wherever, to call me, and I'd look after him.—Because I would, Norris, I'd love to.—But she told me to mind my own business. . . . Well, I did think you ought to know. He's such a darling baby, and it isn't safe for him to be left all by himself. Trouble with Delores, I guess, she's not much more than a baby herself. Just too young to have the responsibility."

Norris did try to talk to Delores about that. He chose an afternoon when Charlie was still out with the truck and Delores was drowsing by the radio. But she set her lips, and her eyes grew veiled; she reached out and turned the radio on louder.

Norris said, "I'm serious about this, Delores. You can't leave a baby alone in the house for hours at a time." He crossed the room and shut the radio off.

She stood up and flounced away with the first real display of temper he had seen in her. "I'm so bored, that's all. I'm so bored I think I'll go crazy if something doesn't happen soon." She whirled on him. "You just don't know what it's like. I'm young, and I have all of my life ahead of me yet, and I never have any fun or get to go out anywhere or see anybody but you and Patricia and Charlie." Her lips trembled; she collapsed on the piano-bench and began to cry. "I wish I'd never married him, that's what; or had the baby or come to Broadfield at all. I hate it here. I might just as well be dead."

"Maybe we have been piling the work up on you," Norris said. "If you want a day off now and then, Betty Lou would be—"

"A day off! Sure, that's all I am, just a maid, just some common servant to the rest of you. No, not a servant even—a slave. I don't even get paid for my work."

"Now, Delores, that isn't the right way to—"

"What good would a day off do me? I don't know anybody. There's nowhere for me to go."

Norris sighed. "Well Laurette's coming up for a week-end soon, and she still knows quite a lot of young people here. Maybe she could kind of introduce you around. I have so many things to keep track of, I'm afraid I've kind of lost track of you." He wished she would look at him. "But you know, Delores, I envy you, really. I'd much rather sit home with David than go down to the paper every day. It's a wonderful time in a baby's life. He's growing so fast—he changes every minute, almost. I could spend all my time watching him."

"Because you don't have to. You don't know how much work a baby is."

Norris smiled. "I've had four children of my own."

"Yes, and who did all the work?" cried Delores, standing up. "Who had all the pain and suffering and then had to do all the work? Your wife, that's who. Do you think she didn't get bored sometimes? Do you think she didn't get sick and tired of the sight of them?"

"Everybody gets a little bored with life sometimes, Delores."

"Nobody but rich people should have children. *You* never had a right to have any children. Look at the way they turned out."

"Now, Delores, you're just upset."

"You're damn right I'm upset. I got a good mind to walk out on the whole bunch of you and never come back." Delores fled upstairs, and Norris wished he had left her alone.

But he remembered now that there had been evenings as well as mornings when Delores simply disappeared. A secretive look would come over her face as dinner drew to a close; then, between the time they rose from table and the time the dishes were stacked in the sink, she would have disappeared, without a word to anybody, and when she drifted in again at half-past ten or eleven or later, she appeared to be almost drugged—she moved with such languor, smiled so strangely, spoke so slowly and remotely; and then she would climb the stairs and shut herself into her room with her child.

Norris asked Patricia about it, finally, as they were washing the dishes one night. Patricia gazed out into the garden, where Charlie was standing with a hose in his hand, sprinkling the lettuce seedlings. "Maybe she goes to the movies."

"Three or four nights a week? And all alone?"

"I don't know, Father. I don't know anything about Delores."

It turned out that Joel had been lingering in the dining room; now he appeared in the doorway and said, "She goes out with different fellows. Buzz Boonstra, he was in Morison Park one night a couple weeks ago, at a wiener roast, and he saw Delores. She walked right past him with a fellow."

Patricia continued to stir a mop through the suds; she fished up one dish after another, until the draining-basket was stacked full; but time seemed to have stopped in the kitchen. Joel leaned in the doorway, looking unconcernedly at his father; Norris stared at him in distress; out in the garden Charlie played the hose over his lettuces. Patricia felt a vast impatience with her father, and made time start again.

"It wasn't very hard to guess," she said.

"But—" Norris pulled out a chair and sat down at the kitchen table. "How'd Delores get way over to Morison Park?"

"There are trolley-cars," said Patricia. "There are even boys with automobiles."

"It just happened, probably. Just that one time," Norris said. "She went over to the park for a little fresh air, and—"

"I've seen her downtown myself," said Joel, with the same bland unconcern. "Going into a movie with a fellow. A different one both times."

"You haven't told Charlie?"

"Naw." Joel smiled; he looked pitying and a little scornful. "Gee, Pop, I'm not that dumb. If Charlie knew, he'd try to beat her up again, prob'ly."

Patricia pulled out the plug and watched the soapy water swirl down the drain. Her father made her impatient but Joel astonished her—where did his innocence stop, and what was the source of his calm? Perhaps Norris was wondering the same thing. He kept staring at Joel, and frowning, and trying to say something more. But when he did manage to speak, the remark was completely inane: "You shouldn't talk like that about your own brother."

Joel yawned widely, and stretched, and wandered toward the back door. "Charlie's really tough, isn't he?" he said, contemplating him through the screen-door—with admiration, it seemed. "But I don't see why he wastes so much time fussing in the garden. . . . So long," said Joel, and kicked the screen-door open and was gone. A moment later, Patricia could hear his bicycle rolling down the driveway.

Norris sat helplessly at the kitchen table, resting his head on his hands, while Patricia finished drying the dishes.

"How long has it been going on, Pat, do you think?"

"Maybe it isn't true, what Joel said. Though it probably is. Delores has always been like that. Charlie told me—" But she broke off and hung the wet towel carefully over the rail. Preoccupied with private anxieties, she could not waste time or energy on Delores; but pity for her father, who always took things so hard, touched her as it had been touching her increasingly of late.

"I think you might just as well give Delores up as a lost cause." She looked out at Charlie, and back at Norris. "You'll have to learn how to be tough too," Patricia said, astonished at the discovery she thought she had made. "You never have been tough enough, I don't think. That's why—" She paused. "You expect too much of people. You can't make them different from the way they are, and it's foolish to—tear yourself to pieces because they—go on being themselves."

"It's my son's life, my grandson's life, I'm thinking about. Pat, I can't be tough about that."

"They'll both be better off without Delores. Charlie's given her up. He has, Father."

Norris stood up slowly, and after a little while he went away to see Betty Lou again. Before Patricia left the kitchen she could hear their voices, murmuring under the sour-cherry tree. She wished he would marry Betty Lou and get it over with and start leading his own life again. There was too much eagerness on the part of parents to go on being parents.

She sat out on the hammock, swinging slowly, and the unrest which had been growing in her all spring was worse tonight. Since that Sunday morning she had felt a kind of shame in Johnny's presence, because she had shown him too much of herself; and Johnny as she knew him now disturbed her profoundly. He filled her with humbleness, but there was no humility left in him—his eyes no longer worshiped her. He was kind and gentle enough, but beneath the kindness and gentleness there was scorn, she thought—not love, but pity.

She wished he would come over, but she knew that if he came she would remain unsatisfied; really it was Vincent she wanted, and Vincent would never come, now. She sat and yearned for him, trying to remember every detail of his face, and what his voice sounded like, and the feel of his hands, gently and subtly bringing her body to life. It was Vincent with a glory shining about him that came into her mind; though all the time she knew he was not like that. If she were sensible she would rejoice at having lost him; but she could not rejoice, and she knew that if he did not come to her soon, she would have to go to him.

She felt a wild excitement at the thought; it almost suffocated her as she sat on the porch. Night after night the same excitement returned, as she remained outwardly so calm; night after night it kept her awake, and she would think of herself drifting away into the dusk like Delores, imagining every step of that walk, up to the moment when she found the house where Vincent was living now; there her mind stopped short, because she still didn't know if she would actually go in, nor what she would say to him if she did.

In the end it really happened—she was overcome by a kind of vertigo, and when it was gone she found herself walking along Johnson Avenue, so much the captive of what she had imagined that it seemed she must still be doing this in imagination only.

It was warmer than it had been all season, more like a July night than one in May. Sprinklers were turning in the front yards she passed, or men in their shirt sleeves were standing dreamily with hoses in their hands, and there was the summer smell of warm earth and warm concrete made suddenly cool and wet. Through open windows the music from radios floated; from front porches came the creak of wicker chairs and the sound of slow drowsy conversation; the leaves on the trees had grown full-size, so that it was dark and still where Patricia walked. The warmth and dark and stillness, the sounds beyond the silence, bore her onward—her feet seemed hardly to touch the pavement, she was moving without volition, and presently there was nothing left inside her but the burning core of excitement. It consumed her fear; it destroyed her own identity: a part of her stood far off and watched a girl in a white dress, a complete stranger, walking through the warm dark night.

Vincent's new address was Number 5 Eustis Court, and Patricia knew where Eustis Court was, though it lay in a part of the city she had always avoided. It was not more than half a mile from Johnson Avenue, and near it were great mansions not all of which had yet become apartment houses; Eustis Court was one of those unexpected pockets of slum which can be found in almost any city.

She began to hear Eustis Court before she saw it. The radios were louder, the voices harsher, and there were children yelling in the street, playing a game of cops and robbers though night had closed in at least an hour ago. Eustis Court was a dead end, a steep narrow street, still paved with cobbles. Patricia paused when she reached the place where it slanted up from Munsing Avenue, and stared into its shadows, and walked on again, pretending that she had only come out for a stroll after all. Vincent probably would not be there anyway, but over with Carola Wilmot, consoling her for the death of Alexander.

But when she reached the end of the block she turned and moved back again, purposefully now, and climbed the steep slope of cobbles, thrusting her way between the children before her courage should desert her. She believed the children stopped their game to stare at her, the people on doorsteps halted their talk to laugh—they all knew why she had come. Still she turned her head calmly enough, looking at the numbers tacked on the wooden porches, until she found Number 5. It was at the summit of the street, and behind it rose a high wall, and beyond the wall a bank sloped up; at the top of the bank, seeming to tower in the dark night, was one of the mansions, with lights shining through its windows.

On one of the thin square porch pillars of Number 5 was a cardboard sign, white letters on a blue background—FURNISHED ROOMS—and even in the dark Patricia could see what kind of house it was, narrow and tall, with a blind wall facing the blind wall of the next house lower down, and small windows in front with lace curtains looped back, and potted geraniums on the sills. Unlike the other houses it was quiet; the voices and the music seemed far away now. On the dark porch a lone woman sat and rocked, flapping herself with a palm-leaf fan.

Patricia moved toward the porch, whose rail was almost flush with the sidewalk; nothing grew in the bare trampled earth. "Good evening," she said to the woman, who was incredibly stout, spreading wide in the chair as if she might burst it asunder, and whose breath sounded loud in her throat.

"Evening," the woman said. "Hot, ain't it?"

"Very." Patricia laid her fingers on the rail; it was gritty to the touch. "Is this where—do you know if Mr. Rourke is in? Mr. Vincent Rourke?"

The woman rocked and flapped her fan. "Yah, he's in. Come back twenty minutes, maybe half an hour ago."

"Oh," said Patricia. When she had imagined all this she had seen herself finding his room without help; but she was beyond the power to feel shame. "I just wanted to tell him—"

"You go around the side," the woman said. "There's a door back there. Just push the door right open, honey, and go on up the stairs. He's on the third floor."

"Well, I wasn't going to—"

"Don't be ascared. Ain't nobody else in that part of the house at all. It's shut off, like. I got two, three empty rooms there now. You wasn't planning to take a room here yourself, was you?"

"No, I—live over across—"

"You know anybody wants a room, you tell 'em about this place, will you? Good clean rooms and soft beds, and only the four roomers, when the place is full, to share the bath. I got a phone too, in my part of the house." Ponderously the woman lifted herself out of the chair and approached the railing; a great gust of cheap scent blew over Patricia as the woman stared down at her. "Ain't never seen *you* before, have I?" she said, and smiled in the darkness. "Go on up and see your boy friend. Guess he's feeling kinda lonesome tonight."

She leaned there on the rail, her fan motionless, the breath sawing in her throat, and it was as though she were pushing Patricia; indeed Patricia was not sure afterwards that the woman hadn't laid a plump hand on her shoulder and given her an actual shove toward the alley between the house wall and the wall that kept the bank from sliding down into Eustis Court. There was a dank subterranean smell in the alley, and Patricia held her breath until she reached the door the woman had mentioned. There was a glass pane in it and a light shone through the pane; after Patricia had pushed the door open and stepped through and shut it again, she peered back along the alley, with some notion that the stout woman might be standing there watching her; but there was only the empty end of Eustis Court, and a vacant house across the way, with its windows boarded up.

None of this could really be happening, Patricia thought; it was only that she was imagining things with greater vividness than ever before. So it did not greatly matter what she imagined next—that she climbed the narrow stairs into the shadows, and paused on the second floor to catch her breath, and climbed on again, into complete darkness and silence and stifling heat; and that her eyes became adjusted to the darkness and found a door, upon which she tapped softly.

Vincent, who had been lying motionless and half drunk in the dark, with his shoes kicked off and the sleeves of his shirt rolled back and his collar open, sat up and groped for the chain on the rickety floor-lamp. His hand struck the shade and the lamp almost toppled over; he swore under his breath as he caught the stand and steadied it; then he jerked the light on and blinked in the dazzle.

"Come in," he said, before he remembered that he'd locked the door. "Just a minute, just a minute," he said, crossing the floor in his stocking-feet, and he thought he had started to drink too soon; he should have been a little more patient. He turned the key in the lock and jerked the door open; then he stepped back in astonishment, because he had not expected to see Patricia Bryant standing there. "Well, for God's sake!" he said.

"Vincent, I—"

He laughed. "Come in, come in." He caught her hand, pulled her into the room, and shut the door again. "Welcome to my elegant abode," he said, gathering up dirty clothes from the old Morris chair and tossing them into the wardrobe, straightening the cretonne covering on the cot, switching on a second lamp that stood on the chest of drawers. "Humble," he said, "but cozy. Too damn cozy on a night like this. I think I'm going to have to move again, preferably into a sub-cellar. . . . Now where did I leave my shoes? I wasn't expecting to entertain a lady tonight." He laughed again, and sat on the edge of the bed while he put his shoes on. "How did you ever find this dump, sweet?"

"I knew the address. You told me. And the woman downstairs—"

"The Madam. You've met the Madam. Well, sweet, you've seen everything now. How she must be licking her old lips. She thinks I'm quite the boyo. Oh, there's a great bond between me and the Madam," Vincent said, crossing the room again. He locked the door and turned back. "I'm not being suggestive. Just a precautionary measure, sweet, so somebody doesn't burst in on us. There's been quite a bit of coming and going here lately. *Quite* a bit." He smiled again, and felt momentarily nervous. Patricia was standing in the center of the room, on a small patch of worn carpet, as if that were dry land and all the rest of the floor water; she was seeing the stains in the plaster, he thought, and the soot in the folds of the lace curtains, and the cracks where the ceiling sloped down toward the side wall; she was seeing the empty beer-bottles on the table next the bed, and the empty glass beside them.

She turned and looked at him—with anxiety, he thought—and said, "Vincent, are you drunk?"

"Only slightly, sweet, only slightly. Cocktails with my dinner and three bottles of beer back here. I seem to be losing my grip. Out on the window-sill are four more bottles of beer. Won't you get a little drunk too? You make me nervous, standing there so clean and pure and innocent in the midst of this shambles." He went to the window, lifted the screen, and took the bottles out of a box nailed beneath the sill. "Somewhere there's another glass: a clean one. Ah, yes, thank you. It really is clean too." He picked up the bottle-opener. "The damn stuff is so warm it squirts all over the ceiling."

"Let me do it, Vincent."

"Gladly, sweet." He dropped on the bed and tilted his shoulders against the wall. "God, you *do* look innocent and pure. In that white dress you look like a shrine. . . . Ah, neatly done," he said, as Patricia opened two bottles and filled the glasses. "Thank you." He lifted his glass. "To your very good health."

Patricia sat gravely in the Morris chair and held both hands around her glass; she continued to look at him with anxiety, and he was filled with a desire to laugh. "Vincent, are you still angry with me?"

"Angry with you? *Angry?*"

"About that Sunday." She looked at her glass. "I'm sorry, Vincent, I wanted to tell you I was sorry."

"Oh, that. Ah, yes, ah, yes. Well, you did a very wise thing. God, it was one of the most ghastly days I've ever spent. I must have lost pounds and pounds, working on Carola's cottage. I still look rather haggard, don't you think? Then, of course, we got back and found out that her old man was dead. It was a charming experience altogether. She broke down," Vincent said, "and I couldn't do anything. God spare me from hysterical women. You're so calm, sweet; you're so beautifully calm, even now, in this curious and compromising situation. It soothes me just to look at you. But oh, you have been unwise; you have been most unwise and reckless. When you leave, you'd better try to disguise yourself as somebody else."

Patricia set her untasted glass of beer on the table. "Vincent, can't we go out somewhere? I can't talk to you here. It's a horrible place. . . . Darling, you mustn't live here any more. I never dreamed—"

"I can't even afford to live here, really. I should be living in a tent. Uncle Bertrand isn't doing so well in the junk business these days, it seems. If he sends me five dollars in the course of a month, it's cause for amazement and rejoicing. . . . Besides, I like it here, and I'm crazy about the Madam. I've reached my own level at last. I'm a guttersnipe. Didn't you know that?" He bent forward and patted her knee. "Go on, drink up your beer, and then have another glass. Being a guttersnipe is a lot of fun."

"You *are* angry with me, aren't you? Still . . . Oh, Vinnie, why do we have to be so—childish about everything? It was childish, what I did that day, but I'll try to do better after this. If you aren't through with me. I've been missing you so much."

"Well, and I've missed you too. It's just been one of the moods again. That and a few little efforts to divert myself. Some successful and some not. You know, when I opened the door and saw you standing there, I thought you were an avenging angel. It's true. You looked so stern. But maybe you don't know anything about my diversions and maybe I never should have brought the subject up and maybe I am somewhat drunker than I thought I was. Open another bottle of beer for me, sweet, will you?" He drained his glass and held it out to her, but she made no effort to take it so he opened his fingers and let it drop and roll away on the floor.

"Won't you come back to our house, Vincent—and have some coffee?"

"And run into the surly watch-dog?"

"We could go downtown, then. . . . I hate to see you like this. Oh, Vinnie—"

"It's because you won't drink your beer. Go on, have some more, please. I know it's warm and nasty, but that's the way the British like it. Pretend you're British, sweet, and toss it off. Just because your father was deplorable in his cups, you don't have to go thinking I'm deplorable too. *I* think I'm being very amusing," Vincent said, standing up. "I'm really at the top of my form. We could be so gay, darling, if you'd drink your beer." He took up her glass and crouched before her, holding it out. "Go on, drink it fast, and it will have more effect. Or am I going to have to force it down you? That would be so messy. You'd get beer all over your lovely pure white dress."

She smiled faintly and took the glass from him. "If I do drink it, will you come out then?"

"Blackmail," he said, crouching there and staring at her; was it because he was a little drunk that he had begun to want her so much? To desecrate the shrine, he thought, and turned his head away; he sat on the floor at her feet. "I feel so nice and peaceful, darling, right where I am. I don't want to go roaring all over town." He leaned his back against the chair, tilted his head sideways until his cheek lay against her knee, and gazed straight ahead of him. "Are you drinking your beer now like a good girl?"

"Yes, Vincent."

"Toss it down the way I told you to." He shut his eyes. "You don't mind if I rest here this way, do you? I've been so tired today, I've been so tired and sad. You have such nice legs, Patricia," he said, opening his eyes again, and touched the back of his hand gently against them. "Such long smooth shapely legs. But how can you afford silk stockings? You haven't any nice Uncle Bertrand to send you five-dollar bills now and then. If I had any money I'd give you hundreds of pairs of silk stockings for your long smooth shapely legs. Oh, darling, I have missed you, yes, I have, I've missed you worse than you'll ever know. I've missed you, I've missed you, but I don't think you've missed me at all."

He felt her lean forward again; this time when she set her glass on the table it was empty, and he said, "God, you really did gulp it down," and then he thought she was touching his hair gingerly, as if it might scorch her fingers. He turned, looking up at her sideways, and said, "Have you? Have you?"

"Vincent—" She looked a little frightened, he thought; she had drawn her hands back, and seemed to be trying to draw her whole body back and away from him, fearing the lightest contact.

"Will you stay all night, Patricia? Will you? I get so lonely in this horrible room, I have such terrible dreams. You will stay all night, won't you?" He rose to his knees; he took her hands in his and pulled them against his chest, against his heart beating thickly beneath the wall of flesh and bone.

"We can make up a story," he said, laughing at her, "and you can call your father on the Madam's telephone. You can tell him you suddenly had to go to Boston to attend a convention of the D.A.R.; you can say you're on your way to Atlantic City to enter a bathing beauty contest. Please stay, darling; please say you will."

But she pulled her hands away and stood up. He laughed again, still kneeling on the floor, because she was so foolish and he was so foolish too, and he didn't know if it was the beer or the spring or his urgent desire that made him feel so strange—lightheaded, so that he had no idea what he was going to say or do next.

He pushed himself to his feet, became giddy, and caught at the edge of the table. "It must be very potent beer. Don't you feel it at all, sweet? Are you still cold sober?"

She was standing on the scrap of carpet again, studying its worn pattern. "If you won't come with me, Vincent, I'll have to go alone," she said, and moved toward the door; but she moved slowly, and he lunged ahead of her, got between her and the door, and set his back against it.

"Oh, no, sweet," he said. "Now you're being unfair. You come around with your mind all made up to seduce me, and you get me all worked up, and then you walk out without even kissing me. That isn't very nice, darling; it isn't the way to behave at all."

"Vincent, please—"

He caught her in his arms and kissed her, holding her body against his until he could feel all the resistance running out of it. "There," he said breathlessly, lifting his mouth only a little way from hers. "There, now, you've changed your mind about running away, haven't you, darling, haven't you, sweet?"

"Please, Vincent, please," she said, but he stifled her words with his mouth.

Presently he stood back against the door again, breathing as if he had just run a great distance. When he was able to speak, he said, "You aren't going to be a foolish little girl, are you, Patricia? You said you wanted to stop being childish. Well, darling, why don't you, then? Come down in the gutter with me, darling; it's time you found out what it's all about." He moved toward her, saying whatever came into his head. "Like mother, like daughter, that's how it is, darling. You know why you came to see me to-night, and you don't really want to run away, do you? When your mother went to New York to see Andrew McBain, do you think she just said hello and good-by and left him lonely in his room? Oh, no, darling," he said, and kissed her. "Your mother wasn't like that," he whispered against Patricia's mouth; "she wasn't like that at all. But she wasn't as careful as she should have been, so that's why you have a brother called Joel, only he isn't really your brother, darling, is he? He's only your half-brother. Did you ever think of that before? Didn't you ever think it was funny that Joel was only your half-brother, and your father never knew? What a joke on your father," Vincent said, and began to tighten his embrace; but strength had returned to Patricia, who stiffened in his arms and then tore herself free, so violently that he almost lost his balance.

The light shone full in her face and he saw something happen in her eyes—not fear, not any emotion he recognized—and felt a pang of fear himself because he had never seen anyone look as she did then, and he thought she was going to strike him. But nothing like that happened. She let out her breath in an abrupt little sigh, turned the key in the lock, and jerked the door open.

He stood swaying where she had left him, listening to her swift footsteps, listening to the door at the bottom slam shut. He moved over and peered down the dark staircase, and then closed his door and locked it again. A blindness came over him, and he beat his fist against his mouth until he tasted blood and realized what he was doing; he lurched across the room and flung himself down on the bed, and the taste of blood in his mouth was like the taste of desire. His whole body was on fire with his need for her, and this enraged him. What a god-damned fool, he said into the pillow, oh, Christ, what a fool.

He pressed his face against the pillow and a terrible exhaustion invaded him; he must have lain there a long time with sickness in his mouth and the dusty smell of cretonne in his nostrils before he remembered that there were still three bottles of beer left and thought it might be possible to become wholly drunk. His clumsy hand shook as he took up the opener, and the beer spurted out of the bottle, running all over his bare arm and down on the floor; but it didn't matter and he drank straight from the bottle because he couldn't see where his own glass had rolled to nor bear the thought of drinking from hers.

By the time he had emptied the second bottle he had begun to feel not drunk, but sober; his shirt was soaked with sweat and he peeled it off, turned out the lights, and sat in darkness by the window, letting the breeze cool his skin. His arms, his hands, his chest all were sticky from spilled beer and drying sweat, and he was shaken by self-disgust; but he had not the energy to go down to the second floor and wash himself off in the bathroom there.

Slowly he forced his mind back through what he had said and done tonight, but it was like trying to recall a dream. She had taken him so much by surprise when he found her outside his door; he had been expecting to see Delores, but had he said so to Patricia?

He was frightened again, and rose to open the last bottle of beer; he wandered about the dark room as he drank it, forcing it down. It was foolish to be frightened; whatever he had said to Patricia, she would not repeat it, she would never tell anyone what had taken place tonight.

He pulled off the rest of his clothes presently and dropped the cretonne cover and lay down on his bed, gazing at the slope of ceiling just above him; the warmth which had beaten on the shingles all day was stored up in them now and struck through the plaster; the sweat ran down his body. He could not continue to live here, or in Broadfield at all. Horror was moving in on him from every side.

Sooner or later he always walked into a trap; he went on and on and learned nothing and with his eyes wide open walked into Eustis Court, and the time might come when he found himself walled up in Eustis Court for good.

Suppose Patricia did repeat what he had said to her? Even if he hadn't mentioned Delores, Patricia might know. She must know. . . .

Carola Wilmot had not been quite so hysterical over the death of her father as he had suggested to Patricia, but she had been bad enough. Infected by her sudden display of nerves he had felt almost guilty himself; and he had wanted to go to Patricia, but found he could not, after the way Norris had looked at him that morning. They hated him, all the Bryants; he could not thrust himself on them any more.

But he could not stay in his room either, and felt too languid to go driving in his car; so he joined the tide of pedestrians which flowed along the streets of Broadfield on warm spring evenings. Dusk, darkness, made them anonymous and he became anonymous too—drifting down the hill, through the little park where the fountain played, to Main Street, and along Main Street to the square where the Civil War monument stood and from which the street-car lines radiated to the corners of the city. Most of the walkers were boys and girls, arm in arm, but there were others who walked alone like Vincent—boys on the prowl for girls, girls hoping to be picked up, and older people, wistful and a little pathetic, who pretended they were on their way to the movies or had just come to look at the lighted shop-windows.

There were two evenings when Vincent had seen Delores without speaking to her—she had been with another man—but the third time she was alone, gazing into the window of a candy-store at a corn-popping machine; the warm greasy smell spread almost palpably across the sidewalk.

Vincent did not clearly understand his impulse. Loneliness, and resentment against the Bryants, and hatred of Charlie, and an unbearable sense of boredom all had something to do with it. But it was also the way he had become anonymous, a part of the slow spring tide of desire, so that it was the natural and expected and almost inevitable thing to pick up a girl. If it had not been Delores it would have been someone else, sooner or later.

He moved up behind her, touched her on the shoulder, and said, "Isn't the machine-age wonderful? Do you like popcorn, Delores?"

She tittered faintly; arm in arm, they joined the other strollers. It was stupid of him; even then he knew how stupid it was, but the fact that he was a little frightened when he thought about Charlie Bryant made Delores more exciting. In a way it was as if he were getting back at Charlie: he would prove his own virility by cuckolding Charlie.—Because from the moment he touched Delores on the shoulder and she turned as if she had been waiting for him, Vincent was quite sure how the evening would end.

"What's become of that nice smooth coop of yours?"

"The tank has run dry."

"Oh, you! I s'pose there isn't any more gasoline left in the world."

"Gasoline costs money. And I haven't any. If I had any money, I'd buy you a double marshmallow hot fudge sundae with crushed walnuts on top. Am I making your mouth water?"

"I could stand a drink," said Delores, squeezing his arm.

"And you a minor! So dissolute, so young."

"I'm not so young. It isn't years that count so much. It's what you been through," said Delores. "I been around with fellows a whole lot older than you are, Vinnie."

"Are you trying to make me jealous?"

Delores tittered again. "What about Pat? Supposing somebody sees us and tells Pat?"

"That's one of the things I like about you, Delores. You consider other people's feelings," Vincent said.

They boarded a trolley-car after a while, and rode as near to Eustis Court as the line went, and then got out and walked again. Vincent had just remembered, he said, that he had some beer in his room.

He was not sure what he was going to say, because he had never known a girl like Delores before; he even felt a little nervous as he uncapped the beer bottles, and wanted to apologize about Eustis Court, and about the state of his room.

"Where's Charlie these days?" he asked. "What's the matter with your husband, letting you run around loose like this?"

"Oh, him!" Delores smiled across the rim of her glass. "I've washed my hands of Charlie. I just can't stand Charlie any more. I don't think I even like him, not really. Charlie is so crude," said Delores. "The thing about Charlie, he just doesn't have any refinement at all."

Neither, as it turned out, had Delores. The room in Eustis Court was where Delores belonged, and it was foolish to have felt apologetic; it was foolish to have worried about what he was going to say, because as long as the beer held out Delores did most of the talking.

Later he couldn't remember very much of what she had said. But he remembered how her voice gave way to the sounds that came in through the open window; and how when a truck went along Munsing Avenue there was an odd lingering echo he'd never noticed before. It reverberated in the boxed-up end of Eustis Court long after the truck had gone by, and then the reverberation seemed to continue inside his own head, and even to grow louder, until it drowned out everything else. And then the feeling of anonymity he'd had on the streets returned to him; this wasn't a dream, of course, but it wasn't really happening to him. . . .

When she left, he walked with her as far as the beginning of
Johnson Avenue. He kissed her in the shadow of a tree, but it was
only a little-girl kiss she gave him in return.

"Will you come again?" he asked.

"You're awful cute, Vinnie. You're the cutest boy I ever knew,
just about." Delores smiled, but began to drift away from him.

"Please come again. Tomorrow night?"

"Maybe. Maybe not. But what about Patricia?"

"The hell with Patricia," he said.

"And I thought you were so crazy about her. . . . So long."
Delores was gone in the shadows.

She had come up to his room three more evenings before Patricia
came there, and each time it was the same; each time the strange
feeling of anonymity captured him. But the last time she turned
remote and indifferent at parting and he thought Charlie might be
growing suspicious at last.

He was glad that it was over; tonight, indeed, he was appalled
that it had taken place. He lay back on the bed, with the ceiling
pressing down on him, prey to the most complete self-disgust he
had ever known.

He almost wished he were fifteen again, and able to start out
again and move along a different path, into a country different
from any he had ever explored. Perhaps all he had ever wanted,
really, was somebody like Miss What's-her-name, who would tell
him he had the face of a poet, and sit with him in a cool dim ferny
parlor, while they took turns reading aloud to each other from the
works of Rupert Brooke and Edna St. Vincent Millay.

18

And as for Patricia—

Unable to see any comic element in her visit to Eustis Court,
she let it become swollen and distorted in her mind, until there
was cast across her life a shadow from which she was sure she
would never escape.

She had not seen him drunk before. She had learned to adjust
herself to his variable nature, but if he had been quite sober the
episode would have been, she believed, essentially the same, with
the same outcome; and she would still have tormented herself
with the same questions. How could corruption wear so fair a
face? and wasn't she corrupt herself since the fair face still moved
her so deeply?

His touch was lethal, destroying the goodness of life as Cousin
Leon and Aunt Maudie and Grandma Bryant had once destroyed

it. She had tried to rebel at their view of the world, but something in her wished to give way to Vincent; part of her mind wanted to believe what he had said about her mother. She lacked a sense of proportion and so it mattered too much whether or not her mother had had a child by Andrew McBain; if she found out that this was true, the struggle would be over; there would no longer be any point in trying to rebel against Cousin Leon and Aunt Maudie and Grandma Bryant, against Vincent Rourke and Carola Wilmot, for they would have been proved right.

They would not have acknowledged their kinship to one another, but they were engaged in the same pursuit; they were all attempting to obliterate Laura Bryant's image. The thought of Laura filled them with disquiet. Then wasn't their very anxiety to deny that anyone like her had ever existed, proof that she had been otherwise than they said?

It was painful for Patricia to have to look at her father or Joel. When they laughed at the dinner table, talking like children of the weather or the garden or baseball or sailing or catching fish, she was terrified and thought how they might be destroyed also if they heard the words which Carola had spoken to Vincent, and Vincent to her.

But she was living in a nightmare, and one evening she told her father herself. She had come in from a session with Charlie on the front porch, believing her father to be still with Betty Lou; but he must have walked in by the back door—he was sitting in his room, with the door open, and when she went past he called to her.

He swung the chair around from his desk and smiled and told her to sit down. His hair was ruffled; the knot of his tie was pulled down and his shirt-collar open; there was a new kind of serenity in his face, and tilting back in his chair he packed tobacco into a pipe he hadn't smoked for years.

After he had struck a match on the sole of his shoe, and blown out a thin blue jet of smoke, he said, "I know I made up my mind, Pat, not to butt in on my offspring's troubles. And I'm not going to—don't worry. This time I want you to butt in on mine. Fact is, I'm going to ask your advice. Want to ask all of you—I'm writing to Laurette; I'll ask Charlie and Joel, I guess, when I know how you feel." He sucked mightily at his pipe and rocked the chair on its springs; he pulled out a drawer and propped his feet on the edge; he looked so much like a boy—half shamefaced and half enormously pleased with himself—that she knew perfectly well what he was going to say.

"You and Betty Lou are pretty good friends again, aren't you? You probably understand her better than I do, in lots of ways, and what I wanted to ask you—" He took the pipe from his mouth and studied it; then he laid it down in an ashtray and forgot all about it. She could have helped him, but she knew he wanted to get to the point in his own time and way, and sat quietly, waiting for him to go on.

"Betty Lou's a pretty fine person, seems to me. What I mean, Pat, she's *sound*. I haven't known so very many women, but I'd put Betty Lou somewhere near the top. She— Well, that's the whole trouble, in a way. Because God knows I'm no prize package. . . . I keep wondering about her husband. What kind of a guy he was."

He jerked his tie right off and dropped it on the desk. "Course I never *expected* to get married again, and it wouldn't be the same, naturally. I'm not the same man I was then. Old and tired and sad —a mess any way you look at me. But I—well, Pat, the fact is I guess I'm pretty fond of Betty Lou. Fonder than I've ever been of any woman, except one. But I don't have just myself to consider, the way I did then, when I was only a kid. Anything I decide to do—it affects all of you. So I have to know how you'd feel about it too."

Patricia was astonished because her eyes were suddenly filled with tears. "We'd be glad, Father. Oh, you don't have to ask us— you don't! You should have done it long ago."

"Whoa, there!" His feet slipped off the desk drawer and came down hard on the floor. "We mustn't go counting chickens. There's still Betty Lou to be thought of."

Patricia laughed and squeezed her hands together. "You could ask her, couldn't you? It wouldn't do any harm to ask."

Norris swung away and stared through the window; he clasped his hands behind his head and said, "Kind of afraid the words might stick in my throat. I'd think I had such a hell of a nerve. She's young still, Pat. If she'd ever wanted to marry again, she'd have done it long ago—she could have had her pick."

"But, Father, don't you know how much she—"

"Proximity, Pat. I keep thinking it couldn't be anything more than proximity with her. Besides, even if— Well, she wouldn't be taking on just me, would she? No telling how long things will keep on the way they are now. And she's such a little thing, and so gay— Sometimes it seems to me there's a blight in this house, and it falls on anybody who comes to live here. I couldn't bear to see Betty Lou blighted."

"That's foolish, Father," Patricia said. "There isn't anything that *could* blight Betty Lou, I don't think. . . . And she's had her eye on you for ages—she has, really—ever since she first moved next door."

"Well," said Norris with a grin, "I've thought so myself, once or twice. Then I took a good straight look in the mirror and knew

I was a vain old fool." He rubbed his cheeks. "I'm blushing, I guess. In the spring an old man's fancy—" He laughed and rocked in his chair; he picked up the pipe and fiddled with it; he stuck the stem back between his teeth and struck another match.

"And then I—" He looked at Patricia intently. "Maybe it's morbid. I don't know. Your mother—well, she's part of me, Pat. She always will be. Seems like it might be unfair to Betty Lou to—"

"But, Father, Betty Lou knows all about that."

"Yeah. Guess she couldn't help knowing. But it isn't just that, either. Any time I seem to do the right thing instead of the wrong one—in a way it's your mother doing it. . . . I don't believe in immortality, I guess. Not the way your grandfather does. I don't know that he sees the next world in terms of harps and haloes," Norris said, smiling faintly again, "but he sees it, all right, and he knows where he's headed: heaven's his destination, no two ways about it. . . . But your mother—she's still just as clear and real to me, Pat, as heaven is to your grandfather. And I keep asking myself how she'd feel about it. That's what I meant about being morbid. . . . I guess you don't remember her any too well. Not the way Charlie and Laurette do."

Norris turned the bowl of the pipe in his fingers. "I still *depend* on your mother. I don't seem able to go ahead with anything, any more, until she's— Hey, what's the matter?" Norris said, and stood up; for Patricia had begun to weep. He put his hand timidly on her arm. "What is it, Pat? God, I didn't mean to—"

"It isn't you, Father. You're so—" Patricia caught at his hand and squeezed it hard. "I know why Mother loved you, and why Betty Lou does too. But the others—they're so horrible," Patricia said. "There are so many horrible people in the world."

"What's happened, Pat? What's gone wrong?"

"The way they talk about you. The things they say—about you and Mother both."

"Who, Pat? What's this all about? Look," he said, sitting on the arm of her chair, "you're probably making mountains out of molehills. Do people still gossip about Laura and me? Do you think we didn't know they used to gossip, Pat, and scandalize? Good Lord," Norris said, "you don't think that ever bothered *us*, do you?"

"But, Father—"

"And they're scandalizing still! It beats everything, doesn't it? But I don't see who there could be who'd say anything to you about—"

"Out at the farm, first of all. Years ago, when I was living there. I didn't know what they meant, of course, but now Carola Wilmot has been talking about it to Vincent, and he—he told me. I'm horrible too. I went to see him last week, I went to see him where he's living now because I—couldn't stand not to any more. I thought he was furious about that Sunday, and I— I don't like him, Father, I think I hate him almost, in some ways, but I still—" Patricia continued to squeeze his hand; she was afraid he was going to let go and walk off in disgust and have nothing more to do with her. "Well, he'd been drinking, and he—I tried to get him to come out with me, I thought if I could make him sober— I wanted to help him, I suppose; I wanted to make him different from the way he is, just like you with all of us. But he wouldn't come out and then he— Well, it was all my fault, really, and I suppose I'd even wanted it to happen when I went there, I wanted him to—make love to me—but everything got all twisted and queer and he started to talk about Mother again. About Mother and Andrew McBain. He says Joel isn't your child."

Patricia looked up, but she could not see her father's face; she saw past him, into the hall, and there in the shadows beyond the open door Delores was standing—rapt in what had been going on, so that for a moment she didn't know Patricia saw her; then she let out a little gasp and moved on.

Now Norris was absently patting Patricia's shoulder; his other hand held hers tightly, and she thought he couldn't have seen Delores. "Oh, Pat," he said presently. "How long have you had such a— Pat, why didn't you come to me long ago?" She could hear him sigh. "Well, I know the answer to that, of course. But I'm glad you've told me at last. It isn't true, Pat. How could you ever think it might be? If you'd known your mother—" He moved back to his place at the desk, and paused there, twirling the chair. "Hell," he said, "even if it had been true, even then it would have been all right. Whatever she did would have been all right; there would have been a good reason for it. But it's crazy, of course, Pat; it's the craziest idea I ever heard of. They're so wrong it's almost funny."

But he did not look amused. He doubled his hand up and thumped it on the back of a chair. "She didn't believe in hatred. Not in hating people. There were plenty of things she hated, but never people. But I can't help myself. When I think of Carola, and that rotten kid from New York—" He turned toward her; his hand opened and fell slack at his side. "Pat, you've got to be strong and get over this—the way you feel about him. He'll wreck your life, and he isn't worth it. Oh, God," said Norris, "when I think I brought him into this house in the first place— I threw you at him. . . .

"Maybe you think I don't know about these things—old men don't remember what it feels like to be young." The faint smile had returned. "Well, there's a poem in that book he gave you, about desire—I know what the poet meant, and so do you. And it isn't anything to be ashamed of. Male and female created He them: He knew what He was doing, though maybe even He didn't foresee quite all the complications. . . .

"The way you feel about Vincent won't go on as long as you live," Norris said. "Some parts of growing up aren't easy, but if you missed all the difficult parts maybe you never would grow up. There are good men in the world too, Pat; and you'll love one of them eventually."

He clasped his hands on the back of the chair.

"Hang on tight," Norris said. "You'll pull through."

He stood a long time in his doorway, after she had gone to her own room, but presently he had to sit down. Surely nothing could be worse than the way he felt now. He had told her the truth, but there was a poison working in his mind which made it look like falsehood.

With so much pressure of belief in Laura's betrayal bearing in upon him it would have been strange if he hadn't, in black moments, felt his own faith shaken. It was one of his secret shames; and as long as it lived in him, how could he help his children?

He clutched at the arms of his chair, remembering the time in his marriage which he'd always tried to forget. It had begun long before Andrew McBain's return to Broadfield—an estrangement far worse than any of the quarrels had been because now he and Laura found themselves moving in opposite directions, along different planes.

He had never, as she did, felt a personal involvement in the war, and the tragedy of Woodrow Wilson had not seemed to him a symbol of incalculable disaster. He hadn't enjoyed writing those editorials, but when she saw that too as part of the universal betrayal she had seemed to him, for the first time, a little absurd. It just wasn't that important; what he or any single human being did couldn't be that important.

Then he was sitting innocuously at a copy desk and thought the storm had blown over. Back to normalcy served as well for their private lives as for the nation.

The passionate part of their marriage was done with. There must be no more children anyway and they would adjust to middle age; he had begun to look the part, although in a performance with the Players, she could create the illusion of being most radiantly nineteen or twenty—as if, in all the years in Broadfield, time had not touched her. She seemed to have forgotten her earnest endeavors; in what hours she had left over from being a mother to her children, which had always been more important to her than anything else, she was going to play. The house was always filled with people; there were many parties.

But when Andy came to Broadfield Norris saw that the gap between himself and Laura had widened. The part of her that she had thought to lay aside forever when she married him came suddenly to life at Andy's touch. The walls of the world in which she lived collapsed; through Andy she could have a wider view than through any of her doors and windows.

All Norris minded at first was that Andy was turning into a success and seemed to patronize him—to patronize him, but not Laura. Andy gazed at Laura in a kind of astonishment, which seemed to ask how it was possible that she existed at all in such a city. But Laura hadn't been dazzled by him; never by the man himself, only by the prospect he unrolled before her.

She was not quite sure she liked him, she told Norris. She couldn't quite see him or touch him or know what there was beneath the charm and the floods of words. But because she was human and feminine she was flattered that Andy should spend so much time with her instead of going about being lionized.

She was gay as long as he remained in Broadfield, and after he left she was disconsolate, and then she became irritable. This wasn't like the sudden blazing furies which had ended in laughter; it was petty sniping. Couldn't Norris go to the barber more often, must he wear that appalling hat until it decayed on his head, didn't he ever throw away any of his neckties? couldn't he, just once in his life, read a *good* book? must he sit like a dolt when there were Players parties at Carola and Hank Wendover's, looking so scared and humble and never opening his mouth? And he failed to understand his children; he was unreasonable and unkind and unjust to them and was particularly hard on Charlie, and hadn't he been a boy himself once, and had he quite forgotten what it feels like to be a child?

It wasn't incessantly like this, of course, and it seemed worse because his own nerves were frayed. But there was a constant fretful overtone and he thought she was measuring him against Andy McBain, that she had in fact fallen in love with Andy; and Norris gave way and indulged himself in the fierce jealousy which had been latent since the night he saw her run laughing out on a stage with a basket of flowers in her hand.

Many details of their final quarrel were gone from his mind, but he remembered waking in the early morning and seeing her sitting up in bed, with her head resting on her knees; he remembered how his jealousy smote him and he accused her of loving Andy.

She flung herself out of the bed, as if proximity were something she could no longer bear, and paced in the dark room while they hurled bitter and foolish words at each other. It was like their earlier quarrels, but worse because this time they wished to wound permanently.

He did not remember any of those words, but he remembered what she had said when the crisis was over and she sat exhausted on the edge of the bed with her back toward him.

"Of course I don't love Andy. Norris, Norris, what do you think I am? I don't love lightly. I could never love a man I didn't know, and there's no way of knowing Andy. He isn't like you—I knew you the moment you came backstage that night. You were so clear then, and there was so much promise in you. Not for material success—I'm not interested in that, I never have been. But after all the shoddy little people I'd known you were a human being again, and I thought that if this was your place, if this was what had produced you, it was the place for me. I thought I might lose my own shoddiness here; I wanted to put down roots. My father was a pioneer, and he was a hard man, he had to be, material things were important to him. But he was in touch with something else, even if he didn't know it. Not like my poor mother, with her silly shabby dreams, hating the earth. . . .

"You were what I needed. You were in touch with something else too, though perhaps you didn't know it either. But what's happened to you, Norris? What's happened to us both? Is it all my fault? I've done something to you, I've tried to make you over, and it hasn't worked. Or is it this damned town that's done it to us? So cramped, so cramped, the lives people lead! They won't look at the big things; they blind themselves by concentrating on the little ones. All of a sudden I can't breathe here," Laura said, flinging back her hair, and she rose again and went to sit at the window.

"We can't go on like this, Norris," she said. "We can't stay here."

"Wouldn't it be the same anywhere else? It isn't the town, or the way I earn my living. It's me, Laura. You were wrong about me, all those years ago."

"No, no, I wasn't wrong!" she cried. "You were twice the man Andy must have been then—you still could be. And you sat off in a corner and sulked, eating your heart out because you thought he was a success. Dear God, Norris, what kind of success is that for you to envy? What has he done, what has he found out, what kind of man has he become that you should envy him?"

"Isn't that what you want me to be? Rich, famous—"

"Don't you know what I've been talking about?" She stood up; she clutched at her head, a little too dramatically, and laughed at last. "Maybe I'm a complete fool. Maybe I've spent all my life in Cloud-Cuckoo-Land. I'm so tired and mixed up." She sighed and presently she came back into the bed; after a long silence, after he thought she was asleep, she said, "I'm going away, Norris. I know it's wrong, but Laurette and Charlie are old enough now, it will do them good to be without me for a while. Maybe it will force you to be more charitable to them. They're too much my children, not enough yours."

"Where?" he asked in sudden terror. "Where are you going?"

"New York, I suppose. And perhaps up to Maine for a little while. I want to smell salt water again; I want to see the fog blowing in. . . . I've gone blind, Norris; I've got to look at this from a distance." She turned over now, so that he could see her face on the pillow, and lightly touched his hand. "We never have had a vacation from each other. Fifteen years. Perhaps that's the whole trouble."

She lost no time; she left the next morning. Postcards came back presently, colored ones, of the Woolworth Building and the Statue of Liberty and the Aquarium and Central Park; and then of the Maine coast, rocks rising steeply from the sea and waves smashing against them. The messages were like the messages most people scrawl on postcards.

Norris thought the men at the paper had a pitying look, his parents and sister and brother-in-law a smug one. He put on a cheerful face before his children and made a great display with the postcards; but time moved so slowly, life was so empty, she was gone so long; and she never wrote him a letter. His children began to talk in hushed voices, as though there had been a death in the house, and there was the night Laurette cried in bed and could not be consoled. He thought then that he had stopped loving Laura.

But when she came back, and stepped down from the train and flung herself at him and wept on his shoulder, with the other travelers pausing to stare and then hurrying on as if they had not stared, he knew that the pain she had caused did not matter and that what she had done was right. Their love flared up more fiercely than it had since the earliest days, and again they lost all discretion. They were frightened when they knew she was pregnant again, but happiness surmounted the fear and she said it would be all right; dear God, after so much practice, she should know at last how to bear a child.

Little by little she began to tell him about her trip. It was just so much dust and ashes—New York was no use to her, Maine was a howling wilderness, without him.

Finally she even told him about McBain. It was a test, he thought; if he could listen calmly to what she said about McBain, he would have proved himself.

"I had to see him just once more, Norris," she said. "It's strange what happens to your mind, once an idea has been planted in it.

He was one of the things I was mixed up about. . . . He took me out to dinner, and then we went to the theater; and a few days later I saw him off on his ship—he's gone to London. . . . Darling, I was right about him. He's nothing at all. He's only the shell of a man.

"I felt sorry for him, almost. He lost his head, just a little. He wanted me to go to London with him. I'm not trying to make you forget he was your best friend once. I'm trying to tell you one of the reasons why I could never love a man like Andy. If you'd been in his shoes, you'd never have done a thing like that. And I think he knew; he was shamefaced about it. . . . He looked very forlorn, standing at the ship's rail. He has to keep on the move, I think, to forget how unsatisfactory his life has been. I don't believe he ever loved anybody; and he wasn't in love with me. It was only a brainstorm."

Norris was able to look steadily back at her, and their happiness continued. Maybe just because she had been so confident that it would be so, she had an easier time bearing Joel than she'd had with the other three—though it was bad enough, God knows, and she was weak for a long time afterwards.

There were only three years between Joel's birth and Laura's death, and it seemed to him now that two of them had been their best years together. The last storms were over; there was a new tenderness in their companionship. Perhaps it was only retrospect that made those years seem so precious, as if they had held on to each moment, guessing there were not many left.

Dr. Cousins had been firm about no more children: it was an edict. But there was such an abundance of life in Laura, despite her frailness; it seemed that she must, as long as she was able, try to give more life to the world. Norris fell into a rage, the day of the last picnic at the big lake—with himself, really, because his love for her had betrayed him into risking her life. This time there was no confidence; it was as if the intensity of his fear had made things go wrong.

As much as anything else, it was his own sense of guilt which had driven him into the pit; what he wanted to forget was the notion that he had in a sense been Laura's murderer. It was so ugly a way for her to have died—failing at what had seemed most important to her. Love should not result in death; love was the giver of life and a bulwark against destruction.

He sat in his room and tried to hold fast to that. Of all the things Laura had tried to tell him, it was perhaps the most important. But the snake coiled in his mind and wherever he looked he saw monstrous and distorted shapes.

Sanity would return, of course; like Patricia, he would pull through. But while he felt as he did, how was he going to face his children? He had found a burden he could not carry to anyone else; he was left alone, groping in darkness, and he believed his strength was gone.

19

By morning, though, the shapes stood off at a distance and he wondered why he had thought them so terrible; if he ignored them steadfastly they would be gone like night mists. There is something about candid early sunlight and the small indignities of preparing to face another day—scrubbing teeth, shaving, putting clothes on, brushing the hair, sitting down to yet another breakfast—that mocks at tragedy, and he thought his fantasy of the labyrinth looked a little foolish. Today would be like other days, filled with routine performances, moments of tedium, minor irritations, trifling satisfactions; he would continue to function as a clumsy and aging and not particularly intelligent animal—he walked on two legs and had certain special skills not given to the apes, but he was no hero in a legend, his Ariadne was long dead, and he suspected he had yet to confront his Minotaur.

Climbing to the third floor of the *Chronicle* building with the sensible taste of coffee still in his mouth, he wondered why the fancy had entered his mind. His childhood was a long time ago, and how had it ever happened anyway that he'd been allowed to read a book of fables, most of which were immoral? It must have been his father who considered that ancient Greece was so very ancient as to have become disinfected, if not entirely respectable.

Those were the days when they thought of turning Norris into a minister, and after he reached college he would learn Greek as well as Latin, and Ancient Hebrew too perhaps; he might make a pilgrimage to the Holy Land and bring back a bottle of water from the River Jordan. . . . Strange he had never thought before that his father's hunger to get close to him must have been as urgent, once, as his to get close to his own children. The same story, generation after generation, and the old men always failed to transmit their wisdom, such as it was, to the young men, who must be left to find things out for themselves. Did the human race ever really take a step forward?

Norris sighed, tossed his hat on the rack, shed his jacket, loosened his necktie, and rolled up his sleeves; he sat down at his desk, and while he clipped items from the *Bugle* he tried to remember the myth he'd borrowed so casually—to lend himself dignity in his own eyes? or to see the shape of his life more clearly by translating it into symbols? Theseus had been a kind of imitation Hercules; there had been earlier exploits before he went to Crete with other Athenian youths and maidens to be sacrificed to the Minotaur; in Crete Ariadne became enamored of him, and gave him the sword with which to slay the Minotaur, and the thread with which to find his way out of the Labyrinth. And so they were married—or weren't they? In either case they didn't live happily ever after because Theseus eventually deserted Ariadne and went on to other adventures.

So it didn't fit; none of it fitted. Unless fate had provided Norris with a second Ariadne in the shape of Betty Lou Hanbury of Muskogee, Oklahoma, and points north. . . .

"What the hell's so funny in the *Bugle?*" Ack demanded.

Norris looked up. "I guess I was just laughing at myself."

"Well, you must be great company for yourself. Hey, we're having a wonderful spring, you know it? No rain for two weeks."

"My brother-in-law won't be so happy about that," said Norris, and then the day settled down and was like hundreds of days in the past, perhaps like hundreds more to come.

Still, the strange balancing of moods—now melancholy, now a mild unreasonable gaiety—went on; and he caught his mind reverting to the fantasy. It pleased and amused him to think of Betty Lou in terms of Ariadne; the darker aspects of the myth could be ignored for the present, and if the opportunity came he would be a faithful Theseus, sadly lacking in dash and swagger.

But Charlie had no myths with which to console himself. He had been pushed out of the world again, and not by strangers this time. First Delores had refused to listen to him; now it seemed that all the others were turning their faces away.

Joel had been a fresh kid and had made rude remarks, which by wounding Charlie had revealed to him that he still possessed vanity; but that was better than being ignored. Now whenever he could Joel avoided Charlie; and at night he kept his face averted, humming a small tune to himself, and only muttered good night as the light was turned off. Even to Joel, it seemed, Charlie had become a bad smell in the nostrils.

And there was Patricia, whom Charlie had begun to pity a little, and to like—when she sat so patiently on the porch, and listened to his unburdenings, he thought she was a good kid after all. But now Patricia was going through some private hell which left her no room to think about him; and when one evening he tried to bring up the subject of Vincent Rourke—he understood the bastard so clearly, and couldn't he talk a little sense into her head?—she lashed out at him, and walked away, and thereafter regarded him as her enemy.

And his father—Charlie would have the uneasy sensation of being stared at, and would look up, and Norris would jerk his head away or leave the room. Charlie concluded that his father had lost all faith in him and was dreading another outbreak of violence. Christ, he thought, what the hell does he expect, does he want me to be super-human?

And his own son—

Now that Delores seemed to have lost all interest in David, Charlie made clumsy advances; but he was too noisy or too rough, and his son screamed when Charlie approached. There were babies who liked to be swung high in the air, or carried around on your shoulder—but not David, not when Charlie tried it. One day he was alone with David, and became terrified as the wild crying went on and on; he lost his head and shook his son, and shouted at him: "Cut it out! Quit it!" This happened in the back yard and Betty Lou came like a fury through the gate they had cut in the fence, and snatched the baby from him. "My lands, Charlie Bryant, you ought to be ashamed! You and Delores both. What's the matter with you, anyway?" cried Betty Lou, rocking David against her shoulder until his weeping subsided. Charlie walked into the house before she was over her temper, so she never had a chance to repair the damage she had done; she too had become his enemy.

The feeling widened; it began to include even the men with whom he worked at the paper. They were less friendly than they had been, it seemed to Charlie, and maybe they had never been really friendly to begin with. They had always resented him, perhaps, because he'd come in from the outside and taken a job away from somebody else, and the warm words they'd spoken of Norris were only hypocrisy.

He went sliding down the slope again, and it was worse this time because he knew what was happening, and understood that nothing would check his descent but a hand held out to him; but the only hands he saw were raised against him.

May was drawing to a close; in another week Andrew McBain would be in Broadfield; but Charlie was given the final push before McBain arrived.

He had known for a long time what game Delores was playing, but thought she was playing it with more abandon than before; the last pretenses were dropping away. Perhaps because he had tried so hard, because for a brief moment he had really hoped to transform his relationship with Delores, his possessiveness was almost dead. What Delores gave cheaply to strangers was not worth having.

His anger against her returned, and became more savage, until he was filled with it; but the emphasis had shifted, and when he spoke to her at last he believed he could keep it under control.

It happened in the morning, before he went to work; a mizzle

225

of rain was falling and he had lost his zeal for gardening. He sat in the living room, trying again to read a detective story, and presently Delores came in with the vacuum-cleaner and plugged the cord in and switched on the current—mostly to annoy him, he thought, since she had lately been neglecting even the housework.

He watched her over the top of his book; like everybody else, she was pretending he wasn't there at all, but at the same time she made little motions with her body which were supposed to taunt him. He had left her alone so long that perhaps she no longer feared him.

But Charlie's was now a cold anger; he watched her over the top of the book and saw nothing attractive in her. He let her go on pushing the cleaner around for a long time before he laid the book aside and crossed the room to jerk the plug from the socket.

"Sit down, Delores," he said. "Something I want to tell you."

"Oh, gee, Charlie." Even now she didn't look frightened. "I just don't have the time. After I finish cleaning I got to take David over to Betty Lou and then go out shopping. In this terrible rain. Why don't you sit in the dining room or somewhere, so you can read in peace."

"Sit down," he said again, and gave her a little push; she dropped on the piano-bench. "There's plenty of time for what I want to say."

"No, Charlie, honest—"

"Shut up," he said gently. "Or do you want me to tie a gag around your mouth?" He clenched his fist. "I don't want to get rough, Delores, but I will if I have to. You're not going to sneak out on me this time."

"Well, if you're going to start talking *that* way again," she said, raising her voice a little, "you might just as well not waste time. We're through, Charlie Bryant, you and me."

"You're damn right we're through. Soon as there's some money, you're going to be thrown out on your ass. I'd like to throw you out right now. I guess you wouldn't have much trouble finding ways of getting along, would you?"

"You just can't keep your mind out of the gutter, can you?"

"No," said Charlie, "not when I look at you." He leaned against the back of a chair and smiled down at her. "But Pop still has a few illusions about you, I guess, and Pop's had a fairly tough life, so when you do get thrown out—well, we'll try to make it look like something else. For his sake. But you're here now, living on Pop's charity, living in the house my mother lived in, with my kid sister and brother. And as long as you do live here you'll have to try a little harder, Delores, and stop acting like a whore. You're not going to turn this place into a whorehouse."

Delores pressed her back against the piano. "You make me sick," she whispered.

"The sentiment is mutual, sweetheart. I'm not setting myself up. I'm a bastard and I know it— What's so funny?" he asked, because Delores had suddenly giggled. "Shut up till I'm through. . . . If you'd stayed and listened to me that night, you'd know I hate my own guts, just as much as I hate yours. But the difference between you and me, Delores, I happen to like my family. An awful lot of people live in this city but it's still a small town and things get around. Maybe Pop doesn't know yet what you've been doing, or Patricia either. Well, you're going to cut it out, see, before they do know."

"If people have been lying about me—"

"Nobody's been lying about you, sweetheart. Nobody's told me a thing about you. But I'm not blind. I suppose you go out every night and play tiddlywinks in the First Methodist Church parish house."

"I don't go out every night! I haven't been out at all for a whole week, and anyway, if I can't take a little walk sometimes without you thinking—"

"A nice little walk, a nice little walk in the warm spring night, and a nice little lay at the end of it." Charlie's voice went up, but his anger remained quite cold; it seemed as if a partial blindness were coming over him—all he could see was Delores's face, encircled by darkness. "You must have been wanting it pretty bad," he said, "but not bad enough, I guess, to give me a break. Your husband, remember? With my body I thee worship. Well, I don't any more, sweetheart." He shook his head to clear away the darkness which kept closing in around her face; it was hardly like a face at all any more, only a circle of light, which kept dwindling until it was not much more than a pinpoint. He clenched his fists, pressing them back against the chair, because he wanted to drive them at the point of light and extinguish it altogether.

"I wouldn't mind you acting like a whore," Charlie said, "because that's what you are, and we have to follow our own nature, don't we, sweetheart? But just try to control yourself, will you, until you clear out of Broadfield? After that you can go to hell as fast as you like. It just so happens my father is an innocent and idealistic kind of a guy, and Patricia is a nice girl, and Joel is a good clean kid, and if you don't cut this out, sweetheart, I'll kill you with my own hands, so help me God."

He pushed himself away from the chair; for a moment the darkness was absolute and when it had cleared a little he had put his hands out and laid them gently against her throat. "It would be so easy," Charlie said, dreamily almost. "I'm pretty strong. Just a little pressure of the thumbs against the windpipe. . . . No, don't look scared. I'm not going to do it right now. I'm giving you another chance." He heard himself laughing at her. "I just want you to know that I'm not kidding," said Charlie, and dropped his hands.

"Charlie—" But there was, at the moment, no breath left in Delores.

He turned and crossed the room. "It's O.K. You can go now. I've finished what I wanted to say. But remember—I mean it." He flipped open his father's cigarette box and took out a cigarette and lit it; his hand seemed quite steady but the darkness remained in the room and all he could see now was his own hand, holding the dead match. He stood there looking at the match and wondered if people knew when they were insane. He became so interested—why didn't it worry him more? why wasn't he scared as hell?—that he was hardly aware that Delores had started to talk again. He watched his hand put the dead match down in an ashtray and looked at it carefully until the darkness cleared again and he was able to see her face across the room.

"What did you say, sweetheart?"

"It's a joke, that's what I said. It's a joke, the way you talk about your mother."

Charlie said nothing; he was fascinated now by what had happened to her face—the fear all gone, the cheap prettiness gone too; it was working with a kind of passion which submerged everything but the staring eyes and the vicious twist of the mouth.

"You and your mother and your wonderful family," said Delores. "Throw *me* out! Throw *me* out! God, what a laugh! When you called yourself a bastard. Maybe you are, maybe you aren't, but Joel's one, all right. Joel isn't your father's son—he's Andrew McBain's. Yes, and everybody knows it too, except you. Your father knows it. He always has. Taking her back like that and trying to make people think Joel's his own son. The crazy rotten old fool. God, I hate you, all of you, the whole stinking bunch. You're right I'm getting out. I'm going to get out and live with decent people for a change."

Still Charlie said nothing; eventually he sat down. The darkness was closing in again, but through it her voice lashed at him.

"You think *you* know so much, but you aren't so smart. There are a few things I know too, see? Your sweet lovely sister Patricia— you think a boy like Vinnie would waste time on a girl didn't give him everything he wanted the first time he took her out? And Laurette—how do you think she got her job in the band? Because she can sing? . . . Oh, I been watching you, all of you; *I* know what the score is. I heard the whole thing, the whole story, the other night. She was telling your father, Patricia was, telling him about her and Vinnie. Yes, and about your mother and McBain too. She asked him if it was true and he said sure, sure it was true,

why not, what difference did it make? You're a fine one to go calling *me* dirty names. . . . Don't you believe me?"

Charlie pressed himself down into the darkness. Oh, let it close
over him completely, let it grow so deep and thick and solid above
his head it would shut out even the sound of her voice.

"Ask them, why don't you? Because you're scared, that's why.
You know what they'd tell you: it's all true, that's what they'd
have to tell you. But I didn't need to hear them saying it. Vinnie
told me. Vinnie told me long ago. Me and Vinnie, we tell each
other everything. We're good friends, see, and I know all about him
and Patricia. He told me. Like taking candy from a baby, Vinnie
said. Pretending she's so pure she doesn't even know what a man
looks like, and all the time—God, what a family! I wouldn't even
spit on you."

There was silence at last; and the silence continued.

But the darkness presently grew less. It was necessary for him
to get up out of the chair and leave the empty house and walk
downtown through the rain, enter the *Chronicle* building and go
out through the din of the press room to the shipping department
and speak to the men there, help bundle papers, distribute papers
through the building, load the trucks and drive his own truck off
through the rain and dump the bundled papers and make the
return trip.

You could do what you had to do, you could follow the same
pattern you had followed on days when the world had still seemed
solid, you could talk calmly to people and make them believe there
was nothing wrong with you. It was even possible to smile into
Vincent Rourke's face and say, Hi, Vinnie, fine weather for ducks,
and think for a minute that he was just another guy, just one of
the men on the paper, instead of the bastard who had debauched
your kid sister and likely your wife too, and your mother. No, that
was where you were getting off the track, it was McBain, McBain,
McBain who debauched your mother, that was the important thing
to remember. You could still keep the facts straight and remember
that Rourke was one bastard and McBain another, and even if
you killed one of them the other would still be alive; and you were
not going to kill either of them, of course, because where was the
point, what good would it do? It would never bring Laura Bryant
back; Laura Bryant was dead, McBain and Norris having killed
her between them; there had been too much death already and
there must not be any more.

As long as you remembered that there must be no more death,
you could know you were not altogether insane; and when your
work was finished for the day you could step into a bar with some
of the guys and have a couple of beers, and then walk home up
the hill in the rain, remembering that there must be no more

death. Pretty soon it was time for dinner and you sat down at the table with the others, who turned their faces from you, who would never look at you now because they believed you unclean, and they did not want to sit at the same table with you, but they had kind hearts and thought it would hurt your feelings if they confessed why they looked away from you, so they went on pretending there was nothing wrong.

And it was almost the end of May now and McBain would be here next week, and that was what was in all their minds: McBain the debaucher would be in Broadfield, standing on a platform and enchanting the ladies, making crystal-clear to them the situation in Europe, the situation in the Far East. All the people sitting at this table were waiting for McBain to come back to Broadfield so they could look at him again and say to themselves, so that's what he's like, there stands the man who debauched Laura Bryant and destroyed her husband's life and the lives of her children. They had been waiting for McBain and turning over and over in their minds the knowledge of what he had done to them. Everybody knew, everybody had always known except Charlie Bryant, the poor sucker lost in kid dreams of an impossibly perfect woman.

It was evening, it was night, and the rain was coming down harder, and everybody was going upstairs to bed, calmly, as if this were a night like any other night, and so you were going to bed too finally although you knew you would not sleep, you would never sleep again. . . .

But the whirl of Charlie's thoughts grew slower. The noise of the rain came in through the open window, and the smell of leaves and soaked earth, and he thought of his vegetable garden. Joel slept soundly in his bed across the room—his deep slow breathing, like contentment grown audible, said peace to Charlie, rest; and he slept too eventually. In the morning the clouds rolled back across the sky and piled themselves into towering snowy ranges against the blue, and then were gone. Broadfield glittered in the sun, and Charlie, gazing through his window, could see the glittering world as clearly as anyone else; the difference was that he knew the shining surface meant nothing.

What he then began to do—instinctively, unconsciously—was to destroy every bright memory to which he had ever clung. The weapon he used was contempt—for his own softness, his silly sickly pleasure in dreaming about the touch of her hands, the sound of her voice reading from *The King of the Golden River*, or telling him in the still night a tale of Indians and pioneers; her smile when she turned to him with bunches of wet lilac in her arms; her gentleness, her kindness, her sudden laughter. Charlie was a tough guy and there was no place in his mind for such memories; he must learn how to be hard all through.

Once or twice something flickered in him, a doubt, a feeling of unease; Delores might have been lying.

No. The flicker was extinguished. The world had always been an abyss, and those who thought they were climbing out, or believed they actually stood on the edge, looking down or not daring to look down, or who seemed to have walked away from the edge and turned their backs on the abyss forever—they were all deceived; they were all at the bottom, lost in the mire, and they would never find a way out; there was no way out; there was only the abyss. He should have been grateful to Delores, the instrument of revelation. Perhaps he was, and it had been a joke after all when he threatened to kill her.

He looked at his reflection in the mirror, as if what he had gone through—to how many men is revelation given?—must have changed his appearance; but he could see no difference in his face; he looked quite ordinary, and his voice sounded ordinary when he spoke to people. He must have looked and sounded ordinary to them, because they glanced at him as casually as ever; or rather did not glance at him at all, but continued to turn their faces away.

Once he passed Delores on the stairs, one day or two or three days after the revelation (it was growing difficult to keep track of time), and said, I notice you haven't cleared out yet, but she went past as if she had not heard him; and he wondered if the scene in the living room, the mizzling rain beyond the windows and the darkness closing in about her face, had ever really occurred.

He struck his own hand against the wall to find out if everything were not illusion; there was nothing illusory about the pain in his knuckles, but the others still ignored him. Except his father, on whose face Charlie still caught, now and then, the old look of bewilderment and doubt. It was necessary to be crafty. He would feel his father staring at him, and pretend not to notice, and then look up suddenly, just in time to catch the look before his father turned away.

But there was at last a day when Norris continued to look so steadily at Charlie that Charlie had to look steadily back.

"Charlie—"

"Yeah?" It was still possible to smile; the brain said smile, and the appropriate muscles went to work.

"Charlie, is there anything—? Are you worried about anything?"

"Worried? Me? Not a care in the world."

"Because if you are, if there's anything on your mind—"

"Hell, Pop, I don't have a mind. Don't you know that? Truckdrivers never have minds." Smile, said the brain, and the muscles went to work. Norris knew about Laura and McBain and Joel, about Patricia and Vincent Rourke, about Laurette and the men in the band, about Charlie and Delores, but he still didn't know about the abyss; and Charlie, who might otherwise have caught at the hand held out to him, wanted his father to go on being soft and foolish, and struck the hand away.

"You're doing all right on the job, aren't you?"

"Guess so. No complaints that I've heard of."

"We'll have to keep our eyes open for something better."

"Driving a truck is good enough for me."

Norris's eyes kept searching Charlie's face. "Well, even so—there are better trucks, Charlie."

"Cross-country, hey? See the world from a truck."

"Mm. . . . It'll do for the present, maybe."

"Yeah, Pop. It'll do." Charlie drifted toward the door. As long as his father looked at him like that the danger existed; he might weaken, after all, and clasp the hand—he could not be pulled upward because there was no up, but his father could be pulled down, for there were always depths below the depths.

"Laurette's coming up next week-end," Norris said.

"Yeah? Fine. That's swell." Charlie could not remember what Laurette looked like.

"And there's going to be a party out at the Wheelwrights' cottage. We're all invited."

"The Wheelwrights, hey?" said Charlie, and went into the garden.

Norris was almost reassured. He had perhaps been worrying about Charlie for nothing. Charlie had seemed no more strange than his other children, and the strangeness was not really there; it was nothing but the twist in his own mind, the battle he had been fighting with himself—for he still hadn't decided whether or not to see Andy tomorrow.

Andy was arriving in Broadfield before the crack of dawn. He would spend most of his day in the hotel, probably, although the Rotarians hoped to lure him to their regular weekly luncheon, where he might be jollied into saying a few words for free. In the afternoon he would possibly go about renewing old acquaintance, though he would be wanting to save his voice for the lecture in the evening.

The lecture was the last of the Literary Ladies' season and it was to be open to the general public; it would not take place in the old vine-covered club building, but in the larger auditorium of Central High School, and the tickets, said Lucinda's story in the *Chronicle,* were in great demand.

Norris wasn't going to attend the lecture; as to seeing Andy at the hotel, he wanted to do what he would have done if Andy had never known Laura and it had been a simple case of seeing or not seeing a very old friend whose life had followed an orbit remote from his. Norris knew Laura had been telling the truth, but the snake still coiled in his mind, and only Andy could scotch it permanently.

After a sleepless night, he walked to work still undecided—and saw Andy smiling up at him from the front page of the *Bugle*. Regarding Andy as its own contribution to the larger journalism, the *Bugle* had gone to the trouble of sending a photographer and a reporter to greet him as he climbed off the train, and had rushed the photograph to the engraver's, and run the cut in the final edition. But the story that went with the cut was brief. The returned prodigal said that it was great to be back in Broadfield; no, he was sorry, he was leaving for Detroit right after the lecture; yes, it was quite possible that if he ever retired, he would come back to Broadfield for good. Here's where I got my start, said Andrew White McBain, and here's where I'd like to wind up.

Norris said nothing to Ack about the story in the *Bugle;* Ack said nothing to him until half-past ten.

"I couldn't decide if we ought to run an interview with Andy or not," Ack said then. "He's the *Bugle's* boy, not ours. But the *Bugle* didn't make out so well. All that crap about Broadfield. Christ, I'll bet he had words with his agent when he found out he was all fixed up for a lecture here. Well, the *Bugle's* bound to scoop us on the lecture itself, so what I thought, I'd send Vinnie down to get kind of a preview, and we'll scoop the *Bugle.*" He looked at the clock on the wall. "About time for him to get going. Hey, Rourke!" he shouted.

"Wait a minute," said Norris. "It's a long time since I've written an interview. How about letting me handle it?"

Ack turned to him. "You really want to?"

"If you could get along without me for an hour—"

"Hell, yes. If anybody can make McBain talk, you ought to be able to. Only no more crap about how much he likes Broadfield."

Vincent had come up to Ack's desk, and Norris studied his face curiously. Didn't he look a little strange too—haggard, as if he had not been sleeping—or was that also just the twist in Norris's own mind?

Ack leaned sideways and spat. "You got the appointment with McBain all fixed up?"

"For ten forty-five," Vincent said.

"O.K., swell. Only Bry's taking over. That's all," said Ack.

"You mean—"

"Bry used to be a good reporter too, you know," Ack said.

Vincent's glance slid from Ack to Norris; their eyes met, and Norris saw that Vincent disliked him as much as he disliked Vincent.

"Sorry, Vinnie. Andy and I used to be friends." He stood and crossed to the rack and took down his hat; he pushed the bell for the elevator, and rode in state to the first floor, and stepped out into the morning, and walked briskly down Main Street to the Hotel Ulysses S. Grant, shoved through the revolving door, crossed the wide lobby, and laid his hands down on the desk.

"Would you tell Mr. McBain, Mr. Andrew McBain, that the reporter from the *Chronicle* is here?" He stood at the desk until the clerk had put the call through, and then wandered off to the bank of elevators with a cigarette between his fingers. He felt quite calm, now the plunge had been made; he felt only a mild amusement as he stood waiting for Andy; Andy was in for a surprise.

But Andy did not immediately recognize Norris, when the glass doors slid back; and Norris thought he would not have recognized Andy, if it hadn't been for the cut in the *Bugle*. His skin was smooth, and brown from weeks of leisure in Florida or Bermuda; but there was almost no flesh beneath the skin, and through its appearance of health the modeling of the skull showed clearly. Andy's hair was quite white—so shining a white that you couldn't help wondering about it: didn't lemon juice make white hair whiter? His double-breasted pin-stripe suit was tailored to suggest width of shoulder and slimness and flatness of waist without being obvious about it. Andy's hand, when at last it came forward to clasp Norris's, was cold to the touch, but it clasped with fervor, and did not let go for a long time.

"Bry," Andy kept saying. "Bry. I'll be damned! I was expecting some kid—I talked to him on the phone. You don't mean to tell me you're pounding the pavements again?"

"Just for today. It's a pretty special occasion."

"Yeah—yeah. God, it's great to see you, Bry. Great." Andy's dark eyes stayed fixed on Norris's face; he and Norris stood there isolated in the hotel lobby while people flowed past them. And what was Andy seeing in his face, Norris wondered—weariness, failure, defeat? He looked into Andy's face and tried to see success in it. But already the new Andy was blurring with the former images: the college boy, the young reporter, the war veteran were becoming one with the man who stood before him in the well-tailored suit, with the brown skull-like face, the shining hair, the slight limp—for now they were moving on again, across the lobby, and Andy's hand lay lightly on Norris's sleeve—they were old friends and good ones, the touch of his hand suggested.

"What does one do at ten forty-five on a May morning?" Andy asked. "Do you think the bar is open?"

"I'm supposed to interview you."

"The hell with that. You can make up anything you like, Bry— I'll trust you."

"I read your book. Good, Andy. Pretty damn good."

"We don't need to go into that. . . . Sure, the bar is open."

They sat down at a small table against the wall. Presently the bartender came out from behind the bar, where he had been washing glasses, and stood, white-aproned, by their table. "What'll it be, gentlemen?"

"I don't want anything but a glass of water," Norris said.

"You ought to have a drink, Bry. I don't usually drink in the middle of the morning myself, but— You got any John Jamieson?" Andy asked the bartender.

"Yup."

"John Jamieson and water, then. . . . I like Irish; like it better than Scotch," Andy told Norris. "Broadfield must agree with you. You're looking great. Really great."

"I happen to know different." Norris didn't see how the conversation could move on from here; there was too much ground to be covered. "How do you like lecturing?" he asked.

Andy grimaced. Now that Norris could examine him more attentively, he saw the fine lines about the eyes and mouth, and the eyes did not stare into great distances and the smile was only a nervous reaction; really Andy was no more a romantic figure than he was—in Andy's face too there were weariness and failure and defeat. Did all famous men look like this? quite ordinary?

The drinks arrived. The bartender had brought John Jamieson for Norris also, but Norris left it untouched.

"How do I like lecturing?" Andy said, after he'd taken a sip. "It's worse than the war, Bry; I mean it. Something comes over me sometimes, as I stand there, looking down at all the ladies— and why is it only ladies go to lectures? Oh, there's a sprinkling of men, sometimes, but you hardly notice them. I stand there and I hear my own voice going on and on, I hear them laughing at what my voice is saying—oh, I'm amusing, I'm damned amusing, you'd be surprised, and the jokes that worked in San Francisco worked just as well in Butte, but how will they go over in Broadfield? I split up into two people, the guy who's talking and the guy who sits back and says, 'For Christ's sake, McBain, what a phony you are, what a god-damned fake.' Sooner or later," McBain said, sipping his drink, "*that's* the guy will get the upper hand, and he'll tell the audience a thing or two they didn't pay their money for.

"Well, another week of it, and I'll be through. My agent wanted to send me out in midwinter, when business is better, but I said if they want to hear me bad enough, they can damn well hear me in April and May. I've had enough snow and ice and slush to last me a lifetime, and I'm wintering in Mexico, I said, and that's that. Acapulco. Great place, Bry. I lay in the sun at Acapulco, and tried to kid myself that I was a famous guy, an outstanding personality, and life lay before me. . . .

"Lecturing," said McBain. "It gets to be a habit, Bry. Not that I wasn't always a talker, but listen to me now. Teachers and preachers and lecturers, they get so they can't keep their traps shut, on the platform or off. Just sit where you are; I'll bend your ears for you." He smiled, sipped, and turned his glass around on the table. "God, I'm glad you pulled this stunt on me. I almost feel like a human being again."

"Hell, you know a whole bunch of people in Broadfield—"

"Yeah, and they've been trying to snag me too. That Wilmot dame—what's her name? She's been married a half-dozen times, I guess—she called me up just now."

"Her father died just recently. I thought she'd clear out, but she hasn't, so far."

"Mm," said Andy, who was not interested. "No, you're the only guy in Broadfield I give a good goddam about. I was going to look you up this afternoon. How's it going, Bry? Life treated you better than it has me?"

Norris smiled at his untouched whisky. "I don't know what you have to complain about."

"Oh, you don't, hey? Well, I'll tell you about that, maybe." McBain's glass was already empty. "If you really don't want that good Irish whisky, I'll take it off your hands. Drinking in the middle of the morning is a brighter idea than I thought." He appeared to be growing a little restless; he glanced about the empty bar, and there was a bleak look in his face when he turned it back toward Norris.

"How are all the kids? I guess I've forgotten how many there are."

"Four. . . . I'm a grandfather."

"Well, I'll be damned!" McBain said softly. "How many times over?"

"Just once. Boy. He's going on eleven months old now. Be walking soon. Living with me—they're all with me, except Laurette. Times are still pretty tough around here, you know. Guess we got hit as bad as any place in the country. It's been really bad," Norris said.

"Well, hang on, Bry. It's going to be worse before it gets better."

"So you claim in your book. You really believe all that? Another war?"

"Just around the corner. I don't know how long it'll take to get around the corner, but it will, Bry. There's no way out. Maybe there never was."

Absently Norris lit a cigarette. "Laura used to think another world war would be the end of civilization. A lot of people used to think that. I guess I think so myself. It just—doesn't seem possible, somehow. Who wants to fight? Nobody around here."

"Want to or not, they'll find themselves fighting. Or going under. Or fighting and going under both. I've reached the point where I don't think civilization's worth saving. I mean that, Bry. I don't like the human race. I've seen too much of it. . . . A war," Mc-Bain said. "It'll be fine, for a while. You wait and see. It'll bring back prosperity. It's the only thing that could bring it back. We're washed up. You and me, the United States, England, France— we're washed up. Tired out, all of us, licked. Maybe that's the only way you ever get to be really civilized—when you're too old and tired to fight. Well, the war will come, and maybe we'll kid ourselves for a little while, we'll forget we're too old and tired to fight, and there'll be money again, plenty of it, and bands playing, and flags waving. It'll look like the last war, on top, but underneath it will be different—altogether different; underneath we won't be kidding ourselves at all, and that's why we'll go down. That's why we're going to lose the next war."

"Cheerful cuss, aren't you?"

"The thing is, Bry, they lap it up—everywhere I go. I don't put it in just so many words, but it's what I mean, and they know it, and it appeals to them. That proves my point, doesn't it? They don't really want to live any more. Death looks pretty good to them. It's the only way they can find peace—by dying. I soothe them; I tell them they don't have to try any more; trying won't get them anywhere so they might just as well fold their hands and go under gracefully. I don't think they're deliberately trying to blind themselves—they make a lot of noise, still, some of them, thumping their chests and flexing their muscles, but it doesn't mean a damn thing. We *want* to go under. Otherwise we'd start tomorrow, building planes and ships and guns, putting the kids in uniform. . . .

"See, I can't keep my trap shut. I started to ask about your family."

"Nothing much to tell."

"Wish I was going to be in town longer. I'd like to see them all." McBain sipped again and looked away from Norris. "That was bad about Laura, Bry. I just happened to be in New York at the time, and somebody told me, I forget who. I wrote you a letter, didn't I?"

"Yeah," said Norris. "Yes, you wrote a letter."

"It was a pretty peculiar letter, now I come to think of it. You've probably forgotten, but I— Well, the fact is, I felt as if I'd lost my best friend, when I heard Laura was dead. Crazy, but that's how I felt. I always envied you, because she was your wife and not mine. I think I'd have married again, if I hadn't met Laura, but after her—well, no other woman counted. She was—

"I wanted to tell you that, when I wrote the letter. It's funny,

237

with a woman like Laura, you think you're the only guy in the world really appreciates her. You'd been married to her I don't know how many years, but I honestly believed, when I heard she'd died, that you didn't know her. Not the way I did. So that's what that letter was all about, really, Bry. I was trying to tell you what kind of woman your wife had been. Jesus, what gall! But I was a little younger then than I am now."

Norris looked at McBain, who was still evading his eyes, signaling now to the bartender for another drink. "I never did read that letter, Andy," he said.

McBain turned his head slowly; his face was quite blank. "No?"

"I tore it up and threw it away; never opened it."

McBain smiled faintly. "Just as well, probably. It was a bad letter." He paused until the bartender had walked away again. "I was a little crazy, I think. I tried to get Laura away from you, Bry. Maybe you guessed, maybe she told you. I'll never forget the way she looked at me. Not angry. Not angry at all. A little puzzled, first, and then sorry for me. Nobody ever looked at me like that before, nobody has since, thank God." He smiled again. "I couldn't take it, not another look like that. Lower than the dirt, that's what I was then. . . . Not that it wasn't a good idea in its way—from my point of view. There aren't enough Lauras to go around. . . .

"So I mean it, Bry; I envied you. I still do, even though she died. How long ago?"

"Ten years. Eleven years next month."

"Getting along without her, after you'd had her. How in hell did you do it, Bry?"

"I made a pretty bad mess of things. Isn't over yet."

"But you have something. Her to remember, and a family, a grandson, more grandchildren after a while, maybe—"

"If the world's going to smash, what's the point, what's the good? Better to be like you, Andy—no hostages to fortune. Nothing to worry about except your own skin."

"I could be wrong, you know. When you're sick in your mind, the world looks sick too. I don't think, really, that I ever got over the war. That nice, cozy little war, that'll look like a Sunday school picnic when the next one hits its stride. Oh, I waste a lot of time and energy feeling sorry for myself. I'm a has-been, Bry. Maybe it doesn't look that way to you, but it's what I am. It's why I let myself be talked into this damn tour. I don't make an awful lot out of it, but I make something, and it keeps the book moving off the shelves for a while. But when the tour's over, and the book's dead—what then?"

"More reporting," Norris said. "If you're right, there's going to be plenty to report."

Andy shook is head. "I'm too old. There's a whole new generation come along, and more coming all the time—kids, bright kids, who know more than I ever knew, all about economics and political science and sociology, steeped in Marx and all those writers I never had the wits to understand. And they have the one blind spot you need for success—they think what they're doing is important, and if they work hard enough and get enough stories and shout about them loud enough, they can change the course of history. They really do, they honestly believe that. You have to burn with that zeal these days, Bry—it's hard work, and sometimes it's dangerous. . . .

"Well, in a way it's the same old story—the same old difference between a good newspaperman and a bad one, all down the line. You have to think your stuff matters. Getting the story matters more than anything else in the world, whether it's about a house that burned down on Broadfield Avenue, or a secret pact between Germany and Ruritania. And the harder the story is to get, the more it matters. Well, I've stopped feeling that way; the facts you risk your life to get may go through, if you're lucky, and if you're really lucky they may make the front page; even so they're forgotten the day after they've been printed. Ephemeral—it's all ephemeral. Even a book—that's forgotten too, six months after publication.

"I know that now, but the kid correspondents don't, so I'm retiring. I'm going the way all newspaper hacks think they want to go—turning my hand to fiction. My agent, my literary agent, she's all hopped up about the possibilities. I try to get hopped up about them myself. Maybe I'll make a living at it, maybe I won't; money goes further in Mexico—it's where I plan to operate from. If nobody buys my stuff, you'll have to find a place for me on the *Chronicle*. You could make me the church editor, and I'd end my days battling with all the god-damned parsons in the town. There's a raft of them too, isn't there? . . .

"Well, as visiting celebrities are supposed to say to you cub reporters, have you got your story? I'll have to cut this short, I'm afraid, Bry. I'm off to Rotary with liquor on my breath."

Andy called the bartender and paid for the drinks. He walked with Norris into the lobby, resting one hand on his sleeve again, and there was a remnant of their old friendship left after all, so that they shook hands warmly, and looked at each other with a kind of sadness, knowing that probably they would never see each other again. What had begun in young manhood with a rivalry which had seemed important, and blossomed into a fine companionship, and fallen away into estrangement, was ending in—what? A recognition that their paths, moving in opposite directions, had reached the same goal?

"So long, Andy," Norris said. "Good luck to you."

"Thanks. The same to you."

Norris went down the steps to the revolving doors, and then turned his head; Andy was still standing up there, and he lifted his hand and smiled again; then he moved toward the elevators and his limp was more pronounced—the effect, perhaps, of three drinks of Irish in the middle of the morning.

It was almost noon when Norris sat down at his desk again; he shut away the sound of increasing chaos, and ripped off three pages of copy, and read them through; he even began to think about heads, a boxed head, the kind that was sometimes used for interviews or feature stories.

Then he looked over at Ack. "You need this story? You leave any space for it?"

"Naw, I thought you were only kidding, Bry—thought you were just going to chew the fat with him."

"I guess maybe we don't want to print it."

"Sure, why give McBain a plug? Kill it," said Ack. "What the hell?"

But Norris did not tear his story up. He folded it and stuck it in his vest-pocket. Ten years from now, or twenty, if he lived that long, he might reread it and see how good a prophet Andy had been:

DEFEATISM

FAMED JOURNALIST SEES END
OF DEMOCRACY IN NEXT WAR

"Too old and tired to fight," the United States, Great Britain, France and other democracies will "go under" in a second and more terrible world war which is "just around the corner," according to Andrew White McBain, distinguished foreign correspondent and author of the best-seller, *Casual Journey,* who arrived in Broadfield Thursday morning on a coast-to-coast lecture tour. The journalist, whose own career began in Broadfield, believes the next war—

Their paths, he thought, hadn't reached the same goal after all; they never would, no matter how long Andy's casual journey, his own exploration of the labyrinth, continued. Maybe Andy was as licked as he said; but I'm not, thought Norris; not yet, not by a long shot.

It might be true, though, that in one or two ways Andrew White McBain had known Laura Bryant better than her own husband had.

"Throw some stuff over, Ack," said Norris. "I need work."

20

IT HAD BEEN a bad morning for Vincent, but so had all mornings lately, and all afternoons and evenings too. What afflicted him was nothing so definite as the mood; it was a kind of gradual disintegration, as though the world had subtly started to go to pieces. Since the night he got drunk in his room nothing had gone right. Disaster was impending—he knew it, as he had known it toward the end of the Anne Bannister business.

Patricia had told her father, of course. It was why Norris had deprived Vincent of the one assignment he'd ever really wanted. And when Norris found out from McBain that the story was false —Vincent was suddenly sure of this—he would have it out with Vincent.

First there was that, and then there dropped on Vincent's desk a letter from his uncle, who said he had not the faintest intention of helping him to quit the job. "I am thoroughly bored with you, Vinnie, and if you leave Broadfield I shall, to employ again a sadly hackneyed phrase, cut you off without a penny. *I mean this.*"

And then it turned out that Vincent, reading Milly Prentiss's society copy the afternoon before, had absently allowed a series of shocking blunders to go through, and now the composing room was in an uproar because the whole society page had to be reset; and Vincent, not Milly, was the object of Ack's quiet venom.

And then he turned in two stories which Ack picked up gingerly and read through with contempt, and carried over to Will Eliot to be completely rewritten; Vincent was left alone at his desk, to meditate on his sins.

Norris came back from his interview with McBain, and apparently wrote a story about it; but nothing about McBain appeared in the home edition. And if Norris knew about the scene with Patricia, he probably knew also about the scenes with Delores; and so must Charlie.

Vincent began to understand what was the matter with him. It was very simple, really—he was frightened. His life, although he sometimes liked to believe he was living dangerously, had been almost free of physical fear; the only other time he had been as frightened as this was at the end of his affair with Anne Bannister.

Charlie Bryant was something like Tom Bannister: more crude, less sophisticated, but fundamentally the same.

Vincent unbent a paper clip and twisted it into a new shape. It was a warm day and a wind that smelled of summer came in through the open windows and stirred listlessly among the papers scattered on all the desks; but Vincent felt very cold.

He had not only maneuvered himself into a trap; with appalling ingenuity he had seen to it that, once trapped, he would be closed in upon by a circle of enemies. And this time there would be no Uncle Bertrand to come petulantly to the rescue; Carola Wilmot, shut up inside the house where her father had so recently died, was not to be relied upon—at any moment she would leave Broadfield forever; and there was no one else. Vincent was alone.

He wondered how much money he would need to leave Broadfield immediately. There were various unpaid bills, but he could leave them unpaid. One hundred dollars would carry him in his car to New Mexico or Arizona or Nevada, all the way out to Southern California; but what then? He would need a backlog to keep him going until he found a job; and maybe he wouldn't find one; and anyway, at the moment he had not more than ten dollars all told, and there was no one who would lend him one hundred dollars.

Unless Carola—

But he hadn't gone to see her since her father's death; he had sent no flowers for the funeral; he had not written a note.

If he called Uncle Bertrand long-distance and explained the whole situation—

No. Uncle Bertrand would be even more revolted by this mess than by the Bannister mess. He managed his own curious life with circumspection, so as to avoid anything really nasty; if Vincent's affair with Anne had been simply an affair, Uncle Bertrand might have taken it in his stride. Instead, it turned into the kind of thing you read about in the tabloids, and Anne had dragged Uncle Bertrand into it, a frantically unwilling deus ex machina.

A week after Vincent thought he had seen the last of her, Anne appeared suddenly late one April afternoon in Uncle Bertrand's apartment. Vincent and his uncle had been about to have a little drink together, and a little dinner at an amusing Armenian place they had discovered, and then they were going to Carnegie Hall to hear the Philadelphia Symphony Orchestra; but there was Anne, her face gaunt and ravaged, her eyes smudged with dark shadows, looking years older than she was as she cast her coat on the sofa, cast herself after it, and told Uncle Bertrand, as she had told Vincent already, that she was going to kill herself.

Vincent stood frozen against the marble mantel; Uncle Bertrand, after a moment of incredulous stillness, went tittuping about the room, flapping his face with a silk handkerchief and saying with pathos, "Do let's try to be *calm* about this. We achieve nothing by letting ourselves *go.*" But Anne let herself go; the story was all out in a few broken sentences.

"Really," said Uncle Bertrand, "really, this is too degrading. It is so disgustingly physiological. You aren't babes in the wood. Didn't you know what to *do?* Must one supply you with textbooks? I can forgive you everything but this appalling carelessness, Vinnie."

Anne said it had not been carelessness; it had been intentional. She wished to save Vincent from himself and had resolved on a desperate expedient.

"Good God," said Uncle Bertrand, and clutched the handkerchief to his brow. "I wouldn't have believed it of you, darling. You are talking the worst kind of rubbish. What has become of your sense of humor? Do have a drink—please do—and make an effort, at least, to talk like a sane and civilized creature." He poured out three drinks, but they remained neglected on the tray.

"The important point at the moment," said Uncle Bertrand, "is this: *Does* Tom *know?*"

He knew she'd been seeing a good deal of Vincent, said Anne, but then she had seen a good deal of a good many other young men before Vincent came along. But he regarded Vincent as a child, and so he probably did not know; though she would tell him, in any case, before she killed herself.

"My poor, sweet, misguided infant, you must stop saying such outrageous things. Really, you must. Women do not kill themselves for love any more. It has gone out, darling; it is simply too absurd and fin de siècle of you. Besides, if Vincent gave in, if you got your divorce and he married you, he would drive you demented. Do try to gather your wits together, darling, and see that."

Uncle Bertrand went to the windows and pulled the curtains across. When he turned he said, "Vinnie, really, it is your turn to speak now. Do contribute *something* to this agonizing debate. It revolves about you."

But Vincent stood frozen against the mantel and said nothing.

Uncle Bertrand sat on a hassock, close to the sofa, and peered at Anne while he toyed with his handkerchief. "You are not going to kill yourself," he said. "We are clear on that point, at least." He looked at his handkerchief. "I abhor indelicacy, but are you sure, darling, are you *quite* sure this couldn't be Tom's doing after all?"

There was no question of that, Anne said.

"Then I must be even more indelicate." Uncle Bertrand let out a small fluttering sigh and gingerly touched Anne's knee. "Darling, can't you possibly *arrange* things to make it seem as if it *were* Tom's child?"

There was a curious hush in the room. Vincent could hear a truck passing in the street; he could hear the rattle of the elevated, far off along Third Avenue, and a ship hooting in the river, and the whole wide murmur of the city.

Presently Uncle Bertrand took his hand away and sat back. "It would be so simple, darling," he said.

Anne stared at him for a long time; then she turned and gazed directly at Vincent, and somehow he had to look back at her; she was still ravaged, but she was no longer letting herself go. "Do you approve, Vincent?" She even smiled faintly. "Do you think it's a good idea?"

Vincent drew a breath, lifting his head so he would not have to see her; and still he said nothing.

"Can't you see—?" Anne's voice began with a little rush, and then stopped; when she went on she sounded tired and hopeless. "A life," she said. "*Your* life, Vincent, and you— Do you really want Tom to think it's his child? . . . There's been so much falsehood," she said. "All our lives we've been tangled up in lies— all three of us. And now when I try to be honest at last— I'm insane, I suppose, but I love you, my darling, and I want to have your child; I want to be your wife. Can't you see what Bertie's asking me to do? The kind of life he's asking me to lead? . . . I can't," she said. "I can't do it."

Vincent lowered his head and saw that she was still looking at him. Inwardly he was panic-stricken, but his voice came out coldly. "I've told you already, it was your idea; it's your responsibility; it's your decision." He paused. "*I* don't see why you have to—go through with it at all."

The hush fell upon them again. Eventually Anne said, "No. You really don't. Do you?"

Uncle Bertrand rose from the hassock. "Perhaps Vinnie's right. Rather nasty now, but simpler in the long run, darling, after all. I mean, suppose it *looked* like Vincent? My grand-nephew. Or niece. *Really,*" said Uncle Bertrand, and became speechless for several moments. When he had recovered, he said, "Naturally you wouldn't know of any suitable doctors, darling. Nor you either, Vinnie, I suppose, in spite of your blithe suggestion. Good God," he said forlornly, "to think that I should be driven, *I* should be, to making discreet inquiries. Well, I suppose some of my dearest friends may have found themselves in this predicament—really, Nature is too ruthless—and perhaps one of them . . . But what will they think of *me?*"

He stood weakly by the sofa, folding the handkerchief into a triangle and then into a square and then into a smaller triangle; finally he tucked it into his pocket, and touched Anne on the shoulder.

244

"I am now going to take you home in a taxi, darling," he said, "and if necessary I shall sit with you all evening. By tomorrow morning I feel sure you'll be able to see things our way. And not a word to Tom, do you hear? Not one single word until we have fixed this all up. . . . As for you," he said to Vincent, "I think it would be a relief all around if you *were* to put a bullet through your head, but naturally you won't. And those *expensive* tickets for Stokowski, gone utterly to waste! I had been so looking forward to this evening; I am so *driven,*" said Uncle Bertrand, and swept out with Anne.

Vincent did not see her again. He had a last note from her, in which she told him that he was in fact a babe in the wood, but a perverted one, and that she had offered him a chance to grow up, and that she hoped he might be offered it again, by a wiser woman, and that he wouldn't turn it down. "You *need* not be eternally damned, my darling," she wrote, and Vincent burned the letter.

Uncle Bertrand had taken care of everything; perhaps he even paid the doctor; and for a while, plumply but gracefully walking a tightrope, he lulled Tom Bannister's suspicions. But in late spring Tom somehow learned that something off-color had been going on, and Uncle Bertrand thought it best to sever relations with the Bannisters and pack Vincent off to Fire Island until he could leave town for good. Finding the job had been his last great effort for Vincent; there would never be another.

But when the end of the afternoon came and Norris still had not looked at Vincent, his fear abated somewhat. The thing to do about fear was to confront it boldly, he thought, wandering along the dusty streets toward Eustis Court; if you looked your fear in the face, it turned into something else—the notion, for instance, that by now Patricia had made allowances for his drunkenness that night and yearned for him again.

He began to yearn for Patricia, who had never been really demanding, or shown any sign of becoming possessive, or seemed to mind when he was in a bad mood. He believed suddenly that she had infinite understanding, an inexhaustible compassion for him. It might even be possible to put the relationship back on its old footing; they could drive out into the country and find a ferny glade and read poetry aloud to each other. That was what she really wanted; it was what he really wanted too—a purely innocent, a merely pretty relationship.

He went down the stairs and around to the front porch and had a little talk with the Madam, and then went into the Madam's living room and used the Madam's telephone. There was still time to catch Patricia before she left her dentists' office.

Her voice sounded cool and forbidding, but he had lost himself now in his dream; he could see the ferny glade so clearly, he could hear his own voice so clearly, reading aloud from *A Shropshire Lad*.

"I've never apologized about that night, Patricia," he said. "I've hardly slept a wink since. . . . I suppose you still hate me."

There was a small silence, and then she said, "I can't talk now, Vinnie, I—"

"You don't know how lousy I've been feeling about it all. I don't know what got into me, to tell such a filthy lie about your mother. It was a lie, you know. Carola's an evil-minded old hag, and she—"

"Vincent, you—"

"I miss you so much. And we're having such wonderful weather. I thought maybe on Sunday, if you *can* forgive me, we'd go driving somewhere. Won't you, Patricia? Please? Because I don't think I'll be here much longer, there's an offer shaping up, and I'd like to feel that horrible degrading evening was wiped out of your mind. I'm not like that really, and it's meant so much to me, knowing you. And I'd like to write to you, after I do get settled in Chicago. Chicago seems to be the next step."

Her voice was deeply troubled. "I can't this Sunday, Vinnie— I'm going out to the lake on Saturday; I have the day off. The Wheelwrights have asked me. I'll be there the whole week-end. They're renting their cottage the first of June, so this is the last chance, you see, it's— The Sunday after—?"

"I may not even be here then. Everything's come up so suddenly."

"But, Vinnie—"

"There's tonight, of course."

"I'm going to the movies with Johnny. And tomorrow night Laurette's getting here from Detroit, and Betty Lou's coming over, and we're having a sort of party—"

"Oh, damn it," said Vincent. "I want to see you right now." He sighed quite effectively. "By the way, darling, don't say anything to your father about the Chicago thing. Because it may not pan out and if it doesn't I don't want to get in wrong at the *Chronicle*."

"Yes, Vinnie, all right," she said hastily, and hung up.

He wandered out and away from the Madam's sticky interest, and strolled downtown again. He had two drinks in a bar and went into the Orchard House cafeteria for dinner, and partly because of the drinks he wasn't frightened any more; there was nothing in him now but a melancholy yearning for Patricia Bryant, who certainly had not told her father anything about that night in Eustis Court.

He dropped in to see a movie, but his mind continued to play with the thought of Patricia, and how foolish he had been to force things beyond the brother-sister point. That really had been Carola's doing; she had goaded him into attempting to seduce Patricia because she was too old to try seducing him herself, fearing that if she tried she might be humiliated, perhaps; she would get her satisfaction vicariously.

Carola, in fact, had been his evil genius ever since his arrival in Broadfield. If it had not been for Carola, he might have fallen in love with Patricia. You *need* not be eternally damned, my darling —and Carola Wilmot had prevented Patricia from being his rescuing angel.

But it might not be too late.

Vincent left the theater. His feet carried him toward Warner Street, and he found himself entering the driveway to Carola's house, and pushing the bell, just as the City Hall clock chimed a quarter past nine.

Not the sad monkey but Carola herself opened the door, and there was no difficult moment. "My dear," she said. "You should have warned me you were coming, and I'd have tried to make myself look a little less dreadful for you."

But in the shaded light of her living room, with the shapes of furniture and the color of flowers in vases glimmering back from the mirrors, she looked quite as handsome as she had last fall; and he told her so.

"Nevertheless, I am a total wreck, darling. The reasons are too complicated to go into, but I'm glad you've come at last—and so very glad you didn't come sooner. There is something so barbaric and defeating about funerals—I am just beginning to get my feet on solid ground again. Will you have a drink? No, let's just talk. It's been so long since I've talked to anybody. And we'll talk about something amusing."

She allowed him to light a cigarette for her; she smiled up at him, waving the smoke gently aside. "You're looking rather fine-drawn, darling, as if you'd been going through a crisis too—but it becomes you, it really does. You look just a little less like a guileless innocent. How goes the affaire de cœur?"

"That was really what I wanted to talk over with you, if it won't bore you."

"Stop teasing, darling, and begin at the beginning, and tell me everything."

"I'd rather begin at the end and work back." Vincent felt that his smile had never been more charming.

"It sounds confusing, but do go ahead."

"Well—you know you said that you'd let me borrow the cottage one week-end, as a reward for my labors—"

"Borrow the cottage *and* me, in the rôle of chaperon. That's what I said, my pet."

"Yes, I know. So if you haven't any other plans for this week-

247

end, I thought we might— Though maybe you aren't quite up to a week-end at the lake just yet?"

"Don't sound so indecently hopeful, darling. Though I'm not, as a matter of fact. All that water, all that sky—I couldn't face them. I feel small enough as it is—I spend most of my time shut into a closet, as I used to in thunderstorms. . . . No, you may borrow the cottage for the week-end, with my blessing. The pump is fixed, the lights have been turned on, the telephone is in good working order—it's for sale or rent, like the Wheelwrights'. . . . But surely you aren't planning to *abduct* the fair young maiden?"

"Not exactly." Vincent smiled again, leaning back in his chair, with his legs crossed. "She's spending the week-end there too, with the Wheelwrights. There's been a kind of crisis, you see. Ever since she went out with Johnny that Sunday, he's been back in the picture, and now she's the victim of doubts and hesitations. I thought if I could be on the spot too—"

"Yes." Carola smiled back at him. "We certainly can't allow Johnny an unfair advantage. Only just don't do anything rash, darling, or anything too crude."

"I'm never rash or crude, I hope."

"Except possibly when one of those moods comes along?"

"They never do, in May. Not this kind of May."

"I begin to wish I could be invisibly present; I should love to watch your technique at work. But do remember that Johnny used to play football, and got knocked out in a Golden Gloves tournament."

"Maybe I could knock him out, if the need arose."

"Somehow, darling, I think not. And you'd look all wrong, with a broken nose, or a cauliflower ear. No, you must avoid pugilism, at all costs."

"I think that can be arranged."

"Of course I shall be consumed with curiosity until you've told me how it all works out. You must come back here *immediately*, darling, and tell me. I shall insist on knowing all the details—that is another of my conditions." Carola sat up in her chair. "I am *so* glad you've come around tonight. I begin to feel almost alive again."

"I'm a little surprised, really, that you're still here. I thought you'd be leaving for Paris the day after the funeral."

"Paris," said Carola, and looked at her hands. "It's strange, Vincent, isn't it, the way things turn out? One remains so unclear about one's own inner workings. Here I have sat for five years, praying that my father would die and release me. But now, somehow or other, the thought of not being caged any more frightens me. I've grown used to my cage. It has all been rather a nightmare, really. I feel so—lost. Or would if I left this house. Cut adrift, and where would the winds and currents carry me? I seem to be mixing my metaphors, darling—would you give me another cigarette?"

"What would be so frightening about drifting to Paris?" Vincent asked, after he had shaken out the match.

"Paris is the past to me now. A city of ghosts, darling. Quite literally. All the friends I had there have gone away long since. You know what an exodus there was after the crash."

"New York, then."

"Your Uncle Bertrand. I suppose he could arrange my re-entry into all that sort of thing. But somehow I don't seem to want that sort of thing any more. I am so thoroughly sick and tired of myself, darling," Carola said lightly. "It would have to be somewhere quite new for me—a new kind of scenery, a new kind of people. I have nothing to draw upon here," she said, laying one hand, half in burlesque and half earnestly, on her breast. "That is the terrible discovery I have made. I have reached the point where I must draw my nourishment from outside of me. . . .

"Am I being very pompous, darling? It's what a death in the family does to you. I keep seeing myself as the last of the Wilmots —all those generations, all those centuries, mounting to a climax in my father—because he was quite a lad in his day, you know, *quite* a lad—and then suddenly here am I, the most dispiriting of anticlimaxes. . . .

"I talked to Andy McBain on the telephone, this morning. Poor dear, he was sleepy and grumpy and I suppose it was inconsiderate of me, but he's seen so many places, and I thought that somewhere in the world he might know of the right place for me. Mexico, perhaps. He'd been wintering in Mexico, and he says it's enchanting. You didn't cross the border, did you, on your grand tour?"

"No. Though I've always rather wanted to go to Mexico myself."

"I suppose it's been spoiled by now. Overrun by the most depressing kind of tourist—schoolteachers and lustful college boys and whatnot. Then there's the language—I don't know Spanish, and I suppose I'd be cheated right and left. Also there are revolutions. Also there is the health problem. I really am beginning to age—in my youth these considerations wouldn't have daunted me. Still, I have been thinking of Mexico quite seriously. If only I didn't have to go alone. That is something else, you see. I find that I am utterly alone in the world." Carola paused; she regarded her cigarette. "I sometimes wonder what has happened to all my friends."

She let the silence draw out, still gazing at her cigarette, and Vincent became unsure about his next line. Had she thrown him a cue, or hadn't she?

"Well," she said presently, "I must be boring you to distraction.

I'd better get you the key to the cottage and send you off home to bed. You're looking tired, and I know how I look." She snuffed out her cigarette and rose; Vincent rose also, anxious now to leave her house.

She went out of the room, and while she was gone he began to see himself in the mirrors again—tired, as she had said, fine-drawn, certainly a little older than he had looked eight months ago; but old enough to make her half-suggestion, half-invitation—if it really had been that—anything but grotesque?

Carola returned and laid a whole bunch of keys in his hand.

"Guard them with your life, darling, and don't let your passion set fire to the cottage. How I envy you," she said, as they moved toward the door. "Really, you know, you ought to be *most* grateful to me. I do think I'm being extraordinarily kind to you, darling."

"You are," said Vincent, dropping the keys into his pocket. The hall light was not turned on; in the dim radiance that shone from the living room, Carola looked tall and mysterious, completely enigmatic.

She held out her hand to him. "Good luck, my pet."

Instead of clasping her hand, Vincent suddenly bent his head and kissed the inside of her wrist, the soft perfumed flesh; and her hand came up and lightly touched his cheek, her fingers strayed over his mouth.

"How Continental of you, darling," she said.

He fumbled for the doorknob; the touch of her fingers, so brief and casual, had interrupted briefly his vision of Patricia in a ferny glade. He got the door open, and looked out into the dark, and then back at her. He was impelled to make the moment prosaic again.

"You didn't go to McBain's lecture," he said.

Carola stood quite still; the silence seemed to continue for a long time. "I'm not one of the Literary Ladies," she said, and turned away into her living room, leaving the door open, leaving him to walk off unwatched.

But of course a great many people who were not Literary Ladies had gone to McBain's lecture. The auditorium of Central High School was filled; there were even people sitting in the balcony seats cut off from a view of the stage by fat round pillars painted to resemble golden oak. Charlie Bryant was sitting behind one of the pillars, and sometimes he leaned sideways, craning his neck to get a glimpse of McBain's face.

There was no violence in him now, only an absolute detachment. When the lecture was over he planned, if he could, to go up to McBain and greet him, shake him by the hand. He wanted to see him at close quarters and find out what kind of man he really was—clarify the childish memory, look as an adult upon the face which had been so important to Laura.

For a long time Charlie didn't listen to what McBain was saying. He heard the easy self-assured voice going on very much as it had in the living room years ago, weaving a spell, making nearly a thousand listeners share experiences which had happened across the world. Sometimes the listeners laughed—softly or uproariously; once or twice McBain's voice was interrupted by applause; he was being received with unusual warmth because Broadfield still felt a proprietary interest in him.

Charlie sank back behind the pillar; the women on either side of him objected to the way he leaned and craned his neck. Now that he couldn't see McBain at all it was difficult to attach the brown bony face, the shining white hair, to the voice. McBain pronounced his words the way Rourke pronounced his—the R's smoothed out and were lost, the A's broadened; he might almost have been an Englishman. But the Middle Westerners didn't seem to mind that McBain no longer had the Middle West in his mouth; he was still their boy, their gift to the world. Charlie gazed at the pillar, and it was Rourke's face he saw, Rourke who was enchanting the audience.

Now the meaning of the words began to penetrate; or rather the meaning behind the words; and a strange excitement stirred in Charlie, because Rourke, or McBain, seemed to be echoing his own thoughts. McBain too was in the abyss, and knew it, and had become reconciled long ago.

Charlie laughed—and was shushed by the women on either side of him—because the audience was a pack of fools; no member of it had any idea what McBain, with such infinite charm, was actually saying. If they had known, being cowards as well as fools and in terror of the abyss, they would have risen up against McBain, they would have torn the seats from the floor and flung them at him until his voice was silenced; for what he was saying, in every rise and fall of his voice, in every little pause for effect, was, Despair, despair, all hope abandon ye who enter here.

Charlie and McBain were one. We know what the score is, thought Charlie. But perhaps, after all, they didn't see eye to eye, because something else McBain was saying was that the abyss has no national boundaries. And Charlie knew that there is a great difference between dominating and being dominated, even in the abyss, and returned to the train of thought which had seemed so important at Christmas, before he had left his club: each nation on the earth is a great beast, and it matters very much to be the strongest beast, the most unscrupulous, the hardest-headed.

What McBain was talking was sedition. He was urging his audience to let their beast give in to another, to go down still blind to the abyss, still feebly waving their beautiful and unsmirched and utterly meaningless banners. McBain was dangerous. McBain might have been sent as the special emissary of those men in Europe who also knew what the score was, and meant to see that it continued in their favor.

God, said Charlie to himself, but he must have said it out loud, because the women shushed him again.

He began to feel restless; he wanted to stand up and refute McBain. But the voice was so persuasive, the charm was so lulling. Charlie could feel himself giving in to McBain. Why trouble, why trouble, after all? since all your acts begin and end in darkness, why not still your hand? So much easier, so much more peaceful, to sink into the deepest mire and let the darkness close over you forever.

Nothing mattered. Nothing had ever mattered. Why had he ever cared whether his mother were saint or harlot? Saints and harlots were part of the illusion, the symbols at which mankind grasped desperately, trying to prove an antithesis where none existed—saint and harlot, good and evil, light and darkness, love and hate, savagery and compassion: these were only words, thought Charlie, and his excitement mounted. His mind had become incandescent and the revelation given him by Delores had grown enormous.

So God must feel, looking down on His creation; only God was one with the devil, and the devil too was part of the illusion.

Like a god Charlie rose when the lecture was over, and godlike walked out of the building, away from the crowds of chattering fools, until the street lay dark and empty before him. His wish to look into McBain's face was quite gone. Charlie was filled with power now—he could do anything, since to him alone revelation had been given.

When he reached his father's house the people who lived there seemed to have moved off to a great distance. He looked upon them as from the summit of a mountain and their gesticulations were absurd, their voices were shrill weak pipings. He could feel sorry for them, almost; they were so trivial, and thought themselves so important.

Sitting on the porch, they made elaborate and foolish plans for the week-end. Their voices went on and on, and Charlie was astonished at what had happened to them—it was as if a great cloud had blown away. McBain had come to Broadfield to tell them the cloud was eternal, and they had laughed at him, as they would laugh at Charlie, if they knew what was in his mind.

But they would never know. They must keep their rickety contraptions and continue to weave their little plans, and Charlie would even allow himself to be caught up into the plans; although all he really wanted was to be left alone with his revelation, which was widening still.

Godlike he left them, still chattering on the porch, and went upstairs and fell at length into a godlike slumber. By tomorrow, or the day after, he would know what to do with the power which had been given to him.

21

HE WAS UP already, working in the garden in a pool of shadow, when Norris arrived in the kitchen to get breakfast. He came in presently and stood at the sink washing the earth from his hands, and Norris's feeling went beyond diffidence; it was almost fear. But this was foolishness, Norris thought, pouring out the coffee, and tried to smile at his son.

Charlie sat down at the table and drank coffee with Norris, smiling remotely back at him. His body was the same, powerful and clumsy; his face was the same, heavy and brutish and too deeply lined; but what looked out from his eyes was no longer resentment or anguish. There was a kind of vast serenity about him, and Norris couldn't think why this should seem terrible.

He was going to meet Laurette this afternoon, after work, Norris said.

"Laurette?" Charlie wasn't really looking out through his eyes at all, and he spoke absently. "Oh, sure. When's the bus get here?"

"Five-thirty, if it's on time. Glad she could come tonight instead of tomorrow. She must need a good rest by now."

"Yeah." Charlie lit a cigarette.

"You ought to eat more breakfast, Charlie. Big guy like you." Norris rose and stacked the plates. There was something about Charlie's unshakable calm that made everything Norris said sound foolish.

"Not hungry."

"You'll be glad to see Laurette, won't you?"

"Yeah, sure. Sure I'll be glad."

"And you ought to have a good time out at the Wheelwrights'. Damn nice of them to ask us all."

"I think I'll stay home, though," Charlie said. "And you can go with Laurette and Betty Lou."

"No, Charlie, it's all settled now." Norris moved to the door. "Oh, by the way, I saw Andy McBain yesterday," he said, glancing back over his shoulder at Charlie. "Changed quite a lot. He—"

"I went to the lecture."

"So that's where you were."

"He made a big hit. Had them rolling in the aisles a couple times. He's pretty funny, isn't he?"

"I thought— Poor Andy," Norris said. "I felt kind of sorry for him. Seems as if the life he's led should have added up to more than zero. Can't think why I was ever jealous of him." He coughed. "I used to envy Andy quite a lot, but not any more." Norris stood a moment longer, staring at his son, and then said, "So long, Charlie," and stepped out through the back door and walked away down the drive, along the avenue, down the hill to work. If Charlie had needed reassurance about McBain, maybe Norris had given it to him. Indirection, said Dick Wheelwright, I try indirection.

And yet Norris couldn't help thinking that Charlie was isolated now in a private world; as if he had retreated from pain into the most secret depths of his being, where nothing could touch him. Norris couldn't bring him back into the world, but maybe Laurette—

All day he clung to the thought of Laurette. But his hope flagged a little when she got off the bus. She looked so garish, her lips were so bright with paint, her face was so thickly masked with powder, her dress clung so tightly; and on the journey from Detroit she had assembled a coterie—there were five young men, including the bus driver, hovering about her now, bidding her ardent farewells, and she did not see Norris, waiting at the door of the bus station.

When she did see him she gave him a hearty smack on the cheek, and then wiped the lipstick off with her handkerchief; somehow she conveyed an air of prosperity.

"Pop, what do you think," she said, after they had found a taxi. "I've quit the beauty racket. From now on it's just singing. The band got a real break—signed up for the summer at a swell roadhouse, and they'll broadcast sometimes, and I'm going along. I'm taking lessons, now, singing lessons, and I've found a swell massoose and she's going to roll off some of the extra pounds and I might find myself with a Hollywood contract yet—who knows? I was singing to 'em on the bus—we had more fun! I told the driver he ought to be in Hollywood himself—he looks quite a lot like Clark Gable, did you notice? We all got to singing, finally, just like *It Happened One Night*. Except an old pruneface said we gave her a headache. Gee, it sure is too bad everybody can't feel like spring when spring gets here."

Laurette squeezed her father's hand and began to sing lightly:

> *Ho hum, spring is here now . . .*
> *Ho hum, sing a song of cheer now . . .*

"It's an oldie," she said, "but it's just the way I feel. You proposed to Betty Lou yet?"

"No." Norris was taken unawares.

"Better hurry up, Pop. Some other guy might come along. It's the season. She'd make a cute June bride."

"And June is just around the corner. Well, I thought maybe this week-end—I'm packing the rest of you off to the lake, except Joel, but he'll be with the Boonstras, most of the time. So the coast ought to be clear."

"Gee, I'm so excited! I sure do wish you luck, Pop. When you wrote and told me, boy, you should have heard the cheer I let out! I don't know her so very well, but she's the kind of person, you can always tell about them, right away." Laurette held his hand tightly. "But what's all this about Charlie?"

"Things have kind of piled up on him, Laurette—he still isn't over what he went through in Detroit, and I guess there's no more hope for him and Delores. Delores—"

"She been playing around again?"

"Afraid so. But it doesn't seem to make any difference to Charlie. I've been trying to figure out if he's had Andy McBain on his mind too, like Patricia." Norris glanced through the cab window. "There was never anything to that, you know, Laurette. Nothing at all. If I'd known what you were thinking, all of you, and told you long ago—"

"Aah, forget it. *I* never lost any sleep over it. My God, we're *modern*. What a thing to get upset about! Pat feel O.K. now?"

"I guess. Only I don't know if Johnny'll ever be as important to her as Rourke was, for a while." Norris clenched his free hand on the strap by the window. "I feel kind of sick every time I look at that kid."

"Well, you know, it's funny the way things work out, and maybe it's all for the best, Pop, Pat falling for him the way she did. As long as no lasting harm was done. Maybe he was what she needed, at that point. She had some awful queer ideas about purity and stuff, and maybe the kid kind of woke her up. Some girls, they need a guy like that in their life. There was one in mine; only me, I didn't exactly need him. He sure put me through hell for a while, though, until I got ahold of myself."

Laurette smiled and said, "Here we are. The old homestead. Say, the place could stand a coat of paint, you know it? You can't ask a bride to step into a dump like that. How'd you like a new paint-job for a wedding present?"

Laurette had brought them all presents as it was—more perfume for Delores, silk stockings for Patricia, a cable exerciser for Joel, a bottle of Scotch for Charlie, a pipe for Norris, and for the baby a board full of holes with colored wooden pegs to stick into them.

"It's supposed to be very scientific," Laurette said. "It's supposed to teach a baby something—just what, though, I wouldn't know.

Prosperity," she said happily, looking at the scattered wrappings. "God but it's swell to be rolling in dough at last. Wish I'd had the time, I'd 've picked out things that were a little more, you know, distangay, but I just grabbed what I could at the last minute. You *used* to smoke a pipe, Pop, didn't you?"

"Still do, now and then. But a Dunhill, Laurette— You won't be rolling in dough very long at this rate."

"Heck, what's money for? Can't spend so much on myself right now—I want to wait till that massoose has done something drastic about my shape. Boy," said Laurette, looking down at herself, craning her neck for a glimpse of her hips, "she has her work cut out for her, all right." She gave herself a slap behind and said, "Why don't I climb into something old and get to work in the kitchen? The hours I been keeping lately, I never get near a stove."

Loud and breezy and cheerful, whistling and singing, she transformed the whole house; and after Betty Lou had arrived and grown merry on two mild cocktails, the voices rose as excitedly, the rooms were as charged with vitality, as in Laura's day.

Once or twice, glancing at Betty Lou's flushed face, Norris was afraid Joel or Laurette might let something slip; and he didn't want to have to propose in public on the spur of the moment. When he contemplated the actual words he might say, his mind boggled—maybe he was an old fool after all.

After dinner, Charlie went out for a walk by himself, and Norris joined the others in the noisier kinds of card game, that are so hard on the nerves and the cards. Laurette screamed, Betty Lou squealed, even Patricia made a racket; and Norris forgot his anxieties.

"I'm a total and complete wreck," Betty Lou said when she stood up to go, and began to adjust flying wisps of hair; she was still flushed, and breathless with laughter. "I declare, I don't know *when* I've had so much fun! Oh, Laurette, honey, it's just such a shame you couldn't get a job singing right here in town. We *need* you."

"Naw," said Laurette. "A little of me goes a long way, Betty Lou. Drive you crazy if you had to see me day in and day out."

Norris escorted Betty Lou to her door and then they found themselves lingering on the porch. This might be the moment— but words fled from him and so did his confidence. He put his hand out stiffly and shook hers; he almost clicked his heels and bowed from the waist. "If you really want to go with the Wheelwrights tomorrow," he said, "you could still change your mind."

"It's a young folks' party," Betty Lou said. "Mr. and Mrs. Wheelwright'll be more than enough of the older generation— not that they're so terribly ancient, Norris, but you know what I mean. Wouldn't it be wonderful if Pat saw the light about Johnny?"

"I guess. They're both such kids, though, and there's the money angle. Anyway, I still don't know about Pat. Wish we'd had Johnny over tonight."

"So do I." Betty Lou pulled open the screen-door. "He doesn't laugh enough either. . . . I like Laurette, Norris."

"Laurette's all right. If she'd just tone down a little."

"Give her time. She's awful young too."

"It's my fault, really, the way she dresses and—all of that."

Betty Lou was inside the screen-door by now. "Don't start blaming yourself for everything again, Norris. Haven't I told you and told you, it's just so foolish. Anyway, Laurette isn't spilt milk, or Patricia either. Anybody ought to be proud to have daughters like that."

"You're a great comfort, Betty Lou."

"Then don't start brooding again the minute you get away from me."

He smiled at her; she was pressing her nose against the screen. "I won't. It's a promise."

But Laurette and Patricia, sitting on the porch swing, told him that Charlie hadn't come back from his walk yet, so he couldn't help brooding for a little while after he'd gone to bed. Then he heard Charlie come in—the heavy tread on the stairs, the muttered words to Joel, and silence. He wondered whether it would be better to propose to Betty Lou in her back yard or in his, and began to see the setting clearly at last: it was Sunday and they were sitting by David's pen, and the words came out with unexpected ease. Norris forgot about Charlie, and about Laurette and Patricia, who had continued to sit on the porch swing, long after Charlie had passed through into the house without looking at them, without saying a word.

"There *is* something kind of peculiar about him, you know," Laurette said. "Even way back, before Mom died, he'd shut up like a clam sometimes. When Pop wasn't as fair as he should have been. And then all the things that have happened since."

"M'm," said Patricia. Now that the noise and the laughter were over, her mind had been invaded by Vincent, his voice on the telephone yesterday, the urgency and pathos, the hint that he might be going away soon. What you thought was dead turned out to be terribly alive; time had been at work on the evening in his room, dimming what had happened, and his words on the telephone seemed true to her. There was no corruption in him; he was only a spoiled child.

She thrust the thought of Vincent away from her and said, "They happened to you too, Laurette, all those things. It wasn't any easier for you than for Charlie."

"I was born tough, I guess. Sometimes I even think women are

257

tougher than men anyway, you know it? By and large, as the saying goes, and what does it mean? . . . No, but what I was saying, Detroit brought me good luck and Charlie bad. I'm kind of disgusted with Delores. I always knew she was a dope, of course, but now—she's just kind of falling apart. . . . You think they'll get a divorce, Pat?"

"It's what they both want, I suppose. But there's the baby. And what would Delores *do?*"

"Oh, heck, she'd get along. Play her cards right, she'd marry some other sucker, eventually. Guess I'll have to give Delores a piece of my mind too before I leave. Pop wants me to tackle Charlie, make him snap out of it. God, I don't know, it's what I kept trying to do in Detroit, but if it hadn't been for this job here opening up, I bet Charlie would be really batty by now. I'm not so sure he isn't slightly batty as it is. The look in his *eyes,* Pat, and that little smile—"

Laurette stood up and went to lean on the porch rail, hugging her arms together across her breast as if she felt cold.

"I think maybe Charlie and me, we better stay right here in Broadfield with Pop over the week-end. We'd certainly blight your party if we came along."

Because Patricia didn't really want Laurette and Charlie to come, and was ashamed, she said, "But it might do him good. To be with people. I think I've felt the way he does sometimes—"

"I vant to be alone. . . . *I* know."

"But then if I *had* to be with people, I began to feel better."

"Sure. Well, we'll see. I don't know why they asked us. Charlie and me, we never knew them very well. I used to think they were high hat. But that was in the days when Pop was a souse and they were in the money and Johnny wasn't old enough to be crazy about you. . . . Come on, baby, time for bed."

After the light was out, Patricia said, "He isn't, any more, I don't think."

"Who isn't what?"

"Johnny. Crazy about me. He—"

"Well, baby, if he isn't, you have only yourself to blame."

"I know." Patricia tried to see Johnny's face, and to remember what it had felt like to be kissed by him, and the old turmoil he'd caused in her—attraction and revulsion—but Vincent was still too vivid. She sighed. "I wish sweet wasn't such a sticky word. Because that's what Johnny is, he's a sweet boy—only it sounds cheap when you say it. Not like Johnny at all."

"I think you like Johnny quite a heck of a lot, and I wish to God you'd break down and admit it to yourself."

Patricia almost laughed. "I broke down and admitted that long ago. Only if he asked me again to marry him— I can't *imagine* being married, to Johnny or anybody. The same man, all the rest of your life, seeing him day in and day out—" But now for a moment Johnny became extraordinarily vivid and she thought strangely, the father of my children, the father of my children. Johnny would want children and he would be a good father, but babies didn't fit into Vincent's scheme of things. "And we'd be so poor," Patricia said.

"No poorer than ninety-nine out of a hundred other young married couples. The thing is," Laurette said dreamily, "you have to really want *marriage,* if you get hitched on next to nothing a week. The trouble with Delores and Charlie—here goes the Voice of Experience again—the trouble with them, they didn't really want marriage, all they wanted was to sleep together. Well, they got over that in a hurry, and now there's nothing left. But an honest-to-God husband—there's a heck of a lot more to it than just wanting to sleep with him. Give and take on both sides—it has to balance out, kind of. Maybe that was one of the troubles with Mom and Pop—she had so much to give, he didn't have anything, hardly. It was all one-sided and that's maybe why he went off his trolley when she died.

"I don't know," said Laurette, "I could be wrong, of course. Maybe he gave her a lot of things nobody but her ever knew about. For some women, just being needed by a man so terribly— it's enough for them. But there was more to it than that, their marriage. . . .

"I'd like to see you get married, Pat, to the right kind of a guy. The right kind of a guy could give you a lot, but I bet there's plenty you could give him too. That's what keeps marriages going, maybe—always finding out new things about each other, helping each other to grow. A good marriage, it doesn't stand still—it begins little, just with a terrific yen for each other, and then keeps getting bigger and bigger, all the years you live together. The kids make it bigger; everything that happens does.

"Yeah, that's how it must have been with Mom and Pop, I think. They didn't stand still; they changed each other. After she died, Pop tried to slide back, he tried to stop growing—but he is growing, Pat; he's different now than he was a year ago. I mean, just compare him with Aunt Maudie, for instance—same parents, same background, but what a whale of a difference between them. Maudie and Homer, they didn't have anything to give each other. . . .

"It's the best way to find out what life is all about, I guess— getting married to some guy you really love."

Laurette sighed profoundly; then she laughed.

"God, listen to me! I'll be talking myself into taking the plunge, if I don't watch out. Trouble is, I don't ever seem to find the guy

I want to take the plunge with. Lots of guys I wouldn't mind sleeping with; a few I have slept with, now and then. But when you get right down to it, I guess I have pretty big ideas about my dream boy. I want the best there is, and being kind of a cheap piece of goods myself, I got no business thinking that way. . . . Nope, the best I can hope for, I guess, is that millionaire with a yacht. And millionaires are so damn old, most of 'em. Jesus, I sure would hate to get into bed with an old man."

Patricia lay quiet for a long time, and then she said, "You're so—casual about it, Laurette."

"Sure, baby, why not? God, it isn't that important. I'm not proud. You try to cover sex up, like people used to, and it gets too important. There's a heck of a lot more to life than sex, baby; but there sex is, so why get fussed about it? I guess that's been one of your troubles, getting all hot and bothered about sex. Well, cut it out. Sometimes I think sex has been overrated. Sometimes I think I'd just as soon have a good alcohol rub. Good night, Pat, and don't toss and turn all night, will you? I don't sleep as sound as I used to."

Casual; if only it were possible to be casual, Patricia thought, and thought it again next morning when she and Delores went over to the Wheelwrights'. She was in a mood now to feel tender about Johnny, about all the Wheelwrights, who never seemed to get fussed about anything; but the Wheelwrights were getting very fussed indeed about starting off for a week-end at the lake and were all in a bad temper.

"Just put your basket down anywhere, Patricia," said Mrs. Wheelwright, "anywhere at all, and then if you'd go up to the attic and help Johnny bring down those camp cots— Tink, *Tink!* Where are you off to now? Did you get all the bathing-suits together? Well, go get them, then, and hurry. Butter. Butter. Dorothy, did you see me pack the butter? Well, then, you'll just have to unpack the hamper and see— *No*, dear, not *that* one, the *big* one. Dick! Oh, good heavens, where's *he* gone to?"

"He's down in the cellar," said Tink, strolling around with an armful of bathing-suits, and a bathing-cap perched on his head.

"What's he doing *there?*" Mrs. Wheelwright flew off to the top of the cellar stairs as Patricia mounted to the attic; she could hear the loud exasperated voice ringing through the house. "Dick! *Dick!* What in the world are you doing in the cellar? . . . *Dearest,* we don't *need* to take pickles; there are shelves and shelves at the cottage and we'll have to bring them all back. I certainly don't intend to leave them for the Oppenheimers. . . ."

"Good morning," said Patricia, as Johnny rose up from behind a trunk with dust all over his face.

"*I* can't get the damn things out," he said. "The damn trunks are on top of them. What god-damned fool ever went and— Oh, it's you, Pat. You want to help me shove these blasted trunks out of the way—the cots are buried." They shoved and strained and grunted; it was warm in the attic and by the time they had freed the cots they were both sweating, and Patricia was in a bad temper too.

"What the hell's Pop doing? Why didn't *he* come up? They're too heavy for you, Pat; they're too *heavy,* god dammit— No, don't try to take it all alone. *Wait* a minute, will you?" He tugged a cot from her and plunged down the attic stairs, collided with a pile of hatboxes, and started an avalanche—boxes, hats, moth balls, broken toys, Christmas-tree ornaments, gushed around him and were spewed out all over the upstairs hall.

"God damn it to hell," said Johnny, and kneeled to clear up the mess.

"Johnny," called Dorothy from the bottom of the stairs. "John-*nee!* Daddy says hurry up with the camp cots, will you? He wants to strap them on the running-board."

"Tell him to keep his shirt on!" Johnny shouted. "We aren't racing to a fire, for the love of Mike!"

The confusion went on. Only Delores remained unruffled—she stood on the front lawn, smoothing her skirt and looking away along the street. But at last everything was assembled and almost everybody had climbed into the car.

"All set?" Johnny asked from his place behind the wheel.

"Where's your mother?" Mr. Wheelwright asked. "Tink, did you go to the bathroom? Because we aren't going to stop between here and the lake."

"I went *long* ago," said Tink, remote and superior.

"Well, you'd better go again then. Hop to it, now."

"There are ladies present," said Tink, scrambling over the door of the car. He slipped, fell, and skinned his knees on the driveway, and went limping toward the house. "Mother! Mo-*ther!* I'm wounded!"

Silence came. Presently Mr. Wheelwright said, "I ask myself, is it worth it? Echo answers, is it? Why do we all go to pieces in a crisis? How did this get turned into a crisis? . . . What in the world are they *doing* all this time?"

"Mother's bandaging Tink from head to toe, prob'ly," said Dorothy. "He'll come out looking like a mummy. You wait and see."

Johnny pressed his hand on the horn, and his mother appeared.

"At last; I'm worn out." She squeezed herself into the back seat between Delores and Patricia. "Where's Tink?"

"We thought he was with you. Being bandaged up," said Dorothy.

"Bandaged up? What for?" Mrs. Wheelwright started to climb out again, but her husband turned his head.

"Stay where you are, stay where you *are*, Trude, for the love of heaven!"

Johnny pressed his hand on the horn again, and left it there.

"Johnny! Stop! We'll be arrested for disturbing the peace." Mrs. Wheelwright beat upon his shoulder. "Stop it. *Stop!*"

"It's stuck now," said Johnny, and climbed out. "Chuck me the screw-driver, Pop, will you?"

By the time the screw-driver had been found, Tink had returned with both knees lavishly bandaged. "I can hardly walk," he said faintly, but nobody heard him because the horn was still blatting. "Open the door for me, Dorothy; open the *door*, I said!"

The horn was silenced; the engine started, the car backed down the drive, and went banging and rattling off along Johnson Avenue.

"Now let me see," Mrs. Wheelwright said, ticking things off on her fingers. "Have we got everything? Food, bathing-suits, blankets, camp cots, the grill, charcoal—"

"Books," said Mr. Wheelwright. "Did anybody pack that book?"

"What book?—Johnny, slow down, I have a horrible feeling we'll have to go back. What book, Dick?"

"*Seven Gothic Tales*. Trude, I told you to be *sure* to pack it."

"But I thought you'd read it long ago, dearest.—Johnny, slow down; you'd better stop altogether."

"Well, I hadn't. I'd just started. . . . Back up, Johnny."

"There won't be any time for reading," Johnny said.

"I intend to spend the whole week-end in a hammock reading *Seven Gothic Tales*. Back up."

Johnny turned the car around and drove back, muttering.

At last, though, they were on their way; and when Broadfield was left behind, when the hilly country was left behind and they rolled onward through the wide flat farm lands, their bad humor was left behind too. Perhaps they all felt, as Patricia did, that although the landscape here was dull and dispirited, the dunes would rise up eventually, like a line of miniature mountains, a barrier shutting off the magic world, the unbelievable lake, from the ordinary world. When she was a small child she had fancied an angel with a flaming sword would be standing in the middle of the road to block them off from paradise; or they would pass the angel safely, and go bouncing along the sandy track, beneath the trees, through a dip in the dunes, and on the other side there would be nothing at all, only an endless waste.

She closed her eyes and held her breath, a small child again, when Johnny drove the car out of sunlight, in among trees—the cool moist smell was quite different; they were in the depths of a forest and the forest would go on forever and the lake could not exist.

"Here we are," said Mrs. Wheelwright, and the car stopped.

Patricia opened her eyes. The land lifted a little, and over the brink, between the shining blades of beach-grass, she could see the immense sweep of water, blue here, green there, flecked with foam, dappled with the mauve shadows of clouds. The waves washed faintly on the sand, and it was all right; paradise was paradise still.

Presently Mr. Wheelwright had gone off to his hammock and lost himself in *Seven Gothic Tales*, and Mrs. Wheelwright was placidly getting lunch, and the rest, in bathing-suits, distributed themselves along the beach. Dorothy went for a stroll, Tink constructed sand towers, Delores rubbed oil on her body and lay apart, in a cup in the dunes, to acquire a sunburn; Johnny and Patricia sat dreamily together watching Tink.

"I still like the lake better than anywhere else in the world," Johnny said.

"I think I do too." Patricia turned her head, looking left and right along the shoreline—the curves of foam washing on the sand, the dunes moving off and off in either direction in almost regular, almost symmetrical scallops, like waves petrified. The sand was white, the beach-grass was shining green, and standing forward, away from the other trees, were occasional clumps of poplars; their leaves shone too, flickering in the wind. Inland a little way, the pines looked almost black among the paler colors of oaks and maples. Off and off went the dunes, until they faded and blurred at last and were lost in a lavender haze. Paradise, a place in a dream; the lake had never seemed entirely real to her. "But I'd like to see an ocean," Patricia said. "I'd like to know how different an ocean is."

"Smell different, anyway." Johnny inhaled deeply and Patricia stopped looking at the distances and looked at him instead. His skin was quite brown already, smooth over the firm muscles, and she could not look away from him—in that moment it happened to her, the old revulsion became remote and foolish. The father of her children; she saw at last that the excellence of Johnny's body was a part of his other excellence. Johnny was all of a piece, but Vincent was not; Vincent was secretly horrified because he was an animal as well as a man, and his animal aspect had grown corrupt, and the corruption had widened until it touched his mind and spirit.

Patricia trembled; she hovered half in Vincent's world and half in Johnny's. She needed Johnny; she believed that he could pull her over the line and make her all of a piece too, and she wanted to speak to him and tell him what she had just discovered. But when he turned his face and smiled at her she was suffocated by the strength of her new emotions; among them was dismay because she had taken too long to see the truth and his smile was kind but quite impersonal: she was only part of the day to Johnny now, and he smiled at her as he had been smiling at the water and the trees.

"The lake is good enough for me," he said.

"My mother used to tell us about the ocean." Patricia's voice was not steady, but she thought he didn't notice. "Every time we came to the lake, she talked about the ocean. She was a little homesick for it, I think, sometimes."

Johnny rolled over and rested his face on his folded arms; she looked down at him as she had not dared to look, at that other lake, when he started to talk about Barrett Street. To keep herself from thinking what she had done then, what she had thrown away, she tried to remember her mother's words about the lake and the ocean. The voice came back presently, but maybe the words weren't her mother's, really—only things she'd long thought herself.

The lake changes more than the ocean (the voice said). The moods of the lake change from one minute to the next—you have to keep watching it, especially on a day when there are clouds, because it never looks quite the same twice. But the ocean's moods go on for a long time, sometimes the same mood lasts all day, with only the difference in the position of the sun to make a difference in the way the water looks. The ocean is stolid compared with the lake, and the ocean is more frightening; you can't make the ocean yours, because it goes on forever, the world being mostly water; but the lake stops, you know that it stops, even though you can't see for yourself, and so it doesn't frighten you so much. . . .

Johnny lay flat on the sand and listened to Patricia talking about the lake. The wind was cool, but through it the sunlight struck hot against his back and legs. He felt a vast peacefulness wash over him, a sense of physical well-being that was almost voluptuous. And Patricia's voice went dreamily on, mixed with the sound of wind in the beach-grass, and of waves.

If you could lie here forever, in eternal sunlight, eternal spring, spring that was almost summer now but better than summer, close to your beloved, listening to her voice, Johnny thought. Forget everything else, all the large anxieties and all the small ones, the state the world was in, the necessity to work, to return to Broadfield on Sunday night and get up at dawn on Monday morning and go down to the plant, back to the noise and the loud voices and confusion and foul talk and rough fellowship; forget Tink and Dorothy and your mother and father; forget that Patricia had loved Rourke and might love him still. Expand this moment of peace and happiness and conviction—life was good, he thanked God for having made life so good—and let it last forever. So great a happiness was too close to sadness, because you knew it couldn't go on, and you knew that if it could, you would value it less highly, you might almost feel bored, lying here close to your beloved and listening to her voice. . . .

"I don't know if she said all those things," said Patricia. "I was so young then, I couldn't have remembered all that. But she loved the ocean, I know that, even if she was frightened by it. Once she said that women could never feel about the ocean as men do. If women had had their way, men never would have built ships and gone sailing out into nothing."

Johnny raised his head and smiled at her. "And where would you be then, and where'd I be? I'm glad the men didn't listen to the women, aren't you, and went right ahead and built the ships anyway? And what about the face that launched a thousand of 'em, and burnt the topless towers of Ilium? And what about Isabella of Spain," said Johnny drowsily, "and what about Elizabeth of England? If it hadn't been for the women, would the men ever have sailed the seven seas?"

He sat up, brushing the sand from his arms and chest, and grinned at her. "God," he said, "oh, God, I feel good. Don't you?"

Patricia, who was still gazing out at the lake, nodded slowly.

"Kiss her, why don't you?" asked Tink, and knocked his sand towers flat with a sweep of the hand. Squatting on his haunches, half in and half out of the water, he looked at them with candid interest. "I wish you would. I never have seen how it's done, except in the movies."

Johnny flung a handful of sand toward him. "Well, you aren't going to now either. I hear the dinner-bell."

The afternoon slid away and the clouds spread out and flattened and became a haze through which the sun shore dimly; the colors of the lake changed, dulled, and changed again; the horizon was drawing in, and tomorrow there might be rain. At half-past five the telephone rang; Laurette and Charlie were coming out after all.

Johnny sighed and went to his room to get dressed. There had been long discussions about asking all of the Bryants instead of just Patricia; Johnny's mother said they had so little fun, most of the time, and they seemed to have so few friends, and life had been rather piling up on poor Bry. Wouldn't it do them all good to be asked, even if they didn't all come?—Our *last* week-end at the cottage, Dorothy wailed; and her father scowled and told her to cultivate the Christian virtues; so all the Bryants had been asked.

They would clutter things up, thought Johnny, buttoning his shirt; he would have to be polite to Delores and Charlie and Laurette, he thought, knotting his tie; he wouldn't be able to give all of his attention to Patricia.

The Christian virtues—what were they? he wondered, brushing

his cropped head, and clapped the brushes together, banged them on the bureau, ran whistling down the stairs, and drove off cheerfully enough to Rivermouth, with Patricia sitting beside him, to collect Charlie and Laurette. Supper would be late tonight and he was hungry already and he wanted to park the car in a quiet place and take Patricia in his arms; and the dance would be in full swing before they arrived at the pavilion; but love thy neighbor as thyself, and mortify the flesh, if necessary.

The bus from Broadfield had reached Rivermouth before Johnny and Patricia, and a sense of desolation swept over Johnny when he pulled the car up beside a drugstore in the center of that strange hodge-podge town, one-third summer resort, one-third lake port, one-third industrial center. Waiting in the dusk, leaning against the plate-glass window, Laurette looked tawdry and Charlie looked like—Johnny couldn't decide quite what: a man in a trance?

"Hi," Johnny said loudly, springing down from the car, heaving the two small suitcases into the back, holding out his hand to Laurette and then Charlie. Laurette returned the pressure but Charlie's hand lay inert in his, cold, the hand of a dead man. "Hope you didn't have to wait too long," Johnny said. "Now we'll see if we can get any speed out of the old bus."

Charlie leaned his head against the back of the seat and shut his eyes. The car bounced and shook and rattled, and there was a knock in the engine; a wind off the lake struck in at him coldly. He shrank from the noise and the wind; he would have liked to stop up his ears and swaddle his face. His senses had grown suddenly too acute, and if he really started to feel again, if he had been dragged down from his mountaintop by Laurette and could never return there—

He had found her waiting for him on the front porch when he got back from work. There was something too purposeful about her; he found himself tugged into the kitchen, where she opened the bottle of Scotch she'd brought him from Detroit. She made him drink it neat, three shot-glasses of the stuff, while she strolled about the kitchen.

"Go on," she said, "you look like you need it, and there won't be any liquor at the Wheelwrights', prob'ly."

Charlie said they weren't really going, were they, and Laurette said she had to call them right now. Maybe it was what he needed, she said, to go to a dance. She went to the telephone while Charlie had a fourth drink, and then in a little while they were riding in a taxi down to the bus station; they were sitting in the bus, and the bus was moving away ponderously through the late afternoon traffic and gathering speed on the open highway. Charlie thought he was not drunk; he did not feel the Scotch, he did not feel anything; but he was so very tired, and it confused him to be sitting beside Laurette in a bus. She must have packed a suitcase for him; he remembered putting two suitcases up on the rack.

"Charlie," she said, close against his ear, "Charlie— You stinko?"

"Naw. Cold sober." His own voice sounded indistinct to him, but she must have seen his lips move; now he felt her take his hand between both of hers.

"Maybe I shouldn't have given you those drinks, but I thought they might—thaw something out. Charlie—listen to me, Charlie—"

"I'm listening."

"You got to break down and tell me. What is it, Charlie? What's it all about?"

"What's what all about?"

"The load on your mind, kiddo. Heck, you always used to tell me your troubles. Is it Delores? You worried about her?"

"I'm not worried about anything," he said carefully. The darkness was closing in again; he could see nothing but the blue upholstery on the seat just in front of him. "What's there to worry about?"

"There must be something. Charlie, don't you know how queer you've been acting lately? I thought Pop was working himself into a stew about nothing, but the minute I saw you— If you'd just tell me, Charlie. That's what I'm for, kiddo— I'm Dorothy Dix, I'm the Voice of Experience. Maybe I could help you, if you'd give me a chance."

The darkness kept closing in. Charlie stared desperately at the circle of blue upholstery, but it was growing smaller.

"If it isn't Delores," said Laurette's voice, "then maybe it's— that thing about Mom and the McBain guy. Is that it, Charlie?"

"Naw." Charlie cleared his throat. "Hell, no." He thought he was smiling. He lifted his fingers and touched his mouth. Sure enough, he was smiling.

"Because that's all a lot of baloney, Charlie. I always did think so but now I know—I've found out. There was nothing to it at all. You know that, don't you? Charlie—"

"Yeah. Sure. Sure I know." He kept his fingers against his mouth; the movement of his lips fascinated him. "What difference does it make?" asked Charlie. "Who the hell cares who Joel's father is?"

For a little while Laurette was quiet. Then she whispered, "Jesus, is that what you thought, is that what Pat—? God," said Laurette, and fell silent again.

Charlie shut his eyes to avoid seeing the darkness close in, but faces floated before him now, his father's, McBain's, Rourke's, Delores's, and they were all twisted and hideous. To watch the darkness close in was better after all, and he forced his eyelids open; but there was no darkness, only the interior of the bus, quite normal, filled with people; and beyond the windows the flat countryside streaming away, bright green though there was a haze across the sky.

"Charlie," Laurette said, "you really do know that's a dirty lie, don't you, about Joel?"

"I just told you. And who cares? For Christ's sake, Laurette, who cares? She died eleven years ago, almost. There isn't anything left of her now. Not even bones. Nothing. Eleven years—even bones rot in eleven years, don't they?" He looked at Laurette, whose head jerked with the motion of the bus; beneath the hat, beneath the paint and the soft plump flesh on her face, she was just a skull too, and her skull would rot eventually, like Laura Bryant's. There would be nothing left of any of them. Even he, even Charlie Bryant, would rot away to nothing in the dark earth, quite alone. "Quit picking on me, will you?" Charlie said.

Laurette was studying the landscape with great care. Presently she turned, though, and spoke more briskly. "I been thinking, Charlie—there isn't any point in you and Delores being together any more. We might just as well start taking legal steps and fix things so you can marry somebody else eventually. Somebody a heck of a lot better than Delores. She doesn't give a damn about the baby now, I don't think, but Pop's crazy about him, and so's Betty Lou. And they're too old, now, to have any kids of their own, probably, but there one is, all ready-made for them, soon as they get married. So what I was thinking—why don't I take Delores back to Detroit with me? And we could go ahead and fix up about the divorce. Honestly, kiddo, she isn't worth worrying about."

"I'm not worried, I'm not worried, I'm not worried," he said, and his voice must have risen, because heads turned, eyes stared, faces sneered. "Just leave me alone, for Christ's sake," he whispered. "Jabber, jabber, jabber. I don't have a chance to think."

It was then that he began to feel the extraordinary and painful sensitivity. The staring eyes hurt him; the smell of the bus, all the bodies and the gasoline exhaust sickened him; the upholstery scraped his palms when he touched it; the noise of the engine was inside his own head. If only the noise of the engine would stop, he could get back the feeling he'd had at McBain's lecture, when his mind soared upward into that dazzling clarity; but even after the bus had stopped in Rivermouth the noise of the engine still throbbed in his brain.

No, it was the noise of the Wheelwrights' car now; and when that was over it was voices again, half a dozen of them jabbering at him, faces staring at him, lights striking against his sensitive eyes and blinding him. He was taken up to the room which he was to share with Johnny and left there alone for a few minutes. Then he was downstairs again and they thrust stacks of paper plates into his hands, bottles of beer, a platter piled with raw pink naked obscene-looking frankfurters. The voices went on, louder and louder, but at least he was outdoors now, away from the wounding lights; he was standing beside Mr. Wheelwright and heard himself offering advice on the best way to get a charcoal fire going.

Only maybe Mr. Wheelwright didn't hear him, because he went right on puttering with the fire in his own way.

Presently Charlie was sitting on the cold sand, fanning gnats away, eating frankfurters and roast potatoes, and drinking beer from the bottle. He could smell mustard and sausage meat and beer, but cleaner smells too, pine trees, cold sand, and the lake, making a faint whisper down below him in the dark. No stars, somebody was saying, not a star in the sky. But let the clean smell of outdoors flow in upon him, let the small peaceful sound of the waves flow in upon him and wash away the clamor—he would be borne up and soar again, so high that none of them could get at him.

The meal was over. Now there was a bonfire, and the light of the flames wounding him, and Tink Wheelwright screeching, casting paper plates into the flames, and beating against the trash-burner with a stick so that sparks went up like fireflies, almost like stars for a moment until the dark sky quenched them. The pines sighed and somebody was saying, Watch out, Tink, watch *out!* The fire died down; the last sparks were gone.

They were walking along the dark beach. Their heels sank into the sand. Laurette said she hoped she was dressed all right; Mrs. Wheelwright said she looked just fine, and Mr. Wheelwright said, Delores has saved her first dance for me, but you'll have to give me the next, Laurette. That's a promise, said Laurette, you can count on it. Gee, she said, I hope it's a waltz, I can tell by looking at you, you know how to waltz. But I'm going to start out with Charlie, said Laurette, and her arm was linked in his again. You might not think it to look at him, he's such a solid-built guy, but Charlie's a swell dancer.

She was laughing quite loudly in the darkness, in the sound of the waves which was mingled now with faint music, with music which grew louder.

Lights shone brightly among the trees on top of the dunes, lights from many cottage windows, lights strung in loops from tree to tree, lights blaring from the great square pavilion as the music blared; now they were mounting a long flight of wooden steps, two by two, and had no breath left for talking.

The tickets, Dorothy was shouting at the top, who has the tickets? I have, shouted Tink, didn't I *tell* you, Dorothy, I have them all; just follow me, ladies and gents, said Tink, just line up here and I'll take care of the tickets.

But the dance had been going on so long that the ticket-taker had joined the dancers, and Tink scattered the tickets into the dark and seized Dorothy around the waist and pushed her out on the pavilion floor, shoving her against couple after couple, working her arm like a pump-handle and saying excuse me, excuse me—his head reached only to her chin and he couldn't see where he was going.

Come on, Charlie, show 'em how good you are, kiddo, Laurette said, and held out her arms to him. Naw, said Charlie, shaking his head, I'll just sit and watch. There were benches along the sides of the pavilion. Charlie sat down on one of them, and shut his eyes, and presently the sound of shuffling feet, the blare of the brasses, the steady bump tiddy bump tiddy bump of the drums was gone; there was nothing but the faint whisper of the waves, running in from the night, falling patiently on the sand, sliding up a little way on the dark sand and sliding back into the huge dark lake.

Nothing but water now, and the immense and unending night.

22

"Is CHARLIE sick or something?" Johnny asked Patricia, after they had been twice around the dance-floor. Over Johnny's shoulder Patricia could see her brother, sitting against a backdrop of trees sharply illuminated. He sat very straight, with his eyes closed, his head tilted back, his hands resting on his knees. Patricia looked away from him.

"I don't know. He must have—he had some drinks before they left Broadfield—couldn't you smell it in the car?—and then all that beer. . . . Oh, Johnny," she said, "my family's so—"

"Hey, cut it out!" He held her closer and guided her away from Charlie, around to the far side of the bandstand. Johnny was not really a good dancer, not at all an enterprising or original one, but he held her firmly, he led her masterfully the way he wanted her to go; his arm was a bulwark around her and she could feel the steady beat of his heart; but there was still the impersonality—so he would have danced with any girl, she thought—and she tried to forget how much she wanted to rest her cheek against his.

"Pat," he said presently, "Pat, are you still—mixed up?"

She could not see the other dancers any more; she could see only his face, so close to hers, she could feel only his arm about her; but it couldn't be true that the old urgency was back in him.

She turned her head; she made herself see the other dancers. "No, Johnny," she said. "Not any more. Never again. But it's too late," Patricia said, looking at the dancers. "It's no good, Johnny."

She did not know how she kept dancing; it seemed she couldn't hear the music at all, because she was listening so intently for his voice. They had moved all the way around the floor before he said, "What do you mean, it's no good?"

"You don't—feel that way about me any more. You couldn't. I've been too— You don't, Johnny. It happened that day we went bicycling. I saw it happen then."

"Crazy," he said gently, "crazy Pat. Don't you know—"

But just then the music stopped; after a farewell dying trill on the saxophone, the players began to climb down from the stand.

Johnny stood back from her, holding both her hands. "Will you say it?" he said. "Please say it, Pat."

Her lips shaped the words, but voices rose about them and she didn't know if he heard her or not. "I love you, Johnny."

He smiled again and she saw him transfigured; and somehow the glory was real, she thought; not an illusion as it had been with Vincent. "Come on," Johnny said, taking her arm in his. "We'll have to sit down and talk this over."

But after all they did not say very much; they just sat, hand in hand, and looked out across the floor, where couples still were strolling or talking; where Tink and other small boys ran hooting, with paper cups of water in their hands, after a band of little girls led by Dorothy, who screamed like banshees.

"Tink ought to be in bed," said Johnny. "He'll run a fever tomorrow—you wait and see."

"What happened to the bandages?"

"Guess he thought they wouldn't look so good at a dance."

Patricia sighed; she still felt incredulous, but there was something else too that there never had been with Vincent: a feeling of safety, of security, because she knew what was in Johnny's mind and that he would never fly off at a tangent; he was all of a piece and what ought to be good would always be good, with Johnny. This feeling lay beneath the more immediate emotions, a kind of bedrock which would still be there though the other emotions might not last forever.

"I've been so foolish so long," she said. "You've been so patient, Johnny."

"You were worth waiting for."

"That's just it; I don't think I was. I don't think I am."

"Crazy," he said. "You're such a nice crazy kind of a kid. You'd have to be crazy, I guess, to want to be a dirty toolmaker's wife. But you do, don't you?"

"If you'll let me, Johnny."

"If I'll *let* you!" He laughed at her. "Crazy. Crazy Pat. . . . Though I don't plan on being a toolmaker all my life. Outdoors," said Johnny. "I want to work out-of-doors. Wouldn't you like that too?"

"A farm?"

"Or something. Maybe I could get to be a forest ranger. Or a state cop." He laughed again. "Tearing the hell around on a motorcycle, arresting people. That could be fun too, hey?"

"Too dangerous. Much too dangerous."

"Well, a sailor, then."

"No!"

"Or a soldier. Or a flyer. An aviator, a lone eagle."

"A toolmaker's good enough for me."

"It won't be forever. But something else'll turn up. Something's bound to. When you want something so much, it happens, eventually. You've happened, now. . . . The orchestra's coming back. Dance some more? Or shall we—?"

"Let's dance just a little more. I've hardly ever danced with you, Johnny. It's— I like the way you dance."

"Oh, you do, hey?" He stood up; they moved off together.

"You're an *honest* dancer, Johnny. Your dancing's like the rest of you—you're all of a piece, darling."

"Hey, you realize that's the first time you ever called me that?"

"I wish there was a new word that nobody else had ever used before. Darling isn't good enough for you."

"Sounds fine, the way you say it. Oh, God, Pat," said Johnny, and held her so tightly for a moment that she felt suffocated again.

"Now look," said Mr. Wheelwright, tapping Johnny on the shoulder, "this is all very well, but you aren't going to *monopolize* the guest of honor. May I, Miss Bryant?"

"With pleasure, Mr. Wheelwright."

He held her very lightly, but he whirled her off and away across the floor with a buoyancy Johnny would never have. They swept about the pavilion, bearing down upon other dancers, seeing other dancers bear down upon them, but always neatly avoiding a collision.

"If I'm trespassing," Mr. Wheelwright said presently, "just tell me, Patricia. But you look so particularly radiant. Have things been happening, or haven't they?"

The glory which surrounded Johnny extended to the other members of his family, and Patricia felt very humble, dancing with Johnny's father. "They've happened," she said. And then she said, "I don't know how you'll feel about it, having me as a daughter-in-law—"

Mr. Wheelwright's mouth twitched. "I'm not completely unprepared. Been steeling myself for years, in fact." They danced on in silence, and he said, after a while, "We'll be very glad, Patricia, all of us. We've been hoping for a long time. . . . I'm prejudiced, of course, but I don't think you could do much better. Johnny's the salt of the earth."

"And I'm not," Patricia said, with sudden sadness.

Mr. Wheelwright's eyes looked gravely at her, as if he were seriously considering her words; in the end his mouth quirked again. "You can pretend, can't you? As long as Johnny's fooled, that's all that matters. And someday, you know, you might surprise yourself. You might find out you'd been—"

He broke off; now somebody was tapping him on the shoulder.

"Cut, please," Vincent said.

Mr. Wheelwright stepped back. "I was afraid of this. No girl has any right to look so attractive. But I shan't let you keep her," he said.

"But, Dick—Mr. Wheelwright—" Patricia tried to move after him, but Vincent's hand was on her shoulder, his hand was at her waist, pulling her toward him.

"Surprised?" he said.

"Vincent, you—" She found herself dancing with him. Around the floor, threading their way between the other couples; past Mr. and Mrs. Wheelwright, now dancing sedately together; past Delores, locked in the arms of a stranger; past Tink, still chasing Dorothy; past Charlie, sitting on the bench with his eyes shut; past Johnny, who was standing on tiptoe, craning his neck to find her in the crowd.

"Do you think I'll be thrown out? I'm a gate-crasher," Vincent said. "What a dreadful, dreary place this is, darling. How I loathe summer resorts. Can't we go somewhere and talk?"

"Vincent, I—" She looked at his face, so white compared with Johnny's, so finely modeled, so shadowed with weariness; at his eyes, so large and bright with excitement. She thought how superbly he danced, so that it was hardly like dancing at all; it was like flying, like skimming the surface of a pool of sound. But no glory shone around him; all she felt for him was a terrible pity—no hatred, no distaste, even, but an aching pity; and that was dangerous because it might make her forget that he was not for her, she was not strong enough to make him whole; she would not be whole herself until she was Johnny's. She did not want to be cruel to Vincent; but whatever she told him would have to be cruel. "I'm engaged to Johnny Wheelwright," she said.

"Oh, now, darling, don't be fantastic! That clodhopper? Foolish, foolish Pat," he said. "Are you trying to make me jealous, darling? Because you don't need to try. I was born jealous. Nobody's going to take you away from me, darling. You're mine, Pat; you always have been."

She held herself stiff in his arms, and made herself clumsy on purpose. "No, I mean it. I'm going to marry Johnny. I don't even like you, Vincent. You're— You'd better go away. Please go away, or there'll be a scene, and— I've been so happy tonight, and I don't want it all spoiled. You always spoil it; you spoil everything."

But Vincent pulled her close against him. He did not believe her, and he continued to laugh into her face, blithely, because he was seeing her in a ferny glade; no, he was seeing her in Carola's cottage, in the dark cottage with the door bolted against the night and the sound of the pines, the sound of the waves, coming through the windows; he was whispering endearments to her, hearing her whisper endearments to him. It would be as Carola Wilmot had imagined it, only it would be better than that, better than anything that had ever happened to him and so much better than anything Carola had ever known.

"Let's go for a walk, darling," he said when the music stopped. "We can't talk sensibly in this racket."

She snatched her hand out of his and ran from him, and he was still so lost in his vision that he stood like a dolt with his mouth hanging open. He had gone to such pains to arrange this evening; he had taken such risks. He had thought for a while that he wasn't going to find her—the Wheelwrights' cottage, when he walked across to it from Carola's, was in darkness; and then, faintly carried on the wind, had come the sound of music, and he followed it until he reached the pavilion, shedding light and sound upon the night. He stood outside the pavilion until he saw her dancing with Johnny, and then with Johnny's father, and his excitement and his need for her carried him forward into the pavilion and across the dance-floor; and his conviction that things were going to happen as he wanted them to was complete, so that he had believed none of the things she said to him; he had not even believed in the stiffness of her body when he held her.

But she meant it. She'd really meant it.

He stood motionless while the music began again and the couples went turning and dipping and swaying and sliding past him to the sweet muted moan of the saxophone, and there was a sudden explosion in his mind, the wildest and blindest rage he had ever felt; at first he did not notice that Delores had come up. Then through his rage he tried to hear what she was saying.

"Lonely, Vinnie? Did Pat walk out on you?"

He looked at her and saw that her face and bare arms were a bright unwholesome red from the sun, and glistening a little with sweat and oil; he smelled perfume and he also smelled sweat and thought that he wanted to puke. Instead, he began to dance with her.

"Gee," said Delores, nestling in his arms. "Gee, but you're a smooth dancer, Vinnie."

He said nothing. He touched as little of her as he could, and his eyes sought among the dancers for Johnny and Charlie. Panic was cooling his rage, but he continued to dance with Delores; he couldn't think what he ought to do.

"Gee," said Delores, "I think you're crazy, Vinnie, to go and break your heart over her. She wouldn't be any good to you, Vinnie; just no good at all." Delores kept pressing her body closer against his; there was no escape from it, and mixed in with his disgust and panic there was almost a shiver of desire, an echo of the violence they had aroused in each other. "She and Johnny, they spent the whole morning necking on the beach," said Delores. "I guess they're going to get married. Patricia, she wouldn't ever do anything for a boy if he didn't marry her first. Isn't that right, Vinnie?" She began to hum softly, rocking in his arms; her eyelids were lowered. "How you happen to be here, anyway? Did you know we'd all be coming? Gee, I wasn't looking forward to tonight at all, but if I'd known you were going to be here—" She opened her eyes wide and looked at him. "Why so silent? . . . You look scared," Delores said. "Why, Vinnie Rourke, aren't you ashamed! Scared of Charlie." She tittered, and nestled her head on his shoulder; they continued to dance together.

"I'm not scared of Charlie any more," she murmured. "Can't do a thing to me. Said he'd kill me but he didn't mean it. Charlie's nuts, you know it? That's what I think; he's nuts. Look at him over there," said Delores, and jerked her chin toward him.

Vincent looked across the pavilion, but Charlie's eyes were no longer closed. He was staring back at Vincent.

Vincent stopped dead and pushed Delores away from him. "Get the hell away from me," he whispered. "What are you trying to do?" He stared at her, and past her at Charlie, and then turned, thrusting his way between the dancers—he was going to puke, he was sure of it—toward the far side of the pavilion; there, with the bandstand and all the dancers between him and Charlie, he leaned across the railing, out into the darkness. The floor seemed to lift and sink beneath his feet on the waves of sound, like the deck of a ship. He was not going to puke after all, but he stood in a kind of paralysis, thinking that it was no use, of course; he had come on a wild-goose chase; Patricia was going to marry Johnny Wheelwright.

He shifted his position, tensed his muscles, and gripped the railing more firmly; he would vault over it and run away. But somebody else was standing beside him.

"Hi, Vinnie." It was Laurette. "Remember me?"

He turned his head, and managed a smile of sorts. "Mae West," he said, "in person."

Laurette was smiling too; she even sketched a slight sway of the hips; but her eyes were impenetrable, like gray stones. "Been wanting to have a little chat with you, Vinnie," she said, and put her hand on his arm. "What say we take a walk?" She sounded friendly enough; she continued to sway her hips a little, burlesquing Mae West's burlesque of seductiveness.

"Charmed," said Vincent. His glance slid away from her and searched the pavilion, but he couldn't see Charlie or Johnny or Delores or anyone he knew.

"Come on," said Laurette; her fingers had closed about his arm. "We'll give 'em all the slip."

They walked along the edge of the dance-floor, through an opening in the railing, out among the trees. Vincent was still suffering from a paralysis of the will, and in a way he was glad of Laurette's hand on his arm, though he was tired of them all now, tired of all women, and beneath his weariness still panicky.

"Where are we going?" he asked. As soon as she let go of his arm he would forget his dignity and run from her back to Carola's cottage.

"It doesn't make so much difference," Laurette murmured. "Just someplace where we won't be interrupted. . . . You spending the week-end down here, Vinnie?"

"At Carola's," he said. "Mrs. Wilmot's."

"Oh, sure, Mrs. Wilmot. A very charming woman, Mrs. Wilmot. Cultured too. And rich. And quite a traveler in her day. You're lucky to know a woman like her, aren't you?"

"Very."

"A lucky boy any way you look at it." Laurette glanced back, and then her pace quickened. "Can you see in the dark, Vinnie?"

But for a while there was light enough shining through cottage windows for them to see where they were going, and they passed other couples, sitting on porch steps or melting away under the trees. The wind was so faint that Vincent couldn't feel it on his face, but over his head the boughs of the pines were sighing together.

Presently the rows of cottages stopped short; beach-grass brushed against Vincent's ankles, and then he and Laurette were out from under the trees and the darkness thinned a little. He could see farther dunes hunched against the sky, and a faint line of foam on the beach below, and the dim shape of more trees ahead; there were no stars in the sky but the sand seemed to give off its own pale glimmer.

The music, which had stopped some time ago, began again, but it came faintly, in broken fragments, between which there was the persistent lap of the waves.

The paralysis was growing on Vincent; if Laurette had let go of his arm now he wouldn't have been able to run away. Whatever she wanted of him, let her have it. They were all the same: they looked at him and they were lost; they had no shame and no pride. Vincent began to pity himself because this was all to be gone through again, the same words, the same skilled motions of the lips and hands, the same final violence of the body. His feeling of sickness returned.

They had been mounting a slope and now they paused. Beneath his feet Vincent could see a hollow of sand, and it looked very smooth and firm in the darkness, like a great basin wedged down among the beach-grass.

"This'll do, won't it?" said Laurette. "Nobody'll find us here."

"Your dress—"

"Hell with that. Going to get me a whole new outfit soon."

They sat just below the lip of the basin, digging their heels into the sand to keep from sliding down. She was very close to him; her thigh lay warm against his, and he tried to forget his sickness and torpor, he tried to imagine her lush soft body stripped of its clothes; but there was a rigidity in his mind and he thought, I can't go through with it; I can't do it; God, I don't even know her.

"You got a cigarette?" Laurette asked. "These damn no-seeums."

Besides, he thought, groping for the pack in his pocket, he had to get away, that was the important thing; he shouldn't have come, he never should have come on this wild-goose chase.

In the brief flare of the match he tried to see her face; but he couldn't tell if she was still smiling, and it was difficult to look at her squarely because any shift in their position would have sent them both slipping to the bottom of the bowl. It was so grotesque, and so undignified; but had it ever been anything else with any of them? He looked back coldly at all the episodes there had been since New Year's Eve in Quebec, and saw himself in all of them as a kind of horrible clown; women had made him like that; they had turned him into a clown.

He drew fiercely at his cigarette, and pitched it away.

"Look," he said, "I've got to—" He pushed with his free hand against the sand, meaning to rise and leave her, but found that his other arm was pinioned. She patted his hand.

"We haven't had our talk yet, toots," she said.

Oh, God, said Vincent to himself; and then he said, all right, then, all right, get it over with, and get the hell out of here. He turned quite suddenly, digging his feet deeper in the sand, and laid his free hand on her shoulder, which was very soft before the bone started, and very smooth. "A little talk," he whispered, running his hand down her arm and up again; he slid his arm behind her shoulders and began to pull her toward him. "There really isn't any point in talking, is there?" said Vincent. She did not resist him; his lips found hers in the dark and he wanted to laugh—it was so easy, it was always so easy—until he discovered that there was no response in her; her mouth was slack beneath his, and her hands, gripping his body, were actually holding him off.

"All right, toots," Laurette said, and calmly, strongly, without apparent effort, pushed him away—he scrabbled and would have fallen down the slope if she hadn't cavalierly hauled him back. "That's enough of that," said Laurette. "I was just curious. I wondered how you started. The fast worker, the great lover." He thought she was laughing now. "You're still just a kid, really, aren't you? I don't think you know a thing about women, toots. Not a goddam thing."

Vincent groped for another cigarette and jabbed it between his lips; his hands were shaking and he had to strike three matches before he could bring the flame up. The terrible thing was that if he didn't get himself under control he was going to cry. He sucked the smoke into his lungs and blew it out again, and said, "Then would you mind telling me what the hell this is all about?"

"Boy," said Laurette, "haughty, aren't we? . . . Give me another cigarette too, toots—remember Emily Post? No, I'll light it. You might singe my eyebrows, the way your hands are shaking." She drew reflectively on her cigarette. "It's very simple, really. I just want to tell you one thing. Get out of town."

"Aren't you being rather elaborate about all this? You could have told me that a long time ago."

"I wanted to tell you in private, toots. Because I mean it. Get out of town."

"The dictatress," said Vincent. "Mrs. God."

"I'm not arguing, toots. I'm telling you. Get out of town before it's too late. You're a pretty little boy, one of the prettiest little boys I ever saw, and I'd hate to see you get all messed up. So scram, toots. Just scram."

"If you'd let go of my arm, maybe—"

"In a minute, toots. But first I want to tell you all the different kinds of bastard you are."

"Really," said Vincent, "this is too fantastic—"

"Yes, darling, it reahlly is, it reahlly reahlly is too utterly fantastic for words, and I do mean reahlly, darling. . . ."

Charlie, who had been approaching slowly—it was so difficult to see in the dark, and he was not sure they had come this way—now began to hear their voices: Laurette's, then Vincent's, then Laurette's again. He must be very close to them, although he could see nothing but the slight upward lift of the dune, and the remote darkness of the sky, and the nearer darkness of other dunes and of massed trees tumbling away into the night. There was the darkness of the night and the other darkness too, and this was worse;

it was like trying to find somebody blindfold, and he kept rubbing his fists against his eyes to push both kinds of darkness away.

Partly because he felt weak, partly because of the darkness, he dropped to his knees and began to creep forward; close to the sand, which was paler than anything else, he might be able to see a little better. He lay flat on the sand, with the smell of it in his nostrils, and inched up the slope until his groping hands found that it stopped; there was space beyond, and now, besides the sand, he could smell Laurette's perfume and the tang of cigarette smoke; but he still couldn't hear what they were saying.

He pressed the whole length of his body, he pressed his cheek, against the sand, trying to hear Laurette's words, but it was impossible to concentrate because part of his mind was trying to think what the sand smelled like; there was sand against his lips now but still he could not think what the smell reminded him of nor why it made him feel so strange.

Everything was so strange, he thought, lying there only a foot or two away from them. How had he come here? what was he doing here? Maybe he wasn't really here at all, but back in the pavilion, sitting with closed eyes while the music played and the dancers shuffled past him. He tried to hear the music, and saw Patricia going past in Rourke's arms, and then Delores; and then Laurette and Rourke were going out into the dark together. That had been back in the pavilion and his mind had been quite clear then, as clear as it had been at McBain's lecture; but now he was here among the dunes and his mind was confused and kept thinking about sand. Charlie lay and laughed at himself for worrying about sand when there was something so much more important to worry about.

Now the excitement was returning; the pain was returning but the excitement was returning too, the immense burning clarity, the terrible violence which had been growing in his body all spring and had found no outlet but which would find an outlet now, because of course he knew where he was and what he was going to do, and why was he wasting so much time about it?

He pushed himself to his knees. There was sand inside his mouth and he spat before he plunged over the edge, but the gritty feeling went on, the strange taste and smell went on, and they would confuse him again if he didn't concentrate, concentrate—

He was sliding, rolling down the slope of sand, and then he was on his feet again and their voices were very loud for a moment. Laurette was screaming and he could see McBain, no, Rourke, Rourke, remember it was Rourke, he could see Rourke scrabbling up the slope of sand to the ridge above the beach.

Charlie went after him, on hands and knees again for a minute because the slope was so steep, but he was at the top and could rise again; and he caught at Rourke's white jacket, swung his other fist wildly and felt it jar against Rourke's jaw, saw Rourke's knees sag in the dark, saw Rourke starting to collapse and jerked him to his feet again and swung his fist again, hurling his whole body against Rourke's.

"Charlie," Laurette was screaming, and she was tugging at his arm. "Charlie, Charlie, Charl—"

But he flung her away; her voice broke off short and there was silence now except for his own breath sawing in his throat, sawing past all the sand he had swallowed, and Rourke's breath coming in sobs through the stillness—

The pain of Charlie's fist against his jaw had been bad enough and was still blinding him, but then Charlie's knee came up savagely into his groin and this time the pain was annihilating and he thought he was dying right now, this minute, before Charlie had had a chance to kill him properly. Maybe he screamed, maybe he yelled a great oath into Charlie's face, but he did not know because the pain obliterated everything else; and when it became a little less (but it would go on forever, it would never be quite gone) the whole weight of Charlie's body was on his and Charlie's hands were at his throat and Charlie's thumbs were pressing his windpipe. He was being killed, he was really being murdered, here on the top of the dunes on a May night he was being murdered by Charlie Bryant and it was so incredible that he would have laughed if Charlie's thumbs had not been against his windpipe.

But it was as if the hideous pain gave him strength, and he could feel his own body writhing beneath Charlie's, tossing itself this way and that, refusing to have the life squeezed out of it; his hands lifted from the sand and clawed at Charlie's face, at Charlie's chest, ripping the shirt, at Charlie's arms, until the pressure on his windpipe slackened a little and he could suck in a gulp of air. He arched his body upward, pressing with his feet and the back of his head against the sand, trying to lift the weight of Charlie's body with his and fling it off and away, trying to roll with Charlie to the edge of the bank. If he could fight his way to the edge and they dropped to the beach he might still escape.

He tried to shout for help (it was not fair, he kept thinking, it was not fair, Charlie was so much stronger than he was, Charlie had struck him foully in the groin) but although he clawed at the arms, Charlie's hands were tightening again and he could see nothing but the wheels of fire spinning in his head, hear nothing but bells ringing, bells ringing incessantly, a perpetual din like the clang of an ambulance. They had called for an ambulance and he would be saved if only he kept clawing at Charlie's arms, at Charlie's fingers squeezing the life out of him.

And then there was no solid ground, only space; they dropped through space and then they were rolling over and over together, still locked tight, down the slope to the beach. The ground came up from beneath and hurled itself against Vincent, and Charlie's body hurled itself against him from above; the bells rose to a wild crescendo and the pain was more terrible than it had been even when Charlie's knee struck him and then everything went faint and far away and there were no bells ringing and the wheels of fire spun and were gone in darkness.

Charlie thought he had been lying on his back on the beach for a long time, for hours, perhaps, gazing upward in the hope of seeing the stars. But there were no stars tonight; not a star in the sky, a voice had said long ago. Charlie lay and listened curiously to the sound of his own breath; it did not come evenly and steadily as it should, but in long shuddering gasps—anyone who had heard him would have thought he was weeping. He listened, hour after hour it seemed, until at last his breath did not make so much noise any more and he could hear the waves again, very close to him; his hand was lying in the water.

Charlie got up on his knees and bent above Rourke.

Rourke was dead, Charlie thought; Rourke was dead.

Christ, said Charlie, oh, Christ, oh, Jesus Christ.

He stood up and looked back toward the pavilion. Lights were moving up there, lights were coming toward him along the dunes and along the beach. No, said Charlie, and began to run away from the moving lights, along the beach at first and then back up into the dunes. He found a steep path in the dark and his feet slipped in the sand and his breath was shuddering in his throat again, but up here in the dunes they would not find him so easily.

He left the path and plunged through the beach-grass, pitched down a slope and fell headlong among bushes with sharp twigs, and got to his feet and ran on again, blindly in the dark, trying to avoid the trees, trying to see where the ground rose and where it dropped, so that he would not fall again. The trees thinned; he ran past the back of a dark cottage, and into the trees again on the far side, and past another cottage, where lights shone in the windows and a dog was barking. Then he returned to the beach because he could run more swiftly there, and would be less likely to meet anybody.

When he looked back over his shoulder he could not see the moving lights any more, but still he ran, on the firm wet sand at the edge of the water, along by the faint glistening line of foam, his feet pounding into the foam sometimes when a bigger wave than most slid up on the beach. The wind felt cold now; he had lost his jacket, his shirt was torn, and there were streaks of fire on his face and chest and arms when the wind blew against him. Scratched—Rourke had scratched him; he'd fought like a woman.

Christ, said Charlie, and spat into the wind because there was still sand in his mouth; there was only sand in his mouth, a rasping dryness, and he was not able to spit.

The last drop of strength was drained from him abruptly and he fell on the sand and lay there breathing carefully, trying to ease the soreness in his chest and throat. But it was not safe to rest because he had murdered Rourke and they were coming after him, even Laurette. That was it, Laurette had known she could not stop him from murdering Rourke, and she had gone off to call the others, to call the cops, so there would be no time lost in arresting him.

Charlie listened intently. He looked back along the beach but he could see no lights, he heard no voices.

Now his fingers moved deliberately. He had some trouble untying the knots in his shoelaces, which were sodden with water and gritty with sand, but the knots came undone finally; he pulled his shoes off and set them neatly side by side on the wet sand, as if he had been setting them under a bed; he pulled off his wet socks and rolled them with equal neatness and put them inside one of his shoes. He knew what he was doing; let them come after him; he wasn't going to let himself be hurried.

He stood up in the dark and gazed out at the lake.

At first the water felt cold on his bare feet. The floor of the lake shelved so gently; he had to walk a long time before the water crept up his legs, plastering his trousers against the shivering flesh. The floor of the lake shelved gently but the water crept up, above his knees, above his loins, above his waist; the water was at his armpits now and his torn shirt was stuck to his chest and back. His teeth chattered but the water was not really cold; it was warm, and caressed him; he began to swim, slowly and powerfully, outward into the dark. They would look for him on the beach or among the dunes; they would never think of looking out here, and in such an enormous expanse of water they would not find him even if they looked.

He unbuckled his belt as he swam (take it easy, take it easy, you can keep swimming all night if you have to) and got his fly undone; his trousers went drifting and sinking away in the water behind him. He had more trouble with his shirt, but in a little while he was set free and was swimming naked in the gentle caressing water. It washed pain away, and violence away, and fear. Why hadn't he done this to begin with? This was what the voice of the waves had been saying to him and there had been no need to murder McBain, or Rourke, or anybody else.

If he had not used up his violence he would not have been so tired now. But he was tired, even in the water; even when he opened his mouth and let the water flow into it to wash away the strange feel and taste of sand he continued to feel tired, and some of the water had gone down his throat and he choked as he swam.

He rolled on his back, hoping the clouds might have blown away; surely now the stars would be above him. But there were no stars; there was nothing but darkness and water, and the darkness was absolute so that he couldn't see the waves as they came toward him, he couldn't watch out for the large waves and avoid them, and the water was not kind after all: it came dancing at him out of the darkness and flung itself viciously at his face, and more of it was going down his throat.

He could not rest; he must swim strongly now and get back to the shore. But he had lost his clothes; he had let his clothes sink away from him in the water and would have to walk out naked on the beach. Then he stopped worrying about that because he had discovered that he did not know where the beach was; the darkness was all around him, the darkness went on forever in all directions.

He was terrified for a moment. How was he ever going to keep himself afloat until daylight? He pushed the terror away, and tried to think what time it must be by now; it was important to know how long he would have to keep swimming before dawn broke. But everything was so confused; he might have been swimming for ten minutes or for a year, and there was no dawn, of course, there never would be. That was what he had found out, that was what they had told him, all those voices: no stars, no dawn, no light of any kind, nothing: only the dark and the cold water, world without end, amen.

Wasn't this what he had meant to do from the start? Had there ever been anything else for him to do?

No, said Charlie, no, it's all a mistake.

He tried to lift his heavy arms; he tried to kick with his heavy legs; but he could not move any more.

No, Charlie said again.

The waves closed over him. The water ran down his throat.

23

THE WHEELS of fire were remote as nebulae, the ringing of bells came as if from the depths of the sea. Then fire and noise rushed at Vincent suddenly from the small end of a funnel, and broke over him in waves of pain; the fantasy fell apart and panic smote him—Charlie Bryant was still there.

But it was Johnny Wheelwright.

Vincent tried to speak and found that he couldn't; all that came out between his lips was a noise half sob and half animal grunt and wholly horrible.

"Had the wind knocked out of him," said Johnny's voice impersonally. "He passed right out, I guess, but now he's—"

Vincent thought of sitting up, but Johnny's hand lay firm against his shoulder. "Take it easy. Everything's going to be all right. . . . Give me that coat, Pop. That's it. Thanks."

Vincent felt the wadded coat thrust beneath his head; beyond the horrible noise of his breath he could hear the waves; beyond Johnny's crouching figure he could see other dim shapes.

"I want—" Vincent said. "I want—" But each time he tried to speak, the words were cut off by the obscene noises forced upward from his chest. For a moment he was ten years old, suffering from whooping-cough, and Aunt Lucy said he was giving in to his illness instead of fighting and besting it.

"Just take it easy," said Johnny's voice, with a remote, slow patience. "You'll be breathing all right in a minute. Don't try too hard."

"Sick," Vincent said desperately, "I'm going to puke," and he did sit up now, despite Johnny's restraining hand, and retched violently.

"On your knees'll be easier," Johnny said, and Johnny was supporting him, Johnny's hand was clamped against Vincent's forehead while Vincent shamefully vomited; his aching body was racked by each spasm and he thought the spasms would never stop. But the shame—they saw him like this, become loathsome—was worse than the pain, worse by far than the taste of bile in his mouth.

"God," Vincent whispered, "oh, God," and sat back, resting his sweaty face on his knees. He was not going to weep before them.

There seemed to be a long silence, and then Johnny said, "Think you can walk now, fella? Can you make it to our cottage?"

"Wash," Vincent said, "I've got to wash off." He lurched toward the water and sprawled in the wet sand, like an animal still, thrusting his hands into the small waves, bending his face down to gulp the water and spew it out again. The coldness of the water shocked him and presently his breath came quietly, although there was still the constriction in his throat. He kneeled while the waves flowed about him and saw that there were by now only Johnny and Johnny's father as witnesses to his shame; though dim shapes were receding along the beach, and farther off there were shouting, flashlights waving, feet crashing through the underbrush on top of the dunes.

"O.K.?" Johnny said. "Give me a hand, Pop, will you?"

Vincent found himself hauled to his feet; his legs buckled at first, but one arm was clamped about Johnny's neck, the other about Mr. Wheelwright's; they lugged him along the beach between them.

"Don't try to take it too fast, now," said Johnny.

"Charlie," Vincent said. "Charlie Bryant, he—"

"Don't worry about Charlie," said Mr. Wheelwright.

They moved on in silence and the strength was coming back into Vincent's legs. He could have walked without support but they kept a firm hold upon him, as if he were their captive. He groped for his lost dignity; he sought frantically for Vincent Vaughan Rourke, Esq.

"I'm sorry," he said. "You don't know how sorry I am about all of this. I—"

"Here we are," said Mr. Wheelwright. "Had we better carry him up, Johnny?"

"I can walk. Really I can. There's nothing—wrong now. No bones broken. Nothing." But it was a long flight of steps and at the top he was breathing hard again.

Mr. Wheelwright was moving ahead into the cottage, snapping on lights, and turned when Johnny followed with Vincent. "Brandy, Johnny, do you think? I don't know if he ought to have stimulants or not."

"Better make sure no bones are broken first. Hey, come on, lie down here, will you?"

Vincent stretched out on a sofa. He stared up at the board ceiling and smelled the universal smell of summer cottages everywhere; a moth was knocking itself against a paper lampshade. Weakness invaded him again and he thought he wanted to sleep. But sleep was denied him; though Johnny had vanished, Mr. Wheelwright was bending over him.

"Better get that shirt off. We'll have to look you over."

To be stripped before them was the ultimate humiliation, and Vincent wished to protest. He smiled thinly and said, "You're a doctor?"

"Just an architect, I'm afraid. But I used to know a little about anatomy. . . . Bring the first-aid kit, Johnny, will you? It's out in the bathroom. . . . If there's anything really wrong, we'll get a doctor over from Rivermouth." His long thin fingers moved serenely, pulling off Vincent's jacket and shirt and trousers; a sour smell of vomit still hung in the air. "You're pretty badly bruised," Mr. Wheelwright said presently, "and there are what they call minor abrasions, I believe, but I think your ribs are sound enough. You're tougher than you look. . . . Oh, thanks, Johnny. The iodine first; and there's some salve, or should be, unless Tink's used it all up. Thanks."

Like everything else, the doctoring seemed to go on for a long time. Vincent tried to stifle his wild impatience; he had never hated them more than he did now.

"All right," Mr. Wheelwright said finally. "You can get dressed again."

He and Johnny walked out of the room. Shivering, his throat aching, his raw scraped flesh smarting from the iodine, Vincent pulled on his clothes. He groped in his jacket suddenly; by a miracle, nothing had fallen from the pockets—keys, wallet, the squashed pack of cigarettes were all there.

When he was dressed, Vincent sat back on the sofa and smoked one of the cigarettes. The lassitude was returning; he didn't want to move or think what he was going to do next, and it was almost a relief when Johnny came in with a cup of black coffee and stood over him while he drank it. It washed away the taste of bile and he thought that at least he wouldn't have to puke again.

While he still sat there, staring away from Johnny, he heard the telephone ringing in another room, and made a show of not listening to Mr. Wheelwright's voice.

"Yes, yes, no lasting harm done, I think. Bit shaken up, that's all; probably suffering from shock. . . . No sign yet? Oh. Johnny," he called, "come here a minute. You happen to remember what kind of shoes he was wearing?" The murmurs went on for a while in the next room, and then Mr. Wheelwright's voice on the telephone again: "Yes, they must be his all right. That rather settles it, doesn't it? It looks as if he'd—▸ Oh, fine, good. Well, I hope they find him before it's too— Call again in about an hour, will you?—Or wait, I'll call you. What was the number? Thank you."

Mr. Wheelwright came back into the room and his glance fell on Vincent; his face appeared to stiffen slightly. "If you're feeling up to it," he said, "I think you'd better let Johnny drive you back to Broadfield. I don't want to be inhuman about this, but you've caused a good deal of trouble, one way and another, and the girls have enough to cope with as it is. Otherwise we'd put you up here for the night and get a doctor in. Not that I think you need one." His voice remained level, but there was contempt underneath, Vincent thought, and it flicked at his nerves.

He stood, setting the empty cup on the table, and his anger made him speak elaborately. "I'm quite all right now. You've been very kind and I'm extremely grateful, but you needn't bother about me at all any more. I'm spending the week-end at Mrs. Wilmot's cottage and I think I'll go back there now, if I may." He began to feel almost like Vincent Vaughan Rourke, Esq.

Johnny stepped forward. "I'll go with you."

"There's no need," Vincent said, inwardly raging. "I tell you, I'm quite all right."

But Johnny walked along the beach with him just the same, and up the steps, and saw to it that Vincent crossed the threshold.

"Sure you're O.K. now?" Johnny said.

"Quite."

"Well—" Johnny hesitated. "Give us a buzz if you want anything. If you want me to drive you over to a doctor in Rivermouth—"

"There's nothing I want less. Good night," said Vincent, and shut the door in Johnny's face.

Johnny returned slowly to the beach. His penance was over; but he couldn't help feeling ashamed of his own sense of triumph, so large and overwhelming that there was no room, really, for anything else. All this was a nightmare which would be gone by morning, and even in the nightmare the only thing that mattered was that Vincent was disposed of and Patricia loved Johnny, she loved Johnny Wheelwright, Patricia Bryant was going to be Mrs. John Spencer Wheelwright. . . .

He began to run along the beach, back toward the pavilion, past the place where Laurette had brought him and his father and they had found Vincent lying on the sand and for an instant believed him dead; past that place and back up the steps to find Patricia again, in the cottage where she had gone with his mother and Laurette, Delores and the kids.

The orchestra was still playing, although most of the dancers had gone off to join in the manhunt. Manhunt, thought Johnny, with a sudden sense of shock, and paused beneath the strings of lights to look at his watch. Incredibly, it was not quite ten yet. So many things had happened in the last hour; too many things.

He looked out at the lake. Far off northward, beyond his father's cottage, beyond Carola Wilmot's, motors were throbbing and searchlights were sweeping the water. Out on the dark lake, back in the dunes, far away along the beach they were hunting for Charlie Bryant, who was sick in his mind and had tried to kill Rourke and by now, perhaps, had succeeded in killing himself.

No, it was not possible. Johnny's own mind rebelled—the world which held his happiness had no room in it for death.

He turned from the lake, but before he reached the cottage, Tink hurled himself upon him. "Did they find Charlie? Did they find him, Johnny?"

"Not yet, I guess." Johnny caught Tink by the hair and shook his head gently. "Come on, we'll collect the others. You and Dorothy should have been asleep hours ago."

"*Asleep!* We're going to sit up all night."

"That's what you think."

"Johnny, Charlie's crazy, did you know that? Everybody says he's crazy."

"Well, you shouldn't pay any attention to what everybody says."

He and Tink went into the cottage. Laurette, Patricia, Delores, sat about a table with strangers—two women, two men—drinking coffee. Mrs. Wheelwright was in a corner, playing checkers with Dorothy. It looked almost like a normal scene; only the expression on the strangers' faces showed how terrible it was. They looked kind enough, the four strangers; there was a strained anxiety to be good, to do what was right, to help; but behind that, beneath it, there was a secret gloating.

"There," said Mrs. Wheelwright to Dorothy, "you've beaten me again. Come along. Time for bed." She rose calmly, putting one arm about Dorothy, the other about Tink.

"The coast is clear," Johnny told her.

"Yes. Come along, girls."

It was a great relief to be out on the dark beach again, although far away the motors still throbbed and the searchlights continued to sweep the water. Johnny walked with his arm around Patricia; he held her very tightly, and was glad when she relaxed a little and let her shoulder rest against his.

But the feeling of unreality returned when they were back in their own cottage. Delores began to whimper, and was taken away by Laurette. Mrs. Wheelwright went upstairs with the two children and sat in the hallway outside their open doors. She read aloud to them from *The Tin Woodman of Oz,* and the placid sound of her voice went on for a long time. Mr. Wheelwright sat reading too, but Johnny, seeing the speed with which he flipped the pages over, knew he wasn't taking in the sense of the words. It was bad to feel such a sense of frustration; there ought to be something more that all of them could do, but there was nothing.

Laurette returned presently and said that Delores had gone to sleep. "You ought to go to bed too, baby," she said to Patricia.

Patricia shook her head. "Shouldn't we call Father?"

"God, leave him in peace for one night, anyway. No point in calling until we know for sure about Charlie. . . . Poor Pop. He was all set to propose to Betty Lou. Well, I sure hope he's gotten it over with by now." She lit a cigarette and walked slowly up and down the room until Mrs. Wheelwright reappeared.

"Patricia," Mrs. Wheelwright said, "really, dear, you'd better try to get some sleep." She had a small box in her hand. "I've found some sleeping-tablets, and I think just this once—" She sat beside Patricia. "Come along, now. There's nothing you can do by staying awake, and perhaps in the morning there'll be—good news. People can be cured, you know; it's like any other illness."

"I'm so ashamed," Patricia whispered. "It's so horrible. Dragging all of you into this. We shouldn't have come. None of us should have come. There's something horrible about us; something wrong with all of us, we—"

"Nonsense," Mrs. Wheelwright said, "nonsense, dearest. Come along to bed now. There's just one thing for you to think about.

You're going to be Johnny's wife, and we're all very happy about that."

"I can't," Patricia said, "not now."

"Come along." Mrs. Wheelwright more or less lifted her from the sofa and they went upstairs together.

Laurette snuffed out her cigarette. "All I can say is, you're just about the swellest bunch of people— God," said Laurette, "I know what Pat means. I could eat dirt."

Mr. Wheelwright laid his book aside. "I think I'll call again and see if there's any news." But when he came back from the telephone his face was stiffer than before. "No good, I'm afraid. Not a trace. Maybe he didn't—"

Laurette sat down. "I never did think there was any real hope. He tried it once before, you know, when he was a kid. There's always been something inside Charlie—he took life too hard, that kid. Maybe it was always going to happen. When a guy won't let you get *at* him—when he makes up his mind to be alone, not to take any help. I don't know."

Mr. Wheelwright cleared his throat. "By the way, I think Rourke's left already."

"He was in no shape to drive," Johnny said. "He—"

"Personally," said Laurette, "I hope he has a smashup. I'm afraid I mean that."

"He's young," said Mr. Wheelwright. "While there's youth there's hope." He smiled faintly. "I like to think so, anyway. I wish I'd known, when he cut in, that that's who he was. The whole thing might have been prevented."

"You start thinking along those lines, you'll go batty," Laurette said. "Never look back at all the ifs in your life: that's my motto."

Vincent had, in fact, been driving like a fugitive. It was possible presently to exult in speed and not to think about anything else; even the ache of his body could be forgotten. But when, just after midnight, he came into the outskirts of the city, he was terrified and lost again. He had, for a few minutes, no idea where he was going or what he would do. He had to leave Broadfield tonight; he must set hundreds of miles between complete humiliation and himself, himself. When he had driven far enough he would forget the sobbing, retching, stinking animal on the beach.

Almost without thinking, he had steered the car away from empty Main Street, up the dark tunnel of Warner Street, and into Carola's driveway. He got out with great care, and with great care shut the car door, making no noise. He climbed the steps, and pushed the bell, and stood there in the profound silence.

She would be awake. She would have to be awake; his need for her to be awake and to help him was so great that it could not be otherwise. And in fact she presently came to the door and pulled it open.

"Vincent," she said, "darling—"

She was wearing a negligee over satin pajamas and her hair flowed back across her shoulders in russet waves, but he did not think she had been asleep. She had dropped his hand, and was standing back from him, staring at him in the light from the hall lamp.

"Vincent—" For a moment her face was incredulous; her fingers went up and she lifted her hair farther from her face; she smiled faintly. "You look horrible," she said. "I thought you were going to avoid pugilism."

Vincent found that he was swaying on his feet. "I've got to sit down," he said. She took him by the arm and, switching on lights as they moved, led him away to the small room out behind the dining room and helped him into the chaise longue there.

"Brandy," she said, and gave it to him in one of her great crystal glasses.

After a few sips he was able to smile at her, although the smile wrenched at the muscles of his face. It was necessary to be debonair, and exceedingly careful, or he might destroy his last chance. Over her face, so calm and still, a tiny shadow of expression flickered, but he couldn't tell yet if it was curiosity or distaste.

"I came to you, you see," he said, "as I promised. And here are the keys, by the way." He laid them on the table.

"But I wasn't expecting you before tomorrow night, darling. And I expected you to come back in one piece."

"I'm quite whole, really."

"Whole, but horrible. Your face is scraped raw, and your chin's swollen, and your throat— Darling, what in the world happened to your throat?"

He shut his eyes for a moment, pressing his hands around the curve of the goblet. "Charlie Bryant tried to kill me."

"Now, really, darling, a good story is a good story, but there *are* limits."

He smiled again. The reality of the moments on top of the dunes was diminished by her voice.

"It's true," he said. "It's completely fantastic, but it's quite true. He tried to choke me to death—he very nearly succeeded—and then we fell down a sandbank together and I suppose he— I don't know quite what happened to Charlie because I was knocked out, but he must have run away, and by now, I think, he's drowned himself in the lake."

Carola sat down. "You are a most unconvincing liar, Vincent," she said, and took up a cigarette.

It was becoming difficult to remain debonair; tears stung at the back of his eyes and the feeling of sickness was beginning again. "You can *see*, can't you? You can look at my face, you can look at my throat."

"I'd much rather not. . . . Keep talking, darling. Presently I shall begin to believe you. *Why* did Charlie Bryant try to kill you? I thought we'd cast Johnny as the heavy."

"He's insane, I think."

"Johnny? Oh, you mean Charlie. Well, it isn't surprising, I suppose. Did he just select you at random, darling, or had you given him good cause?"

"He probably thought he was protecting American womanhood. That's the way his mind would work."

Carola was not amused by his effort to be amusing. "I hope all this didn't take place in my cottage. I shall have to have it fumigated. Really, it's rather nasty, the whole business." Under the surface she meant what she said so lightly; her nostrils had widened.

Weariness assailed him; he was losing his temper. "It took place outside, on the dunes—nowhere near the cottage. I told you."

"Yes, pet. Don't raise your voice." She smiled. "I can quite see that a narrow escape from murder must be rather shattering, but you gain nothing by growing hysterical."

"Hysterical!" Vincent sat quiet for a moment. "Do you think this is a joke?"

She gave him a sidelong glance, and began to examine her fingernails. "Since you ask me, yes. Not a very pretty joke, perhaps—but what a thing to happen to you!" She sat in silence, still examining her nails, and his weariness became insufferable—there was no hope. But there had to be; she was all he had, now.

"I see what you mean," he said. He set the empty glass aside and absently touched his throat; then he clasped his hands together on his knees. He had made another mistake, of course. He should have gone to his room and slept this off.

"What are you going to do about it, darling?" Carola asked. "Are you going to sue?"

"I'm leaving," Vincent said, and watched her carefully; he peered at her still face, seeking for some gleam of hope; but she merely smiled.

"Running away. Do you always run away from your messes, Vincent?"

"I suppose so. There's no point in—wallowing."

"If you must *make* messes. But why, darling? Why do you?"

He looked at the floor. "They just happen, somehow. Again and again. When I came to Broadfield, I was running away."

"I'm sure you were. Only somebody really desperate would come to Broadfield from choice. . . . Where are you running away *to*, Vincent?"

He turned his face back to her and smiled winningly before he remembered that his smile couldn't possibly be winning tonight. "That's really what I wanted to talk about. You mentioned Mexico the other day. I've always wanted to go to Mexico myself. Carola, I thought maybe—" He couldn't finish his sentence because of the way she was looking at him. There was a cold alertness in her face now; her eyes were wide open, darker in color than he had remembered, and he thought that always before she had kept her eyelids lowered a little.

"Yes," she said. "Go on. You thought maybe—"

"We might go together," he said.

The silence became dreadful. He wanted to look away from her and could not. He had played his last card, and played it badly. Panic made him lose his head, and he stood up.

"It's what you want, isn't it? You've always wanted it. It's what you were hinting at the other day—of course that's what you meant."

He paused because hatred was getting into his voice, and then went on more quietly, trying once more to smile.

"Carola, please, darling, do it! We could leave in a few hours. Haven't you always liked to do things on the spur of the moment? Crazy things? You can pack right now, what you'll need—we could leave before daylight. By tomorrow night we'd be well on our way. You have a lawyer. You could let him fix up about the house. Please," said Vincent, and took a step toward her.

"If you don't do it now," he said, "you never will. It's your last chance. You don't want to stay shut up in Broadfield, with all these people who don't like you, for the rest of your life." In his mounting excitement he snatched at her cold hand. "Oh, darling, we could have such a wonderful time. You know how beautifully we get along together—I've never liked anybody as much as I like you. We'd amuse each other so—we'd always amuse each other. It's the right thing for you to do, it's the only thing. In sunlight, all that sunlight, in Mexico— In Mexico it would be all right, don't you see? Nobody would know us, nobody would think it was strange; they'd think I was your son. I'm young," Vincent said, "but I'm not like other young men. You couldn't find another young man like me if you spent the rest of your life looking."

"I'm quite sure of that," said Carola. She drew her hand away, stood up, and crossed the room. When she turned she was smiling again.

He stood a moment longer; when he saw there was no hope, he sat down. "You're such a hypocrite," he said. "You want all of the fun and none of the danger."

"Speak for yourself, darling," she said composedly.

"It's all your fault, everything that's happened. You wanted it to happen—you drove me into it. You wanted me to seduce Patricia because you didn't dare hope I'd want you. Vicarious: you needed the vicarious satisfaction." If only there had been a break in her composure, the slightest rift; but he couldn't even hurt her. "I know," he said wearily, "I know what women are like. . . . All those lies about Laura Bryant. You knew they were lies, but you wanted me to use them. You didn't care who got hurt, as long as you had your cheap little thrill." He was appalled to discover that his cheeks were wet, his voice shaking.

"So now we turn on the tears," she said. "The whole repertoire. It's a shame your face is so banged up. If you still looked pretty, the tears might be rather effective."

She moved again, but not toward him; she leaned in the arch-way leading to the dining room, turning a fresh cigarette in her fingers.

"I wonder," she said. "I do wonder, Vincent, how much truth there is in what you've been saying. Fascinated me—yes, you've always fascinated me. But maybe the fascination was a little more special than you guessed, or than I've known myself, until now. I've never been—*quite* sure about you, darling. Like uncle, like nephew, I've sometimes thought; but that wasn't right, was it?"

She turned the cigarette slowly in her fingers.

"I believe I knew, the very first afternoon you came to see me, that you thought you could play a little game with me. I wasn't just goading you on, darling, to corrupt Patricia Bryant; I kept wondering how long it would take for you to betray yourself, one way or another. And then I thought perhaps you never would, and perhaps that's why I became so obvious, toward the end. My burn-ing curiosity. . . . Well, I have my reward, now, haven't I? And what satisfaction does it give me? That is the dreadful thing— nothing ever turns out to be really amusing in the end, does it? I merely feel rather sick."

He heard her sigh.

"Yes, there must be a good deal of truth in what you've said," she went on presently. "Although I didn't foresee that Charlie Bryant would go out of his mind and try to kill you. That was a Gothic elaboration I had not expected. . . .

"Do stop crying, darling! After all, you're twenty-four, twenty-five—young enough to be taken for my son, as you so delicately pointed out, but old enough not to cry, just the same. And you looked deplorable enough as it was."

She paused again; he heard her strike a match.

"And yet—if I'd *really* wanted what you think, I could have had it, darling. I could have it now, couldn't I? I could have had it the day we went to the cottage— Maybe that was why I took such care to make you repulsive then too. I don't know. One's own motives

—I'm almost forty-six," said Carola, "and I think I'm a little weary of the flesh. There was so much of that sort of thing, until just a few years ago, but it was never really amusing in the end, any of it. I suppose this has been a new kind of experiment for me."

She was still leaning in the doorway.

"I wonder if you'll ever know anything about yourself. You have been looking so hard at yourself, all these years, that you've almost snuffed yourself out of existence. What is Vincent Vaughan Rourke? Nothing, now, but a small bundle of nastiness. . . .

"Off to Mexico, hand in hand, the two of us. A very pretty picture. It would serve you right if I accepted your charming offer —it would serve me right. A just punishment for our sins, a really glorious and crowning mess, eventually. . . . I'm tempted, darling; yes, even now. But would Mexico be any better, really, than Broadfield, before the mess happened? No, you may go off by yourself, and leave me to rot in Broadfield, as I suppose I shall. I am so terribly tired; I don't want to try any more. I rather wish Charlie Bryant had chosen to kill me. Because, like you, I should never have the guts to kill myself."

She moved forward a little way and stood by the table, looking at her cigarette. "I don't understand people who are not like me— Laura Bryant, for instance, or Johnny Wheelwright— But you, my pet, I think I've understood you from the first. Or knew I would eventually. You'd never kill yourself, just as I never should, even though we have nothing to live for. Have we? Nothing. Nothing. It's a rather terrifying discovery, but it has taken me forty-five years to make it. You've made it at twenty-four. I almost begin to pity you. . . .

"Well, darling, Mexico is a long way off. Don't you think you'd better be starting?"

Vincent stood up and made himself look at her; he made himself say what he had to say. "It's no use. I have no money."

"And now you expect me to play Lady Bountiful? After all this?"

"No," he said.

"But you do, darling, you do. What a pity that it happens to be Saturday night; what a pity you're dead set on leaving for Mexico this minute. Because if you hung around until Monday, I might give you a check to get rid of you. Can't you restrain your impatience, darling, until Monday?—On the off-chance that I might decide to play Lady Bountiful after all?"

"Good night," Vincent said, and started toward the archway.

"No, no, do wait a minute!" She caught at his hand. "I insist on spoiling your exit. Come with me, darling. I have enough to get you as far as—where is it Bouncing Betty Lou comes from?—

Muskogee, Muskogee, Oklahoma. Send me a postcard when you reach Muskogee, and tell me what it's like."

She kept hold of his hand and led him upstairs with her. He went submissively, into her bedroom, where the covers were flung back from the bed and a book lay open face down and an ashtray was filled with dead stubs; there was a smell of perfume and stale tobacco smoke—the heavy curtains were pulled against the May night.

"I won't take any money from you," he said, stranded now in the middle of the room while she pulled back a picture from the wall and began to turn the knob of a small safe.

"I think you will," she said. The safe was open; she lifted out a thin packet of bills and began to lay them down on the bedside table, one by one, counting under her breath. "One hundred dollars," she said when she was finished. "It should take you at least as far as Muskogee, and perhaps in Muskogee you can find another Lady Bountiful." She came toward him, holding out the bills. "Now please, darling, be sensible and take them. There has been more than enough melodrama for one night."

He needed the money so desperately; he had to have it.

He took it from her, and put it in his wallet, and shoved the wallet back into his breast-pocket.

"I'll pay it back, of course," he said.

"And don't try to play Johnny Wheelwright either." She linked her arm in his again and led him back down the stairs. "I'm glad you're looking so repulsive tonight. It makes our parting a little easier. I shall try to remember you as you look now—it will help me not to feel any regrets."

They had reached the lower hall, but she kept hold of his hand a moment longer. "Good-by, my pet," she said. "If I thought it would do any good, I'd offer you some advice. I'd say to you that there will never be anything except messes, one after another, never anything else for you until you learn— No, there's no point in telling you, and I dislike platitudes. Perhaps because there is too much truth in too many of them. I hope you have a lovely time in Mexico, and do be careful about what you eat and drink."

She gave him a little push, and he was out on the front steps, and the door had closed behind him; he could hear the bolt sliding into place.

"Bitch," he said aloud, and returned to his car.

An hour later he had left Broadfield. It was foolish, perhaps, to drive at night, when he was feeling so weary, but he would not fall asleep at the wheel. He knew that as clearly as he knew Carola had been right when she said he would never have the guts to kill himself. Presently it was possible to stop thinking about the past, all of it; he drove on rapidly in the dark, thinking of the enormous empty lands into which he was going, the sand and the sagebrush and the whirling dust and the lifeless eroded mountains sprawled along the horizon and the incredible heat of the sun. He was returning to the desert, where the darkness would be burned out of him, where he would become as empty as the sky, and could be at peace with himself at last.

24

JOHNNY must have dozed off, eventually. He found himself jerking his head up, and saw that the lamp on the table looked a little foolish because of gray light now coming through the windows. The voice of the lake had grown much louder, an angry tumult on the sand, and the wind was a huge disturbance among the trees.

Johnny shivered and stood up. There was a stale taste in his mouth and his head felt thick; it took him some time to see that the room was empty save for Laurette, who still slept, her face turned to the back of the sofa. Voices murmured together on the porch, under the noise of wind and water, and Johnny found his parents out there. They smiled as he came toward them but in the cold pale light they looked wearier than he had ever seen them.

"Well," said his father, "you got forty winks, at least."

"Any news?"

Mr. Wheelwright shook his head. "They've given up. There's a storm brewing now." They turned, all three, and looked out at the slaty lake, flecked with foam as far as they could see—the gray sky bent down and touched the water, it seemed, only a mile or so out. "The lake's too damn big," said Mr. Wheelwright, and rubbed his forehead. "I find the greatest difficulty in believing that any of this has happened. Even when I remember that poor boy's face last night. Wishful thinking: we won't see there's anything wrong until it kicks us in the face."

Mrs. Wheelwright began to shift the porch chairs, propping them against the wall of the cottage. "I hope the Oppenheimers will decide to buy the cottage," she said.

"Yes." Mr. Wheelwright almost visibly shook himself. "There's plenty of work for us to do today. But I think, Johnny, you'd better drive the girls home right after breakfast."

"Yeah. No point in hanging around now. But about Bry—"

"I called him just a few minutes ago," Johnny's mother said. "I thought he'd better have a little time before they all got back." She had set the last chair in place against the wall, and came toward her husband and her son, and put her arms lightly about them. "It was easier to tell him than I'd expected. Almost as if he'd known, when the telephone rang, what it was going to be."

Her hand tightened on Johnny's arm; she sighed. "I'm glad Patricia has you, dearest."

"Yeah."

"This doesn't change anything between you and Pat, Johnny," his father said, but there was almost a question at the end.

"Of course not. I'm just worried she'll go on thinking—the way she was last night. What happened to Charlie—it doesn't have anything to do with Pat and me. It can't have. I won't let it." He felt a fierce resolve and a great tenderness; his happiness was so powerful, his view of the future so clear, that he had, really, no doubts at all about Patricia.

"Patricia's going to be all right," said his mother, "but I'm worried about Bry. It's taken him ten years to get over Laura's death; he was just beginning to—" She broke off, moving toward the door, and smiled a little. "Well, crêpe-hanging doesn't help anybody. I'll see about breakfast."

Johnny and his father stood in silence; the bending sky seemed to draw even closer, and presently the rain had started; the lake was shut away behind the gray curtain.

"I apologize, Johnny," said Mr. Wheelwright.

"What for?"

His father glanced at him; his mouth quirked up at the corners. "Doubting your love for an instant. It was only for an instant, and only because I haven't had any sleep. . . . It isn't going to be easy, Johnny, but you'll win out. Fortune and victory—they're still there. I can see them clearly." He turned his face to the rain again and said, "I suppose it may be better if they never find Charlie at all. I don't know. . . . Anyway, they probably never will."

But Charlie's body was washed ashore near Rivermouth, a week later, at the end of a series of unseasonable storms. Norris had to go out to Rivermouth; he was ashamed of himself for feeling nothing but a sense of physical nausea, and for turning so quickly away, for hurrying so unceremoniously through the necessary arrangements.

What water had begun, fire ended. It was as clean as death could be and in some obscure way Norris felt he was making amends to Laura for at least the smallest of his betrayals. There would be no grave for Charlie, no sign that he had ever lived at all.

. . . Except for his son. David was almost a year old, and had begun to walk. With the death of Charlie, the departure of Delores, he seemed to acquire a new vitality. Watching him stagger around the back lawn in the sunlight of early summer, his strong legs spraddled wide, his small fat belly bulging outward, his shoulders thrown back and his spine erect and his arms churning the air, seeing his scowl of concentration and hearing his sudden yells of delight, Norris tried to remember that it was life that mattered.

But the monster was with him always; he wondered if he would ever have done with it.

It had been like history repeating itself, to go downstairs in the early morning to answer the telephone; but the day of Laura's death had turned out fine, and that Sunday the rain started, and went on intermittently for more than a week. The pall which had never quite lifted from Norris's house was back again; if it hadn't been for the baby it might have closed completely over Norris and Patricia and Joel.

But the baby and the job kept Norris sane for a little while. In daylight the monster withdrew to the farthest corner of his mind and could almost be forgotten. Night was the bad time; alone in his dark bedroom Norris wondered how long he could endure the struggle. For a dollar or two he could buy a temporary assuagement and he was frightened because he thought it was what he was going to do, sooner or later. It would be worse than the other time because he was so much older and more weary now; if he gave in at all, he would be lost. He just wasn't strong enough, he thought; he had never been strong enough to cope with life. He yearned quite terribly for the blurring, the softening, the deadening of pain and guilt which drunkenness would bring.

History was repeating itself, but the accent was different. Losing the only woman you had ever loved was not like losing your first-begotten son, who had all his life been a stranger to you, a more tormented being than you had ever dared let yourself see. It wasn't really Charlie's death which appalled Norris so much; it was the brevity and confusion of his life. At night, in the darkness, while rain fell into the restless trees, he could not avoid morbidity; he tried to imagine what must have been going through Charlie's mind in those last weeks, and wished he could believe that at the final moment Charlie had wanted to live—death welcomed seemed more horrible to Norris than death fought against. The brevity and confusion of Charlie's life, the inability of human beings to give one another aid when aid was needed most: this was what Norris wanted to forget by drinking. Eleven years ago he had drunk to forget that without Laura he was lost.

Eleven years ago he had resented the diffident sympathy of the men with whom he worked; but this time he was grateful for it. It revealed itself in small ways, all of them clumsy; a few of the men tried to say something about what had happened, but more of them made a valiant pretense that everything was quite normal. Ack even cursed him more than usual, and piled extra work on him. But whatever any of them did they betrayed their affection for Norris, and this moved and humbled him. He was not worth it, he thought; they were wasting their sympathy. They were good men, though as awkward about the emotions as he was himself; he was constantly astonished at the goodness of human beings.

The feeling was there, wherever he turned—in his own children, in Betty Lou, in the Wheelwrights, everywhere except at the farm, and he hadn't expected to find it there; he did not deserve to, having cut himself off so long ago from his parents and his sister. They were shocked when Norris gave Charlie's body to the fire; it was pagan, they said; and behind their eyes was the smugness which had been there when Laura died. Norris had sinned with Laura, and a relentless God was punishing him still. Even his father believed that.

There were times when Norris's mind wavered and he almost believed it himself. This was the pattern his life had made because he had loved her too greatly—he had worshiped a woman instead of the power that shone through her. There was somehow a terrible irony in what had happened, and he kept going back in his mind, searching the past for the place where the wrong turning had been made. He wanted to see the irony clearly, and discover why it had existed.

Such enormous consequences resulted from such casual and unthinking actions; fate might hang on the smallest gesture. Sometimes he thought that Charlie had died because he, Norris Bryant, had boarded the wrong trolley-car one October afternoon and gone to the cemetery instead of Rush Lake. If he hadn't gone to the cemetery he wouldn't have been given a lift by Vincent Rourke; if he hadn't been in an overwrought state that afternoon—renascence, it had seemed then, after years in a half-world—he wouldn't have asked Rourke to supper. Rourke would have remained just a young man he knew at the paper, and Carola Wilmot's lies would never have been spoken, or if spoken would never have filtered through to Patricia, to Delores, to Charlie. And Norris's foolish belief that he had re-entered the world of the living, that now his life which had always drifted would begin to march, had helped drive Charlie to his death: there was no way of calculating the effect of the letters he had written about Laura.

But of course it was far more complicated than that. The root of the trouble lay so much farther in the past, and all the things that had happened to Charlie in the past were a part of the pattern. But those too were mostly Norris's fault; only the hard times could not be blamed on him. For the hard times, for the state the world was in, he shared the blame with all men—for the indifference which had allowed the darkness to triumph. But he could not escape the conviction that he was his own son's murderer.

The irony stood forth clearly now. Laura had meant life to him, and he had killed her. After ten years of trying to kill her in his memory also, he had attempted a kind of resurrection. He had set the image up before himself and his children, and bowed down before it, and thought to draw life from it; and beside this betrayal of Laura all his other betrayals dwindled into nothing.

The belief overwhelmed him and he knew he could not endure it much longer.

There was a night when he tried to tell Betty Lou what he was feeling, but the clarity fogged over as soon as he tried to put it into words. He fumbled on, in the dusk of her garden, under the shadow of her sour-cherry tree; she sat on the string hammock, bending her head and pushing with her toes at the ground, swinging back and forth gently.

"Oh, Norris," she said finally, breaking into the middle of a sentence, "I wish you wouldn't! I just wish you wouldn't!" She leaned forward and clasped his hand. "What good does it do to torment yourself like this? Aren't you starting in all over again, the same way, doing just what you said you shouldn't have done before? You can't get Laura back, or Charlie back. If you've made mistakes—and Lordy, Norris, we all make them, all the time—you've made them, they're over and done with, you can't go back and repair them."

"But such terrible mistakes," he said. "If I can see why I made them, maybe I won't make such terrible ones from now on."

"The worst mistake is to think too much about the past. It's now that counts. Tonight, and tomorrow, and maybe the day after, but not any farther ahead than that. You're no help to yourself or anybody else as long as you go on brooding." She sighed and lay back in the hammock, staring up into the leaves, into the dim boughs where the fruit had begun to form.

"And in a way," she said, "in a way, Norris—now I'm not trying to be mean, I don't want to hurt you any more—but in a way it seems like you attach too much importance to yourself. Even if you did do terrible things to your children, it isn't *all* your doing, Norris. Your children aren't puppets—they work their own strings; you have to let them; you can't protect them always. You can't live their lives for them, or take all the pain. You can help them, of course, in lots of ways; but not when you sit off in a corner and beat your breast and say it's all your fault."

She swung gently while a breeze stirred the laden boughs, and said, "I'm not what you could call religious, I guess; but maybe we shouldn't look too closely at the ways of the Lord, Norris. There's a lot of things, I think, we maybe aren't meant to understand.

"And what's happened, Norris—it isn't all bad. I guess I sound like Pollyanna, but— No, I don't, I'm being hard-boiled, really. . . . There's David. Maybe it's terrible to say he'll have a better life now than if— But he will, Norris— We do learn from our mistakes, and you're so much wiser now—you could be if you'd quit brooding—you're so much wiser now than you were when your own children were growing up. There's David to think about," said Betty Lou, looking up into the tree.

"And there's Patricia and Johnny," she added presently. "That Rourke boy, he meant her nothing but harm, but it didn't work out that way. Whatever was wrong with Patricia—and something was, Norris—he cured it."

"That's what Laurette said. But it's so— Good coming out of evil. It doesn't make sense. It leaves you no ground to stand on."

"I don't know, Norris. It's too deep for me, I guess. But it's true just the same— She needed a shock, and he gave it to her. He did something for her Johnny all alone never could have."

She sat up again now and spoke with increased urgency. "I wish they'd hurry up and get married. Who cares what people think? It's the right thing for them to do. I don't believe in long engagements. Norris," she said, "if Laura was alive, she'd tell you the same thing; I know it. David counts, Patricia and Johnny count, *you* do, *your* life—"

Suddenly she sounded very tired, and his own weariness flooded in upon him. He said, "If I just didn't want a drink so badly. You don't know what it's like, Betty Lou. I'm scared even to touch beer now. I'm scared to walk past a bar— When I see a bar looming up, I cross to the other side of the street. Scared my feet will take me in before I know what's happening."

"Shoot! That's just stuff and nonsense."

"I wish it was."

"Well, you *have*n't gone into a bar yet, have you?"

"I will, though. Tomorrow, or the day after, or the day after that, I will. It's so easy to be a drunk, now. Eleven years ago you had to know the right places in the wrong part of town. You had to keep in touch with a good bootlegger. It would be so easy," Norris said, "so terribly easy. I could walk downtown this minute and be blind drunk before closing time."

"Why don't you do it, then? Why *don't* you go this minute?"

"Because I—"

"Go on, go on downtown and get drunk, get it over with. You'll wake up tomorrow with a perfectly terrible hangover—and believe me, Norris, there's nothing I don't know about hangovers. I declare, Sam Hanbury had the worst of any man I ever knew—and you'd feel awful all day, and then you'd be over it. I know that,

Norris. Go ahead and get drunk if you want to; it won't be the first step to perdition. You're a whole lot stronger than you think. Oh, Lordy," said Betty Lou, "you're so mixed up—you're conceited about the wrong things and humble about the wrong ones too. You're a whole lot stronger than you think you are, and I'm just not worried one little bit."

She had been talking almost with her old vehemence; too vehemently, perhaps, he thought after he'd left her, to cover up her anxiety. Though what right had he to assume she'd feel any anxiety about him? He was glad, he thought, that Mrs. Wheelwright had called him so early in the morning, long before he'd had a chance to ask Betty Lou to marry him. The question would never be asked now. He was a derelict and had burdened her too much already. Marriage was for the young, for Patricia and Johnny.

There was another night when he stood between the living room and the dining room, where Joel was sitting with books spread all about him, studying for his final examinations. Norris still didn't know about Joel; perhaps he never would. So calm, so solid, so stolid too, most of the time, except for the occasional flashes of impertinence, which might be Joel's own formula for showing filial affection. Norris hadn't told Joel about Charlie on the Sunday morning; he had let him go off to the Boonstras' in the rain, and possibly Joel had gone to church with them; it was no day for sailing.

How was it, anyway, that the Boonstras' puritanism relaxed enough to countenance sailing on the Lord's day? The question had never occurred to Norris before, and he almost asked Joel now; but instead stood and watched his son scowl. That was all Joel had done when he returned from the Boonstras' on the Sunday evening; he had scowled, and drawn a breath, and gone down to the cellar for a workout on his punching-bag; and since then he had been as calm and solid and stolid, and as hungry, as ever.

"How's it going?" Norris asked.

"Not so good."

"That's what you get for neglecting your homework all year."

"Yah."

"Maybe next year you won't neglect it so much."

"Maybe not." Joel clapped a book shut; he began to bounce a pencil on the table, dropping it eraser-end down and catching it as it came up. "I made up my mind I want to go to West Point after all," he said.

"Oh?"

"I read a book," Joel said, "a book by that guy you used to know. McBain. It was in the school lib'ary and I read it for a book report. Well, he says there's going to be another war. When the war comes, maybe I'll have to fight in it. So I want to go to West

Point. I'm going to join the ROTC too, soon as I'm old enough, and get a head start."

"McBain could be wrong, you know."

"Yah. But it's good exercise, anyway. Good discipline." Joel continued to bounce the pencil; his gray eyes—so much like Laura's —looked past Norris's. "Pop," he said, "did Charlie kill himself because he thought McBain was my father?"

As soon as he was able to, Norris moved forward, pulled out a chair, and sat down at the table. He sat for a long time, rubbing his tired face with tired hands, trying to think what to say. Would he never learn to prepare himself for shocks?

"In the first place maybe Charlie—didn't kill himself. He was kind of sick, Joel—sick in his mind. It isn't anything to be ashamed about, you know; that can happen to people just like mumps or measles. And I think he just thought suddenly he wanted to go for a swim—and then swam out too far. That's all. That's the way to think about it, Joel. It isn't a bad way to die, you know, doing something you've always liked doing."

"Sure." Joel drew a diagram on a sheet of paper, and began to play noughts and crosses against himself. "Charlie was a good swimmer."

"And about the other thing—you know it isn't so, Joel, don't you?"

"Oh, sure." Joel considered for a long time before he drew a circle on his diagram. "I wouldn't want *McBain* for a father. But Charlie " He drew a cross in the box beside the circle. "Well, he used to get mad at Delores, the way she went around with other fellas, so I thought maybe he thought Mom was the same way. Girls are funny, you know it? I don't think I understand them very well yet. Buzz's sisters—" He made another circle and studied it carefully. "Mom sure was a good-looking lady, all right. Anyway, from that picture."

"The best-looking one there ever was. The best. . . ."

Joel made another cross. "Betty Lou isn't so bad. Considering her age."

"Wait till you're that age. You'll think it's the prime of life."

Joel's game had come out an impasse, a jumble of noughts and crosses. "Charlie was strong, all right," he said. "You think I'll ever be that strong, Pop?"

"You'll be stronger, Joel. A whole lot stronger," Norris said, and went upstairs to his room.

And there was another evening, when he was sitting out on the porch, and Johnny Wheelwright came over.

"I'll call Pat," Norris said, and started to get up.

"Naw, Bry, I wanted to speak to you first."

"All right, Johnny. Sit down."

303

But Johnny just leaned against the porch rail, with his hands in his pockets. "I wanted to ask you first how you'd feel about it. I've been talking it over with my family, and they—don't see any reason why Pat and I should wait much longer. If it's all right with you, I mean. Some people'll be shocked, I guess, so soon after— Well, they'll be shocked, but—"

"I don't think you need to bother about them."

"You mean it's O.K. with you?"

Norris nodded. "As long as Pat—"

"Yeah."

"Come on inside, Johnny." Norris touched his arm. "I'll get her down."

He left Johnny wandering in the living room, and tapped on Patricia's door. "Pat."

"Oh. Just a minute." She came to the door presently and pulled it open. She was very pale; there was a stillness about her, almost like the old stillness, but it was not quite the same. She looked older, he thought; she looked almost like a woman.

"Pat," he said, "it's Johnny. He wants—"

"Yes. I know."

"If you want it too—and you do, don't you? Well," Norris said, "go ahead. It's all right. All right with me, I mean. There's no reason why you shouldn't. We can't—mope forever, you know."

"Yes, Father."

She remained still another moment, and then smiled fleetingly, and turned toward the stairs. He followed her a little way; he stood and watched her descend slowly, he watched Johnny move across the room toward her. She hesitated, and then almost ran to Johnny.

It was right, Norris thought, and went back to his bedroom.

They were terribly young, they would be very poor for a long time and maybe always, and a threatening future hung over them. The small pattern they would make of their lives might be disrupted soon by enormous patterns involving all mankind; but it was the right thing for them to do. This moment, and tomorrow, and maybe the day after, but not any farther ahead than that. No use to look ahead; make what you can out of the present.

. . . And there was, at last, a morning when Ack Guion swung his chair toward Norris and said, "By the way, Bry, been meaning to speak to you a long time, but I didn't know just how you'd feel. We're having the spring picnic Friday night, and we're all hoping a lot you'll decide to come."

"Oh." Norris stared down the long room.

"Do you good, Bry, maybe. Forget your troubles for a while."

"Yes," said Norris, and reached for a sharper pencil. "Just so long as I'm not a skeleton at the feast."

"Hell," said Ack, and spat. "We need that rich baritone of yours. *Sweet Adeline* wouldn't be the same without you."

The test had to come, sooner or later. Get it over with, Norris thought; get it over with and find out about yourself.

So he went with the others, after work on Friday, out to a boys' camp on the river ten miles from town, which hadn't been opened for the season yet and had been rented for the picnic by the editorial staff. The tent platforms, over which the tents hadn't yet been pitched, stood in a semicircle in a grove of trees. There was a long trestled table under the trees, with a string of Japanese lanterns hanging above it; when dark came there would be a bonfire.

It was like all the *Chronicle* stag parties Norris had ever been to—doomed at the start, it seemed, because of the curious shyness that came over the men when they saw one another deprived of the familiar background of desks and typewriters and telephones and drifts of paper. They had become strangers to one another; they were now their private selves, and unease had gripped them —they regarded one another warily, and were too worried when the small-talk languished, and laughed too loudly at one another's mostly feeble stories.

But a keg of beer was broached and the food passed around and their hard and separate edges thawed and began to merge; good fellowship was born in the grove by the river, and the voices rose, the stories grew fouler and funnier, the laughter became real.

Norris, although he'd had nothing to drink, was caught up into the warmth for a while. He felt himself sitting at the table, while the river flowed past over its shallows and the sun went down among dazzling banners in the west; he felt himself throwing his head back, he heard himself laughing; he heard himself telling a story or two, loudly and insistently, stories he hadn't known he remembered, and they were so old that they seemed new. He had made a contribution to the laughter and was one with the rest of them.

His liking for them increased. They had nothing in common but their work; few of them were friends away from the office and some of them were enemies all the time; but this could be forgotten while they sat about the table as darkness came, and crammed food down their throats, and shouted for more beer, and presently began to sing.

They sang under the trees, under the early stars, while the river went on making a cold hushed laughter over its stones. The aim was noise; the more noise they produced the stronger the feeling of fellowship would be. Norris, who had been thinking so much in symbols lately, sought for a symbol in this too—and stopped seeking, because somehow there was a tall stein of beer in his fist.

He pushed it away and became self-conscious. Ack was looking at him gravely, no longer singing, and a little farther along the table young Will Eliot had stopped singing to look at him too. Will Eliot, who'd been a boy as young as Charlie when Laura died, but who knew the stories about Norris, of course; Will Eliot who, like Norris and not like Vincent Rourke, would stay with the *Chronicle* until he had grown old at the job, who would remain rooted in one small city in one state of the union all his life, a failure like Norris, a failure. There was pity for Norris in Will Eliot's dark earnest gaze, and Norris suddenly rebelled against the pity and reached for the stein.

When it was empty he got up from the table and walked over to the beer-keg and turned the spigot. He stood with the full stein in his hand, at some distance from the table, watching the others, listening to the loud discordance they made in the quiet night. The lanterns were lighted now; beyond the table the bonfire blazed up, and the glow spread wide, the sparks poured into the trees. The singers were flat black shapes against the light of the fire, but welded still, a single creature.

Norris wandered away into the dark and found one of the tent platforms; he sat down, with the stein beside him on the planks. At this distance the singing was less discordant, and lulled him into a dream. It seemed that his mind was quite empty for a little while, and when the dream was over the stein was empty too.

He was not drunk, of course. He was only as far from sobriety as he had been that afternoon in October when Johnny and Patricia returned from their bicycle ride and found him drinking beer with Rourke. A long way, he thought vaguely, we've all come a long way since then.

He sat alone on the tent-floor, looking at the men sitting around the table, and knew that he was not quite sober. But there had been no need to worry; he didn't want anything more to drink. He even wished he had not drunk so much, because it made clear thinking difficult.

Some of the notions that had moved through his mind in the last few weeks were right, but some of them were not. He tried, said Betty Lou, to attach too much importance to himself; in some ways he was conceited; and he pitied himself, although she had not quite told him that. There was more to it than this, though. Only an exceptional human being could be complete in himself, and even in such a one, perhaps, the feeling of completeness was a form of lunacy. As for Norris, he was an ordinary man, incomplete, filled with terrible flaws and blind more often than not; and so there could be no finality in any of his actions, and almost nothing that he did could be called absolutely good or bad. So often the right impulses led to disaster, the mistaken ones to an unexpected triumph.

In the months since October, he thought, he had made at least a few valid discoveries; the moment in the cemetery had not been altogether an allusion. Since then he had continued to fumble and grope and take wrong turnings, but there were times when he had marched. The old blindness, that came from a fixed regard for self, would not return to him now, he hoped. It was incredible that learning to see had taken so long. Even then, eleven years ago, in the depths of his grief, how could he have forgotten his children? That was the one absolutely bad thing he had done—to turn his face from his children, who were the living part of Laura.

And David, he thought—David was as much her grandchild as his.

Have done with ghosts; the living laid upon him an obligation to share life with them. Forget self; if he was lost in his own laby-rinth, so were all men in a greater one. A greater monster threat-ened all of them, but to each a sword was given, to each a thread, and together they might one day slay the Minotaur and walk out into the light.

Norris smiled. He stood up and went back to join the singers at the table.

25

It was a fine mild October Sunday and they'd had it in mind to ride out to Rush Lake and hire a rowboat; but when they reached the amusement park at the end of the line, and climbed down into the sunlight, they found that the little excursion steam-boat was blowing its whistle at the pier, and decided to go for a ride on that instead.

It was an absurd little steamboat, hardly larger than a toy, as Rush Lake was hardly larger than a pond. Norris thought how strange it was that Broadfield insisted on calling the smallest body of water a lake, when such an enormous lake began less than thirty miles westward. He smiled at Betty Lou, and took her arm, and together they strolled along the deck to the bow; they leaned side by side, gazing out at the water, amber beneath them, blue as the sky farther out, and flashing where the brisk wind whipped it into waves.

With a great deal of churning, with loud shouts from the crew, with a last frantic blast of its whistle, the little steamboat put out from the pier. The noises of the amusement park—the music of the merry-go-round and the rattle and sudden downward roar of the roller-coaster and the screams of those who rode it—were left behind. Foam spread outward from the blunt prow and the steamboat left a respectable wake, in which rowboats and sailboats, also like toys, rocked wildly for a moment.

All about the green shores stood the houses of the rich and mighty; many of the rich and mighty were less so than they had been before 1929, and some of the houses stood empty, and some of the lawns had run to weeds; but from the deck of the steamboat, in the middle of the lake, the houses shone white as palaces and the lawns were incredibly smooth.

"Keep an eye open for Joel," said Norris. "He's sailing with the Boonstras."

There were not many other passengers aboard, this trip; Norris and Betty Lou had the bow to themselves, and he pulled two chairs close to the rail, and they sat down.

Betty Lou adjusted her hat; she had to hold it down because of the wind.

Norris sighed faintly, and to keep from feeling nervous thought about Johnny and Patricia, who had come across the street to look after David for an hour or so. By March, Norris would have become a grandfather twice over, and he ought to be feeling much older than he did, and much more worried. They were too young, he thought; they were much too young to start a family; it had come too soon.

Betty Lou seemed to know what he was thinking.

"I'm betting on a girl," she said.

"Kind of premature, aren't you? But they'd like a girl, I guess. . . . They should have waited, Betty Lou."

"I think it's fine to have your children young. Then you aren't decrepit by the time they've grown up."

"No. . . . *I* feel like Methuselah."

Holding her hat down, Betty Lou looked at him sideways. She looked at him for a long time and because the light was in his eyes, striking downward from the sky and upward from the bright water, Norris couldn't tell whether she was grave or smiling. "You're still brown," she said at last, "from working so hard in the garden. With the gray hair it looks just fine." She paused; he decided she was smiling. "Did Joel give you that necktie?" she asked.

"Guess he did. For Christmas, once. How'd you know?"

"Oh—I just thought it looked like Joel's idea of a good-looking tie."

"Isn't it yours?"

"I guess men and women never do see eye to eye about neckties. The arguments I used to have with Sam!" She leaned toward Norris and began to make adjustments in the knot; when she had it more to her liking she patted it smooth and tucked the ends back beneath his jacket. "There," she said. "Now I see what Joel meant."

She began to take her hands away, but Norris caught them and held them fast.

"I'm as old as Methuselah," he said, "and I'm a failure—"

The boat had turned and the light fell differently; the sun was out of his eyes and he broke off because Betty Lou was looking so tremulous. The wind had blown the veil on her hat down into her face, but her hands were in his so she couldn't lift it away.

"I'm a failure and a derelict," Norris began again firmly, "and I have no right to say this, Betty Lou, and if you want to put me in my place, you go right ahead. I *could* get along without you, I guess, but I—I can't see life that way any more. So I'm going to ask you to marry me."

She looked away across the lake; all he could see was the side of her cheek, the edge of her chin, the veil on her hat blowing in the wind.

"I know what a nerve I have," he said. "I've been so much of a burden to you already. But you said once—I remember you said you'd always wanted to be a grandmother, eventually. It's a funny kind of a thing to offer a woman, but it's about all I have."

Still she gazed away from him. The veil fluttered, and beyond the veil he saw white sails moving against the bronze and yellow trees; her hands, though he held them so firmly, seemed to tremble a little.

"It would only be by proxy, kind of," he said, "but—"

"You don't know," she said. "You just don't know what you have to offer. If you did, maybe I wouldn't love you, Norris." At last she turned. "Oh, Norris," she said, and abashed and incredulous at the look in her face, he dropped her hands.

"This wasn't the right place, maybe," Norris said, "or the right time, or— I never do anything the right way. There's so much you'll have to put up with, if you—"

But Betty Lou was struggling with her veil.

"It's the nicest place and the best time I can think of," she said. The veil was up at last, out of her eyes. "Norris—"

But a gust of wind came along the deck and blew the veil down again.

"This *hat!*" she said. "Oh, shoot!" said Betty Lou, snatching it off, and kissed him.